# WORKBOOK

# Student Notes and Problems

# BIOLOGY 20

## Alberta Edition

**CASTLE ROCK**
RESEARCH CORP

Canadian Cataloguing in Publication Data

Rao, Gautam, 1961 –
**STUDENT NOTES AND PROBLEMS** – Biology 20
**ISBN:** 978-1-55371-675-4

   1. Biology – Juvenile Literature. I. Title

**Published by**
Castle Rock Research Corp.
2000 First & Jasper
10065 Jasper Avenue
Edmonton, AB T5J 3B1


10  9  8  7

**Publisher**
Gautam Rao

**Contributors**
Markus Chan
Robert Hempel
Dr. Brent Kilback
James Kropfreiter

Dedicated to the memory of Dr. V. S. Rao

# STUDENT NOTES AND PROBLEMS WORKBOOKS

Student Notes and Problems (SNAP) workbooks are a series of support resources in mathematics for students in grades 3 to 12 and in science for students in grades 9 to 12. SNAP workbooks are 100% aligned with curriculum. The resources are designed to support classroom instructions and provide students with additional examples, practice exercises, and tests. SNAP workbooks are ideal for use all year long at school and at home.

The following is a summary of the key features of all SNAP workbooks.

## UNIT OPENER PAGE

- summarizes the curriculum outcomes addressed in the unit in age-appropriate language
- identifies the lessons by title
- lists the prerequisite knowledge and skills the student should know prior to beginning the unit

## LESSONS

- provide essential teaching pieces and explanations of the concepts
- include example problems and questions with complete, detailed solutions that demonstrate the problem-solving process

## NOTES BARS

- contain key definitions, formulas, reminders, and important steps or procedures
- provide space for students to add their own notes and helpful reminders

## PRACTICE EXERCISES

- include questions that relate to each of the curriculum outcomes for the unit
- provide practice in applying the lesson concepts

## REVIEW SUMMARY

- provides a succinct review of the key concepts in the unit

## PRACTICE TEST

- assesses student learning of the unit concepts

## ANSWERS AND SOLUTIONS

- demonstrate the step-by-step process or problem-solving method used to arrive at the correct answer

Answers and solutions are provided in each workbook for the odd-numbered. A SNAP *Solutions Manual* that contains answers and complete solutions for all questions is also available.

# NOTES

# CONTENTS

## Human Systems

## Answers and Solutions

# THE BIOSPHERE

When you are finished this unit, you will be able to...

- describe the flow of energy in the biosphere
- explain energy storage in the biosphere as a balance between photosynthesis and cellular respiration
- interpret the biosphere as a thermodynamic system and show how all stored biological energy is eventually lost as heat
- describe a steady state equilibrium
- list the different ways in which matter is cycled through the biosphere to maintain a steady state equilibrium
- summarize and explain the carbon, nitrogen, and phosphorus cycles
- explain how water is cycled through the biosphere using characteristic pathways
- identify the properties of water—such as the freezing point, hydrogen bonding, specific heat and density—and explain the relevance of those properties to the hydrologic cycle
- determine how matter exchange and the balance of energy maintains a steady state equilibrium in the biosphere as an open system
- describe how gas exchanges in photosynthesis and cellular respiration affect the atmosphere
- evaluate the impact of human activities on the equilibrium of the biosphere

## PREREQUISITE SKILLS AND KNOWLEDGE

Prior to starting this unit, you should be able to...
- define an equilibrium as a dynamic balance
- understand that most of the energy used in the biosphere comes from the sun.
- describe the basic chemical properties of atoms and molecules
- list dynamic processes, such as evaporation, combustion, and dehydration
- describe the scientific method of experimentation and develop skills of conclusion

## Lesson 1   THE BIOSPHERE

The biosphere can be defined as the parts of Earth that can support life. Generally speaking, the biosphere encompasses a thick layer that begins approximately 9 000 metres below sea level and extends to over 11 300 metres above sea level. Within these confines, there are three separate components in which life can be found.

**The biosphere interacts with three components of Earth: the lithosphere, the atmosphere, and the hydrosphere.**

The biosphere interacts with three different components of Earth: the lithosphere, atmosphere, and hydrosphere. The lithosphere is composed of solid matter, such as soil and rocks. The atmosphere is composed of gases that surround Earth. The hydrosphere is composed of all ground water, such as ponds, lakes, creeks, rivers, and oceans. These three components are interrelated and interact dynamically with one another.

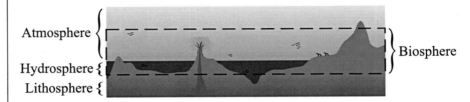

The dynamic nature of the biosphere involves a number of processes that are constantly changing and interacting. Birth, growth, production, breathing, consumption, movement, reproduction, death, and decomposition occur continuously and simultaneously throughout the system. All of these activities require energy.

The biosphere is considered an open system because both matter and energy are exchanged between the biotic, or living parts of the globe, and the abiotic, or non-living parts. For example, when volcanoes erupt, gases and solid matter that were previously beneath Earth's crust enter the biosphere and interact with biotic matter. In the ozone layer, oxygen is cycled through three different molecular structures. It ascends and descends through different atmospheric levels and moves between biotic and abiotic strata.

The biosphere is predominantly powered and energized by the sun. Of the total amount of solar radiation that strikes Earth, about 30% is reflected back into space. Much of the radiation that passes through the atmosphere is absorbed by the pigments in plants and is stored chemically for future use. This storage ability is what makes it possible for all organisms in the biosphere to live and function.

**Light reflected from the surface of Earth is called the albedo.**

The radiation that is reflected back into space from Earth's surface is known as the **albedo**. Different surfaces have varying albedo values. For example, fresh snow reflects 95% of the solar radiation that strikes it, while water reflects only three to five percent of the sun's light.

**Autotroph means "self-feeding."**

Plant life absorbs more radiation than it reflects, with an albedo ranging from 10% to 25%. The energy absorbed in this way is used to manufacture food in the form of glucose. Plants are called **autotrophs** and **producers** because they are able to feed themselves using solar radiation. Plants store energy chemically in polymerized forms of glucose called as sugars and starches.

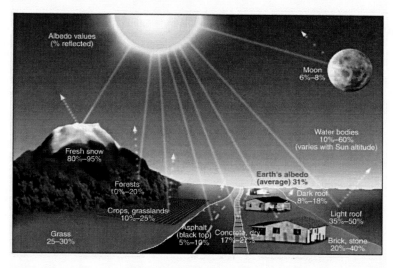

Animal cells are unable to use sunlight for any major purpose aside from warmth, vitamin production, and vision. The inability to produce nutrients from solar radiation means that animals are dependent on other food sources. As a result of this dependence, animals are called **heterotrophs** and **consumers**. The sugars and starches produced by plants form the foundation of the system that allows solar energy to make its way into the metabolisms of heterotrophs.

Heterotroph means "other-feeding."

The biological processes that maintain organic life are known collectively as metabolic processes. Those that require an input of energy in order to build organic material are endergonic, which means that more energy goes into the reaction than comes out as a result of the reaction. Chemical reactions that build or construct organic materials are known as **anabolic reactions**.

Metabolic processes can be either anabolic or catabolic.

Chemical reactions that break apart organic materials to release energy are described as exergonic, which means that the net result of the process is to release more energy than was required to begin the reaction. These reactions are known as **catabolic reactions**.

The anabolic process used by plants is called **photosynthesis**. Sunlight energizes a component of plant cells called a chloroplast, which takes molecules of carbon dioxide and water and recombines them to form glucose and oxygen. Both animals and plants then use the glucose as a source of energy for all living functions. As the glucose is broken down, it releases energy, carbon dioxide, and water. The energy is stored in a molecule called adenosine triphosphate (ATP).

Photosynthesis and cellular respiration are opposite reactions. The products for one reaction are the ingredients of the other.

The process in animal and plant cells that breaks down glucose to form ATP and release heat is known as **cellular respiration**.

Cellular respiration is basically photosynthesis in reverse.

Where photosynthesis takes carbon dioxide, energy, and water to make glucose and oxygen, cellular respiration takes glucose and oxygen to make carbon dioxide, energy, and water.

**Photosynthesis and Cellular Respiration**

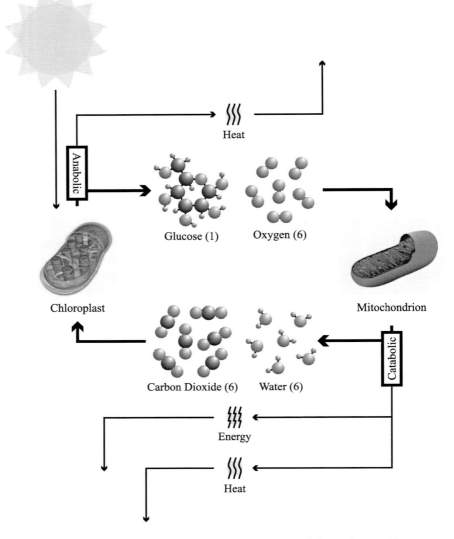

It is important to note that while the molecular materials exchanged in photosynthesis and cellular respiration are exactly balanced, the amount of energy involved in the two processes is different. In other words, when glucose is used for biological processes in both plants and animals, energy is lost in the form of heat.

Adenosine triphosphate (ATP) is a molecule that takes chemical energy from cellular respiration and transfers it to the tissues of plants and animals. Whenever an organism draws energy from an ATP molecule, as in the case of a muscle contraction, heat is produced.

Microbes such as bacteria, fungi, and mold actively break down dead plant and animal organisms into their basic components. This process is called **decomposition**. In order to convert the carbon and glucose in organic material into carbon dioxide, cellular respiration is used, which results in a net output of heat.

Decomposition can either occur in the presence of oxygen (aerobic decomposition) or without the presence of oxygen (anaerobic decomposition). Aerobic decomposition generates more heat, whereas anaerobic decomposition tends to produce sulfurous organic compoundsthat are most directly detected as a result of their pungent odours. Anaerobic decomposition is also known as **fermentation**. It releases carbon in the form of a gas called methane.

Energy from the sun warms and illuminates Earth. Some of that heat and light is radiated back into outer space. The solar energy that penetrates the atmosphere can be used by plants to manufacture glucose from water and carbon dioxide during photosynthesis. The relationship between photosynthesis and cellular respiration is a sustainable, continuous process. Each instance of one reaction creates the ingredients for the other. This activity forms the basis of the steady-state equilibrium within the biosphere and can be performed perpetually, so long as there is sunlight and a balanced amount of components.

Equilibrium means balance. A steady-state equilibrium can sustain itself indefinitely, as long as the fundamental conditions remain the same.

## Example 1

Name the three subdivisions of the terrestrial environment that interact with the biosphere.

*Solution*

The three subcomponents of Earth's environment are the lithosphere, the hydrosphere, and the atmosphere. These three subdivisions interact with the biosphere and exchange matter and energy with the ecosystems that maintain life.

## Example 2

Describe the ways in which solar radiation is stored and used in the biosphere.

*Solution*

Energy from the Sun is stored chemically by plants through the process of photosynthesis. Photosynthesis stores energy in the form of glucose in an endergonic reaction that is also anabolic. Glucose is then transformed by biological organisms into metabolic fuel in the form of adenosine triphosphate through the catabolic process of cellular respiration.

**Example 3**

Compare anaerobic decomposition with aerobic decomposition.

*Solution*

The decomposition of glucose is accomplished through cellular respiration in microbes. When there is oxygen present, microbes can use the process of aerobic decomposition. Aerobic decomposition produces more heat and fewer sulfurous odours than anaerobic decomposition, which occurs in the absence of oxygen. Aerobic decomposition produces carbon dioxide, whereas anaerobic decomposition produces methane.

**Example 4**

Explain how the biosphere is an open system.

*Solution*

A closed system does not have any transference of energy or matter with an external environment. The biosphere exchanges matter and energy with the areas of Earth and space that do not contain life. The sun provides energy input in the form of solar radiation, and there are parts of the lithosphere, hydrosphere, and atmosphere that transfer energy and matter into the biosphere.

## PRACTICE EXERCISE

1. What are the three divisions of the biosphere?

   **a)** Atmosphere, lithosphere, dynasphere    **b)** Atmosphere, lithosphere, aquasphere

   **c)** Lithosphere, stratosphere, atmosphere    **d)** Lithosphere, hydrosphere, atmosphere

2. What is the term used to describe light from the sun that reflects off the biosphere and into space?

   **a)** Albino                   **b)** Albedo

   **c)** Lumbago            **d)** Albumen

3. Which of the following terms can be used interchangeably with *autotroph*?

   **a)** Entropy             **b)** Producer

   **c)** Consumer         **d)** Decomposer

4. Which of the following compounds is a product of cellular respiration?

   **a)** Glucose             **b)** Methane

   **c)** Polysaccharide     **d)** Adenosine triphosphate

5. Which of the following organelles has the ability to perform photosynthesis?

   **a)** Chloroplast        **b)** Chloroform

   **c)** Chlorophyll        **d)** Chromosome

6. Which of the following elements is **not** involved in the process of anaerobic decomposition?

   **a)** Mercury           **b)** Oxygen

   **c)** Sulphur            **c)** Carbon

7. Which of the following terms does **not** describe a metabolic reaction whereby organic molecules are broken down in order to release the energy harnessed inside their chemical bonds?

   **a)** Endergonic        **b)** Exothermic

   **c)** Catabolic          **d)** Organic

# Lesson 2  THE BIOSPHERE AND ENERGY

NOTES

The vast majority of energy that is exchanged and manipulated within the biosphere comes from the sun. Solar radiation provides the power for most of the cycles within the biosphere.

The biosphere radiates energy into space through two central channels: the reflection of sunlight (albedo) and the emission of heat in the form of long-wave radiation.

The fundamental atoms in the biosphere are neither created nor destroyed, merely cycled and reused.

Matter within the biosphere is conserved and recycled, whereas energy is not. In other words, in order for the biosphere to function, it requires a constant input of energy from the sun, which is eventually reduced to heat. The carbon, hydrogen, nitrogen, oxygen, phosphorus, and sulfur atoms that compose most of the organic material in the biosphere do not break down into smaller components and are neither created nor destroyed.

These building blocks cycle through plants and animals and act as agents that conduct energy flow. Of these elements, carbon is the element that forms the fundamental basis for all organic life in the biosphere.

The components of the biosphere can be divided into two categories: biotic and abiotic factors. Biotic factors are living processes that involve organisms and cells. The following are examples of biotic factors:
- photosynthesis
- cellular respiration
- fermentation
- growth and reproduction
- parasitism
- disease
- population density

James Lovelock expressed the dynamic of biotic cycles on Earth in the Gaia Hypothesis, which states that life influences its environment in such a way as to make conditions favourable to reproduction and metabolism. The comparatively stable atmospheric components, the stable salt content of the oceans, and Earth's relatively stable surface temperature suggest that life regulates its own homeostatic conditions. The fact that these conditions have remained relatively static and unchanged over thousands of years is used as further evidence of the stability of the biosphere.

There are five "guilds" of organisms: photosynthesizers, herbivores, carnivores, scavengers, and decomposers.

Studies show that there is a definite framework for nutrient recycling in all forms of biotic life, which include photosynthesizers, herbivores, carnivores, scavengers, and decomposers,. Dr. Lovelock called these groups *guilds*. The waste products of one guild provide the low-energy food for another.

Abiotic components of the biosphere include all the non-living processes and materials that occur on Earth. The following are examples of abiotic factors:

- temperature
- water
- sunlight
- wind
- humidity
- rock and soil
- salinity (the saltiness of land and water)
- ocean currents

Both biotic and abiotic factors affect biogeochemical cycles of matter in the biosphere by either speeding processes up or slowing them down.

One major abiotic factor that helps regulate the carbon dioxide levels in the atmosphere is ocean water near the polar ice caps. Gaseous $CO_2$ can diffuse directly into cold ocean water, thus reducing the amount of carbon in the air. Other abiotic factors, such as volcanic eruptions and forest fires, increase the amount of carbon dioxide in the atmosphere.

Water is tremendously important in the functioning of the biosphere. The bright reflectivity of water when it is in the form of ice and snow increases Earth's albedo and reduces the amount of solar energy entering the system.

When water is in the form of gaseous water vapour, it functions as a greenhouse gas and traps heat within the atmosphere. As a liquid, water stores oxygen in the hydrosphere and can dissolve carbon dioxide from the atmosphere.

The biosphere acts like an enormous greenhouse, where sunlight enters the system and is then trapped by biotic materials such as plants and by abiotic factors such as the carbon dioxide, ozone, methane, and water vapour in the atmosphere. These greenhouse gases act as insulation and are one of the central regulatory components of the biosphere.

Energy predominantly enters the biosphere as solar energy and is cycled via a number of matter processes, beginning first with producer photosynthesis and then energy transfer through cellular respiration. Energy is finally released through the process of decomposition. The final product of these biological cycles is a net loss of heat energy, which is partially trapped in the biosphere by greenhouse gases.

Water vapour is the most influential greenhouse gas

Of the greenhouse gases, water vapour causes between 36% and 70% of what is referred to as the *greenhouse effect*. Carbon dioxide causes between 9% and 26% of this effect, while ozone causes between 3% and 7%.

NOTES

The greenhouse effect is necessary for the normal functioning of the biosphere because without the conservation of heat energy within Earth's environment, the sun would only be able to heat the surface of Earth to an average of approximately –18°C. This system of thermal recycling actually causes the surface of the planet to remain at an average temperature of 14°C. Of the total heat and energy present in the atmosphere, approximately 62% is recycled to the surface, and 38% is lost to space.

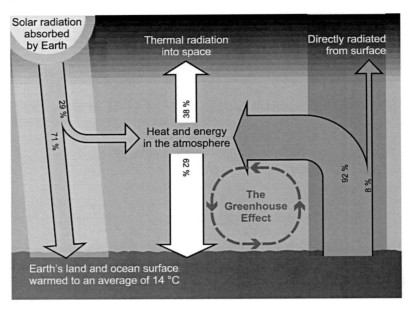

A number of dynamic equilibriums maintain the homeostatic balance of the biosphere.

The biosphere successfully operates as a system because of a series of equilibriums that conserve matter, but not energy.

**Example 1**

List two of the biotic factors that can affect biological processes and cycles within the biosphere.

*Solution*

The following are biotic factors that play a role in the various functions and cycles in the biosphere.

- Motility: When a person runs or exercises, he or she breathes in an increased amount of oxygen and exhales an increased amount of carbon dioxide.
- Population: The greater the population, the greater the amount of cellular respiration.
- Disease: Bacteria, viruses, and other vectors of disease strongly affect the life/death cycle of animal populations.
- Competition: In some environments, there may be two or more sets of organisms that require certain nutrients to survive. If those nutrients are of limited availability, it can lead to biological conflict.

10

**Example 2**

List two of the abiotic factors that can affect the dynamic interactions within the biosphere.

*Solution*

The following are abiotic factors that can speed up or slow down functions and cycles within the biosphere.

- Combustion:  Any kind of hydrocarbon that burns will always consume oxygen and produce carbon dioxide.  A forest fire transforms trees into their component elements faster than decomposition.

- Sunlight:  If a plant receives an increased amount of direct sunlight, it will fix carbon more rapidly into glucose and will use more cellular respiration to grow.  It will cycle carbon out of the atmosphere and then back in.

- Nutrients:  If an area of land is rich in nitrates, phosphates, and water, it could provide a nutritious environment for a large population of autotrophs.

- Lightning:  Lightning can change free oxygen in the air into ozone. It can also start forest fires.  Both of these effects of lightening significantly accelerate different biogeochemical cycles.

**Example 3**

Define the characteristics of the greenhouse effect and discuss its impact on the biosphere.

*Solution*

The greenhouse effect acts as a global insulator by conserving heat and energy in the atmosphere.  Earth's climate is dependent upon greenhouse gases in order to maintain an environment that is able to support life.  Because cellular respiration, combustion, and decomposition all produce greenhouse gases, the greenhouse effect is constantly produced and renewed.

## PRACTICE EXERCISE

1. Which of the following conditions is a biotic factor in the biosphere?

    **a)** Salinity  **b)** Motility

    **c)** Humidity  **d)** Alkalinity

2. Which of the following is **not** a significant element in the composition of organic material?

    **a)** Sulfur  **b)** Silicon

    **c)** Hydrogen  **d)** Phosphorus

3. Which of the following elements is necessary for matter to be considered organic?

    **a)** Oxygen  **b)** Carbon

    **c)** Nitrogen  **d)** Phosphorus

4. Which of the following two gases are considered to be greenhouse gases?

    **a)** nitrogen and oxygen  **b)** methane and propane

    **c)** carbon dioxide and methane  **d)** nitrogen and carbon dioxide

5. Which greenhouse gas has the **greatest** effect in terms of recycling both heat and energy?

    **a)** Ozone  **b)** Nitrogen

    **c)** Water vapour  **d)** Chloroflourocarbon

6. Which of the following processes does **not** produce a greenhouse gas?

    **a)** Cellular respiration  **b)** Decomposition

    **c)** Photosynthesis  **d)** Combustion

7. Which of the following groups is **not** a *guild* of life forms?

    **a)** Carnivores  **b)** Xerotrophs

    **c)** Herbivores  **d)** Decomposers

# Lesson 3   THE CARBON CYCLE

Matter and energy cycles in the biosphere are precisely balanced in order to maintain perpetual cycles. Energy flows from the sun, through Earth's atmosphere, and into the lithosphere and hydrosphere. Solar energy is metabolised and stored chemically by autotrophs through the process of photosynthesis. The producers use some of that energy for growth and reproductionand store the rest as carbohydrates, which are then consumed by heterotrophs. The waste and storage material from producers nourish the consumers. The consumers also help nourish the producers.

The amount of material used in the process of photosynthesis is exactly equal to the amount of material produced as a result of cellular respiration. These two processes perpetuate one another and create a balance that is self-sustaining. The relationship between photosynthesis and cellular respiration is just one of many such equilibriums that serve to maintain a relatively static and stable environment.

With only a few, rare exceptions, matter is neither created nor destroyed and neither enters nor leaves Earth's confines . The net mass of the materials on the planet and in the atmosphere remains constant. The movement and reuse of matter through the biosphere occurs through a number of cycles and processes that balance with one another in order to create a net steady state equilibrium.

The balance between the different biotic and abiotic processes forms a steady-state equilibrium in the biosphere.

The conservation of a certain form of matter as it moves through different forms and configurations in the biosphere is what defines a biogeochemical cycle. Carbon cycles through the three sections of the biosphere and reacts with other elements, such as hydrogen and oxygen, in order to form molecules that can be solid, liquid, or gaseous.

The following diagram shows how carbon cycles through the biosphere.

## The Carbon Cycle

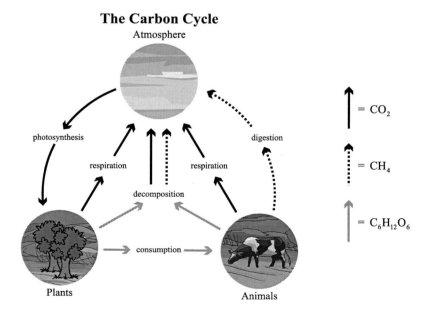

$CO_2$ is carbon dioxide.

$CH_4$ is methane.

$C_6H_{12}O_6$ is glucose.

NOTES

Carbon dioxide is a by-product of cellular respiration in animals and is exhaled as a gas. Although the concentration of carbon dioxide in the atmosphere is very low, it is critical to climate conditions in the biosphere.

## Carbon Dioxide
### ($CO_2$)

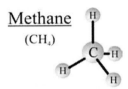

One major abiotic factor that helps regulate the carbon dioxide levels in the atmosphere is ocean water near the polar ice caps. Gaseous $CO_2$ can diffuse directly into cold ocean water, which reduces the amount of carbon in the air.

Other abiotic factors, such as volcanic eruptions and forest fires, increase the amount of carbon dioxide in the atmosphere.

In addition to forming an equilibrium of gas exchanges between plants and animals, carbon dioxide and another carbon-based gas, methane, contribute significantly to the greenhouse effect.

## Methane
### ($CH_4$)

Over 99% of the atmosphere is composed of nitrogen ($N_2$) and oxygen ($O_2$), but the tiny amount of carbon-based gases found in the air has an extraordinary impact on Earth's temperature and climate. Remember that the biosphere loses energy in the form of reflected light and radiated heat.

Carbon in the atmosphere helps keep heat in the biosphere. If the carbon content of the atmosphere becomes too high, the planet could overheat, which could lead to the creation of deserts and the depletion of polar ice caps. If the carbon content of the atmosphere falls too low, the biosphere could enter into an ice age.

Carbon forms covalent bonds easily, which allows it to create long chains and rings in huge macromolecules. Biological and organic macromolecules such as carbohydrates, proteins, lipids (fats), and nucleic acids are all composed of interconnected carbon-based structures. Glucose can undergo polymerization through a process called **dehydration synthesis** in order to form massive chains called cellulose.

## Glucose
($C_6H_{12}O_6$)

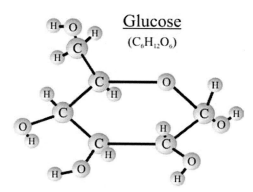

Dehydration synthesis involves the release of a molecule of water from two bonded molecules. Looking at the molecule of glucose, it is not essential to know the exact structure. However, notice the (OH) groups that branch outward. When two glucose molecules combine, a single hydrogen atom from one molecule will break off and bond with an (OH) from a second molecule. This is how $H_2O$ is formed.

Carbon polymerizes using dehydration synthesis.

## Cellulose

Single Glucose Molecule

Water
($H_2O$)

Water
($H_2O$)

Glucose polymerizes using dehydration synthesis to form cellulose.

Cellulose is a carbohydrate that is anabolically produced by plants as a result of photosynthesis. It is an important nutrient in the diet of a healthy animal. In addition to light, photosynthesis requires two chemical ingredients: water and carbon dioxide.

When a producer in either the hydrosphere or the lithosphere draws carbon from the atmosphere and uses it to build an organic compound, the process is known as **carbon fixation**. Photosynthesis is a good example of carbon fixation because it uses carbon dioxide and water to produce glucose and oxygen.

When there is a large quantity of solid carbon compounds that are physically cut off from the atmosphere, it is known as a **carbon sink**. Swamps, bogs, and deep ocean floors that are compressed and driven deep into Earth by tectonic or volcanic forces over thousands of years eventually transform into a different form of carbon, such as coal, graphite, or natural gas (principally methane).

When an autotroph takes carbon dioxide from the air and uses the carbon to build an organic compound, it is known as **carbon fixation.**

**Carbon sinks** are deposits of organic materials that have ceased to cycle through the biosphere.

**Aerobic** decomposition requires oxygen and produces carbon dioxide. **Anaerobic** decomposition takes place where there is no oxygen and produces methane.

The lithification of carbon sinks creates diamonds, and it is also the process that creates all of the fossil fuels that people can burn for energy. Burning these fossil fuels releases the carbon that was previously locked in the lithosphere back into the atmosphere. Remember that combustion releases carbon dioxide into the air and carbon in the form of ash into the lithosphere.

In short, a carbon sink is a large deposit of carbon that has stopped cycling through the biosphere because it has stopped interacting with the atmosphere. Because a lot of these deposits are combustible hydrocarbons, they can be excavated and burned as fuel, which releases carbon into the atmosphere. Many modes of transportation and industrial processes, are responsible for increases to the greenhouse effect.

Because of its chemical reactivity and ability to polymerize into macromolecules, carbon is an essential biological component. It can also be exceptionally deadly when combined with certain elements. Animals need glucose and carbohydrates to live, but they cannot breathe either carbon dioxide or carbon monoxide. Both are toxic to the respiratory systems of animals.

Another important factor in the carbon cycle is the function of decomposers. Fungi and bacteria consume plant and animal wastes as well as dead tissue. As they use these materials for cellular respiration, their activities create heat as a waste product.

Decomposers fall into two groups. Most are **aerobic**, which means that they cannot survive without oxygen. Members of the other group are **anaerobic** (without oxygen). Anaerobic decomposers are able to draw metabolic energy from organic mass, but instead of producing carbon dioxide, as the aerobic decomposers would do, they produce methane.

**Carbon Compounds**
- There are more than one million known carbon compounds.
- Carbohydrates are nutrients that provide energy. This category of compounds includes sugar and starches.
- Carbon dioxide is an important ingredient in photosynthesis, a waste gas from cellular respiration, and helps regulate the planet's climate.
- Carbon disulfide ($CS_2$) is a highly flammable, colourless, and poisonous liquid.
- Carbon monoxide is a highly poisonous, tasteless, odourless, and colourless gas produced whenever another carbon compound is oxidized, as in the engine of a gasoline-powered vehicle.

## Carbon Factoids

- Chemical Symbol: C
- Atomic Number: 6
- Carbon does not melt. It sublimates from solid form directly to gaseous form at 3 550°C.
- All living things in the biosphere are based on carbon compounds.
- Carbon only makes up 0.032% of Earth's crust.
- Carbon occurs naturally in elemental form in four ways: diamonds, graphite, amorphous carbon (such as coal, lignite, and anthracite), and fullerenes (a rare type of molecule that can be found in things like candle soot).
- Carbon does not react chemically at room temperature.
- Diamond, graphite, and amorphous carbon do not dissolve in solvents.

Amorphous is a term that means the carbon atoms lack organization and have no definite pattern. By contrast, graphite and diamonds have carbon atoms that are arranged in patterns.

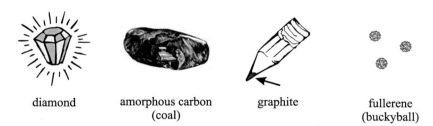

diamond        amorphous carbon        graphite        fullerene
                    (coal)                                (buckyball)

## Carbon Cycle Summary

- Animals and plants release carbon into the atmosphere in the form of $CO_2$ as an end result of cellular respiration.
- Plants, as well as some other autotrophs, pull carbon from the air and use carbon fixation to make glucose and other organic materials. The solid waste products and dead animal and plant matter store carbon in the lithosphere and hydrosphere.
- Cold ocean water can also reduce carbon dioxide in the atmosphere by dissolving it into the hydrosphere.
- Burning carbon compounds from carbon sinks releases carbon into the atmosphere, which increases the magnitude of the greenhouse effect.
- Decomposers, such as bacteria and fungi, use the organic wastes from plants and animals to put carbon back into the atmosphere in the form of $CO_2$ if the decomposition is aerobic or $CH_4$ if there is anaerobic decomposition.
- The rate, or speed, at which this cycle operates depends on biotic and abiotic factors.

**Example 1**

List **biotic** factors that act as vectors for cycling carbon into the atmosphere.

*Solution*

The following are biotic factors of the biosphere that cycle carbon into the atmosphere.

- Cellular respiration in all forms of life, including plants and animals, operates through an intake of oxygen and produces carbon dioxide, which is gaseous and enters the atmosphere.
- Decomposition produces two types of carbon-based gas. Aerobic decomposition produces carbon dioxide. Anaerobic decomposition produces methane.
- Digestion in animals produces waste products, including methane.

**Example 2**

List **abiotic** factors that act as vectors for cycling carbon into the atmosphere.

*Solution*

The following are abiotic factors that can cycle carbon into the atmosphere.

- Combustion: Any kind of hydrocarbon that burns will always consume oxygen and produce carbon dioxide. Candles, paper, and wood are all composed of hydrocarbons and produce carbon dioxide and water vapour when set aflame. Materials from carbon sinks, such as coal, oil, gasoline, and natural gas, behave in the same way.
- Volcanoes can erupt and eject carbon dioxide into the atmosphere from the lithospheric levels beneath the biosphere.
- Cellular respiration, which occurs in both plants and animals, uses oxygen and glucose to produce carbon dioxide and water. The carbon dioxide is then passed into the atmosphere by terrestrial organisms and into the hydrosphere by most aquatic organisms.

**Example 3**

How do human activities affect the functioning of the carbon cycle?

*Solution*

The various ways in which human activities interact with the carbon cycle include the following:

- decomposition
- digestive waste
- cellular respiration
- combustion of fossil fuels for power and heat

## PRACTICE EXERCISE

1.  Which of the following processes is a biotic factor in the carbon cycle?

    **a)** Erosion                          **b)** Combustion

    **c)** Respiration                      **d)** Precipitation

2.  Which of the following compounds does not contain carbon?

    **a)** Glucose                          **b)** Methane

    **c)** Cellulose                        **d)** Ammonia

3.  When glucose molecules polymerize, or link together in a chain, one product is a carbohydrate. What is the other product of this type of reaction?

    **a)** Water                            **b)** Oxygen

    **c)** Hydrogen                         **d)** Carbon dioxide

4.  Which two gases act as the primary source of carbon in the atmosphere?

    **a)** Nitrogen and oxygen              **b)** Methane and propane

    **c)** Carbon dioxide and methane       **d)** Nitrogen and carbon dioxide

5.  Which of the following types of organisms are able to perform carbon fixation?

    **a)** Producers                        **b)** Consumers

    **c)** Decomposers                      **d)** Heterotrophs

6.  Carbon sinks are deposits of carbon-based organic material that have ceased to interact with the biosphere. If people mine or excavate these carbon sinks and burn the contents for energy, what impact would the consequent increase of carbon in the atmosphere likely have on the biosphere?

    **a)** Earth's albedo would decrease.         **b)** Earth's climate would grow warmer.

    **c)** The ocean tides would become erratic.  **d)** The hours of sunlight per day will decrease.

7.  Which process is used in the polymerization of glucose?

    **a)** Combustion                       **b)** Photosynthesis

    **c)** Dehydration synthesis            **d)** Active transportation

## Lesson 4   THE NITROGEN CYCLE

Nitrogen is an important structural component in a number of essential biochemical molecules. As with most of the elements that form the building blocks of life on Earth, a balance is necessary to maintain a stable living environment. Too much or too little nitrogen can endanger organisms. Nitrogen can be lethally toxic in a number of forms: in gaseous compounds and when combined with water. With the assistance of numerous microbes and bacteria, nitrogen is balanced, cycled, and regulated so that the levels and concentrations are suitable for plant and animal use. As a result of the number of forms in which it can be found and the different methods of exchange between the atmosphere, lithosphere, and hydrosphere, nitrogen can be said to have its own biogeochemical cycle.

Within the biosphere, nitrogen can generally be found in two basic forms. The first is called *free nitrogen* because it is not combined with any other elementsor molecules. It appears as the chemical formula $N_{2(g)}$ and is a colourless, odourless gas that forms 78% of the gases in the atmosphere. Nitrogen can take a second important form in conjunction with other elements. Those molecules are called **nitrogenous compounds** and act as critically important parts of proteins and genetic materials.

Nitrogen can be found in a free, gaseous form, or in a nitrogenous, compounded form.

Free nitrogen has a very stable molecular structure, and for that reason, both animals and plants have difficulty metabolizing it.

### Free Nitrogen
($N_2$)

$$N \equiv N$$

Humans, for example, inhale free nitrogen with every breath but are unable to absorb any nitrogen into their blood. They therefore exhale it as waste. Gaseous nitrogen is transformed into usable nitrogenous compounds by bacteria and microbes using a process known as **nitrogen fixation**.

Some bacteria are symbiotic and live in the nodules of roots of certain plants called legumes. Legumes include such plants as beans, peas, and clover.

**Nitrogen fixation** transforms gaseous free nitrogen into ammonia ($NH_3$) or ammonium ions ($NH_4^+$).

Bacteria and microbes that have an enzyme called **nitrogenase** participate in two different nitrogen-fixing processes: ammonification and nitrification. Ammonification creates two main nitrogenous compounds, ammonia ($NH_3$) and ammonium ions ($NH_4^+$).

### Ammonia
($NH_3$)

### Ammonium
($NH_4^+$)

Plants and other autotrophs are not able to metabolize these molecules until they have been nitrified into compounds that contain oxygen. Nitrification transforms the ammonia and ammonium ions into nitrates ($NO_3$) and nitrite ions ($NO_2^-$), which can be metabolized.

Abiotic factors can also transform free nitrogen into nitrogenous compounds. For example, lightning can convert nitrogen gas into nitrates, which can be washed into the soil through rainfall. Farmers often notice significant crop growth after a lightning storm as the root systems of the plants absorb the nitrogenous nutrients.

Plants can transform nitrogenous materials into a number of different important organic compounds, but the three most important categories are **amino acids**, **nucleotides**, and **adenosine triphosphate**. Since animals are unable to fix nitrogen themselves, they are dependent upon plants to form the foundation of the food chain, which eventually distributes these nutrients to all of the organisms in the biosphere.

The following diagram illustrates how nitrogen is removed from the atmosphere and directed into the lithosphere and hydrosphere.
It also shows how nitrogen migrates through the nitrogen cycle and back into the atmosphere.

> The three important types of nitrogenous compounds are **amino acids**, **nucleotides**, and **ATP**.

### The Nitrogen Cycle

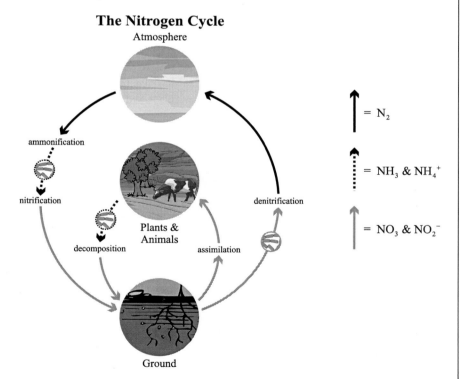

Animals are unable to store protein or other nitrogenous compounds in the same way as they store carbon compounds, such as glucose.
Therefore, excess metabolized nitrogen must be excreted as waste.
Digestive and urinary tracts function as means for the nitrogenous waste products to be returned to the nitrogen cycle.

NOTES

**Decomposers** transform nitrogenous organic material into ammonia and ammonium.

**Nitrifying bacteria** convert ammonia and ammonium to nitrites and nitrates.

**Denitrifying bacteria** return nitrogen to the atmosphere.

Nitrogenous waste in humans is expressed in solid form as feces and in liquid form as urine. Other animals, such as insects and fish, excrete uric acid or urea. All of these excretions inevitably migrate to the ground or to a body of water, at which point a variety of bacteria work to decompose the material.

The first bacteria to transform nitrogenous waste are known as **decomposers** and perform the same job as nitrogen-fixing bacteria: they producing ammonia molecules and ammonium ions. A second group of bacteria, known as **nitrifying bacteria**, convert the ammonium and ammonia into biologically usable nitrites and nitrates through the process of nitrification.

Too much nitrogen in soil or water can be damaging and even deadly to plants. If the nitrites and nitrates in fertilizers and organic waste leach or run off into water supplies, they can cause deadly diseases. There is, however, a third group of bacteria known as **denitrifying bacteria** that break down nitrites and nitrates into free nitrogen gas.

Bacteria and microbes are extremely important in the regulation and balance of the nitrogen cycle. They fix nitrogen gas in the atmosphere into nitrogenous compounds, nitrify those compounds into usable materials, and can either denitrify or decompose materials to release nitrogen back into the air.

**Nitrogen Compounds**
- Nitrogen tends to bond only with itself. Therefore, a lot of nitrogenous compounds are very unstable. Nitrogen atoms tend to revert toward a free nitrogen state.
- Nitric acid ($HNO_3$) is a powerful acid that is used as a chemical reagent. When mixed with hydrochloric acid, it can be used to dissolve gold and platinum.
- Nitroglycerin ($C_3H_5(ONO_2)_3$) is a powerful explosive that is the principal ingredient in dynamite. Trinitrotoluene, also known as TNT ($C_7H_5N_3O_6$), is another explosive nitrogenous compound.
- Nitrous Oxide ($N_2O$) is a colourless and odourless gas that tends to numb sensations. Also known as *laughing gas*, it is used by physicians and dentists to make patients unresponsive to pain.
- Ammonia ($NH_3$) is used as a fertilizer, cleaning agent, and refrigerant.

Liquid nitrogen

Ammonia

Trinitrotoluene

Amino acid

## Nitrogen Factoids

- Chemical Symbol:  N
- Atomic Number:  7
- Nitrogen is non-metallic and is most commonly found in nature in diatomic form as free nitrogen.
- Free nitrogen is colourless, odourless, and flavourless.
- By volume, nitrogen comprises 78% of the atmosphere.
- All organisms require nitrogen to live.
- Nitrogen is a part of the building blocks of amino acids, nucleotides, and ATP.
- Liquid nitrogen is colder than $-195°C$ and is used by scientists for experiments in cryogenics, super conductivity, and many other areas of research where refrigeration is necessary.

## Nitrogen Cycle Summary

- Nitrogen-fixing bacteria live in nodules of legumes, soil and water. They fix free nitrogen from the atmosphere by converting $N_2$ into ammonia ($NH_3$) and ammonium ($NH_4^+$).
- Nitrifying bacteria convert $NH_3$ and $NH_4^+$ into nitrate ($NO_3$) and nitrite ($NO_2^-$), respectively.
- Plants are able to assimilate nitrates and nitrites through their roots.  Animals ingest nitrogen by eating plant matter or other animals.
- Denitrifying bacteria convert nitrates into free nitrogen.
- Decomposer microorganisms release nitrogen from waste and dead matter back into the atmosphere as diatomic elemental nitrogen.

## Example 1

What is the name given to plants with nitrogen-fixing nodules attached to their roots?

### Solution

Plants with nitrogen-fixing nodules are referred to as legumes. Leguminous plants include beans, peas, alfalfa, and clover.

**Example 2**

Compare the carbon and nitrogen cycles.

*Solution*

The following is a list of some of the similarities between the carbon and nitrogen cycles.

- They both use of all three parts of the environment: the lithosphere, hydrosphere, and atmosphere.
- Both cycles have a significant impact on the atmosphere. The carbon cycle is a major factor in the greenhouse effect, and free nitrogen is the largest component of the atmosphere.
- All five guilds of organisms are featured in the cycles.
- Both cycles are affected by abiotic and biotic factors.

The following list contains some of the differences between the carbon and nitrogen cycles.

- The nitrogen cycle is very much dependent upon microbial and bacterial life, whereas the carbon cycle tends to be more macrobiotic.
- The nitrogen cycle involves fewer abiotic factors than the carbon cycle.
- Because nitrogen has a chemical tendency to remain in the atmosphere, more energy is needed to form nitrogenous compounds.
- Carbon is directly involved in both photosynthesis and cellular respiration, whereas nitrogen requires two separate processes—ammonification and nitrification—in order to move from the atmosphere into organic processes.

**Example 3**

What are the products of ammonification and nitrification?

*Solution*

Ammonification produces ammonia ($NH_3$) and ammonium ions ($NH_4^+$). Nitrification produces nitrite ($NO_2^-$) and nitrate ($NO_3$).

**Example 4**

What are the three major types of organic materials that require nitrogen?

*Solution*

The three major organic materials that require nitrogen are amino acids, nucleotides, and adenosine triphosphate (ATP).

## PRACTICE EXERCISE

1. Which of the following processes is a biotic factor in the nitrogen cycle?

   **a)** Fixation                        **b)** Respiration

   **c)** Photosynthesis            **d)** Phosphorylation

2. Which of the following compounds does **not** contain nitrogen?

   **a)** Adenosine triphosphate      **b)** Ammonium

   **c)** Ammonia                   **d)** Glucose

3. How do animals obtain the nitrogen they need from the biosphere?

   **a)** Digestion                  **b)** Inhalation

   **c)** Respiration              **d)** Ammonification

4. What molecular structure describes the **most stable** and common form of nitrogen?

   **a)** $N_2$                       **b)** $NO_3$

   **c)** $NH_3$                    **d)** $NH_4^+$

5. Which of the following substances can be dissolved by aqua regia, which is a mixture of nitric and hydrochloric acids?

   **a)** Hydrogen              **b)** Polypeptides

   **c)** Hydrocarbons        **d)** Precious metals

6. What approximate percentage of the atmosphere is composed of nitrogen by volume?

   **a)** 50%                    **b)** 66%

   **c)** 78%                    **d)** 99%

7. What are the products of nitrogenation?

   **a)** Nitrate and nitrite       **b)** ATP and carbon dioxide

   **c)** Ammonia and ammonium   **d)** Nitrous oxide and nucleotides

8. Which of the following substances is not a common commercial use of ammonia?

   **a)** Fertilizer              **b)** Refrigerant

   **c)** Preservative          **d)** Cleaning agent

# Lesson 5  THE PHOSPHORUS CYCLE

A key function of phosphorus is the transfer of chemical energy through the biosphere.

Phosphorus is an important biological element because the chemical bonds within phosphoric compounds involve a tremendous amount of energy. When bonded to oxygen, phosphorus forms compounds known as **phosphates**. Inorganic phosphates have no carbon and are often found in ionic form. They are represented by the letter P and a lower case i ($P_i$). Adding an inorganic phosphate to a molecule such as ADP stores chemical energy, while removing a phosphate releases energy.

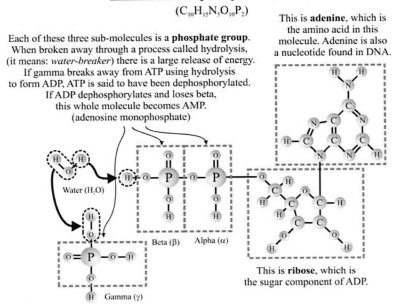

Adenosine Diphosphate (ADP)

($C_{10}H_{15}N_5O_{10}P_2$)

Each of these three sub-molecules is a **phosphate group**. When broken away through a process called hydrolysis, (it means: *water-breaker*) there is a large release of energy. If gamma breaks away from ATP using hydrolysis to form ADP, ATP is said to have been dephosphorylated. If ADP dephosphorylates and loses beta, this whole molecule becomes AMP. (adenosine monophosphate)

This is **adenine**, which is the amino acid in this molecule. Adenine is also a nucleotide found in DNA.

Water ($H_2O$)

Beta (β)    Alpha (α)

Gamma (γ)

This is **ribose**, which is the sugar component of ADP.

If an organism cannot metabolize phosphorus, it cannot make the ATP necessary for cellular respiration and will consequently die. Phosphorus also acts as a principal component of nucleic acids, which carry the genetic codes of every life form in compounds such as DNA and RNA. In animals, phosphorus forms the structural basis for bones and teeth.

Phosphorus is also a key ingredient of compounds called **phospholipids**. These compounds have an interesting property when water is involved. One end of the molecule is known as the *tail* and is repelled by water (**hydrophobic**). The other end is known as the *head* and is attracted to water (**hydrophilic**).

**Hydrophobic** means that a substance *repels* water. **Hydrophilic** means a substance is *attracted* to water.

The tails of phospholipids are also attracted to one another. In solution, they will form a bilayer of molecules that act as a semi-permeable membrane. Bilayer phospholipid membranes are found in all plant and animal cells and are thus an essential part of all living things.

26

This is choline, which is an essential nutrient, classified as a "saturated amine." Notice that the nitrogen atom has formed four bonds. This makes this end of the molecule ionic, and strongly attracted to water. As the "head" of the molecule, this part forms the outer part of cell membranes. The term for the end of a molecule which faces water is **hydrophilic**. Different amine groups here determine the identity of the phospholipid.

The phosphate group, or groups are a part of the polar "head" of the molecule. Some phospholipids can have several of these groups linked together

This glycerol sub-molecule is what holds the head and the tail of the molecule together.

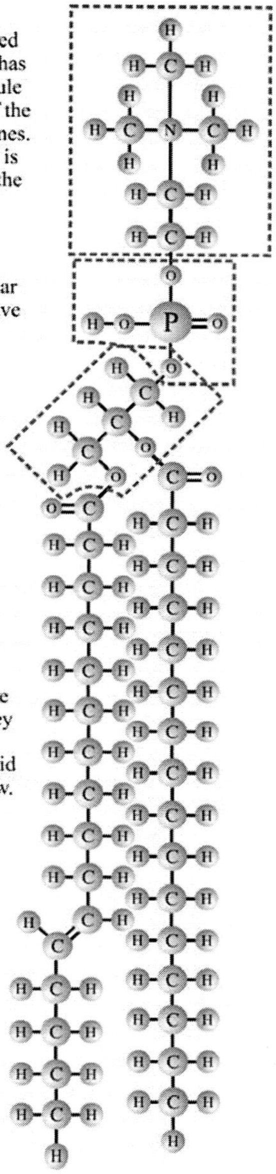

### Phosphatidylcholine (Phospholipid)

($C_{42}H_{82}NO_8P$)

The two fatty acid strands that form the tail of the molecule are **hydrophobic**, which means that they repel water. Tails of phospholipids attract one another, so that when placed together, phospholipid molecules will form a **bilayer**, as illustrated below. Bilayers form cell membranes within a cell.

### Bilayer Formation of Phospholipids

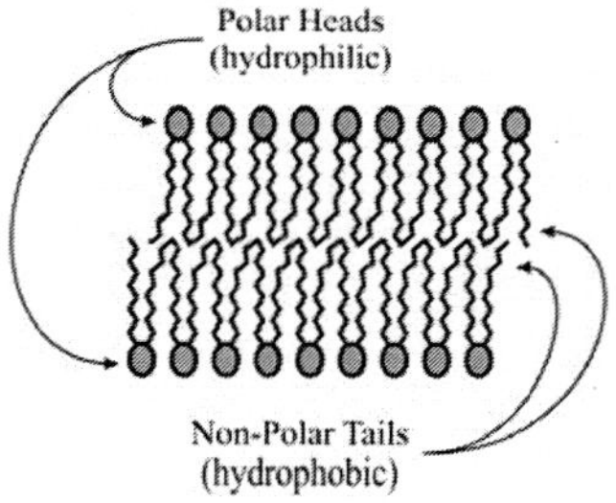

Polar Heads (hydrophilic)

Non-Polar Tails (hydrophobic)

Because all organisms within the biosphere are composed of genetic material and cells, it is necessary for phosphorus to cycle through the environment. Unlike nitrogen and carbon, phosphorus does not cycle through the atmosphere. It is only present in the lithosphere and hydrosphere. Phosphorous is also less abundant and forms heavier compounds that tend to be less soluble in water than the compounds formed by other biogeochemical cycles.

The phosphorous cycle and the nitrogen cycle have a similar reliance on bacteria and other microbes. These organisms help regulate the exchange of phosphorus within the biosphere. Nitrogen, however, is more likely to be found in its gaseous state ($N_2$), whereas phosphorus tends to form heavy, relatively insoluble states and is most commonly found at the bottom of water bodies and as solid sediments in soil.

NOTES

Because phosphate nutrients are not available through respiration, consumers require alternate sources of phosphorus. Most plants and animals have nucleic acids and ATP, which contain phosphorus. The required amounts of phosphates are absorbed and metabolized, and the excess is excreted. Organic waste products and dead animal and plant matter are decomposed by bacteria. This process releases phosphates into the soil or water.

Producers are able to assimilate the available phosphates through their roots by using water to transport the phosphate ions ($PO_4^{3-}$) and hydrogen phosphate ions ($HPO_4^{2-}$) into their cells. Ammonium phosphate (($NH_4$)$_3PO_4$) is often used as a fertilizer in agriculture because it is a phosphorus compound that is very soluble in water. The phosphates are then metabolized into nucleic acids and ATP.

When heterotrophs feed on producers, the primarily biotic part of the phosphorus cycle begins again.

**The Phosphorus Cycle**

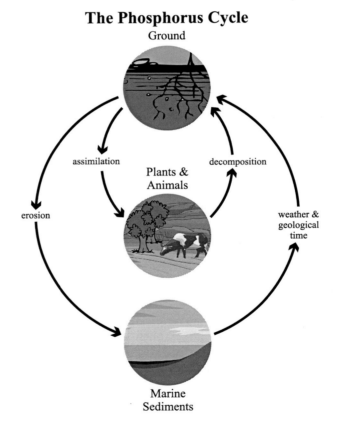

Other biogeochemical cycles store matter differently. Nitrogen is primarily stored in the atmosphere, carbon is stored in carbon sinks filled with fossil fuels, and water is stored in the polar ice caps. Phosphorus is predominantly stored in rock and sediment.

NOTES

The part of the phosphorus cycle related to plants and animals is a relatively rapid one. The storage of phosphorus in rock, however, is much slower.

Weathering and erosion by wind and rain leaches phosphorus from sedimentary rock such as limestone. Phosphorous can then soak into the soil for plant roots to absorb or enter the hydrosphere as runoff. Once it is in an ocean or a lake, phosphoric compounds can be consumed by aquatic life, particularly phytoplankton. When aquatic life dies, the phosphorous settles to the bottom of the water body. This is where it remains until time and pressure transform it into sedimentary rock—and the cycle begins again.

If a lake or pond accumulates too many phosphates and nitrates, it may experience what is called **eutrophication**. Eutrophication occurs when the concentration of nutrients causes a massive growth in the population of aquatic plants, such as weeds, algae and cyanobacteria (photosynthetic bacteria). As a result, biogeochemical cycles within the water body accelerate. This causes an initial increase in biodiversity and population growth. Eventually, the algae and bacteria can take over the area, which can have a deadly impact on many other organisms. Biodiversity decreases, and the ecosystem becomes unstable and fragile.

Eutrophication involves an initial explosion of growth and a possible weakening of the ecosystem itself.

Although eutrophication occurs in areas where there is no human activity, sewage treatment plants, deforestation, the raising of livestock, and the over-fertilizing crops have all been identified as agents that can facilitate the onset of eutrophication.

The Hartbeespoort Dam Lake in South Africa was identified as an example of human-caused eutrophication. Scientists began trying to reduce its phosphorus content in August, 2003. The nine wastewater plants that were discharging over 200 metric tons of phosphorus in the water system annually are now being reformed. Managing the flow of nutrients into a lake and reducing the amount of fertilization and livestock grazing on surrounding farmland are ways people can help achieve a balanced concentration of phosphorus and other nutrients.

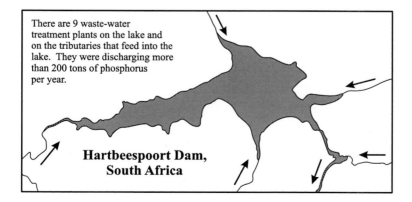

There are 9 waste-water treatment plants on the lake and on the tributaries that feed into the lake. They were discharging more than 200 tons of phosphorus per year.

**Hartbeespoort Dam, South Africa**

Phosphorus Compounds

- Phosphorus is found in every living cell on Earth. Phosphorus acts as a fuel for metabolic energy. It also is a key part of reproductive genetic information, and forms part of cell and body structures.
- Adenosine triphosphate (ATP) and adenosine diphosphate (ADP) are the 'batteries' of chemical energy in the body. ATP splits into a phosphate and ADP, which releases a large amount of energy that is needed for cellular respiration.
- Deoxyribonucleic acid (DNA) and ribonucleic acid (RNA) are molecules that contain the information necessary for the replication of cells and the procreation of organisms.
- Phospholipids form membranes within cells. They also provide structure for organelles and the surface of animal cells.
- Calcium phosphate, in the form of hydroxylapatite $(Ca_{10}(PO_4)_6(OH)_2)$, is found in the bones and teeth of vertebrate animals.
- Ammonium phosphate $((NH_4)_3PO_4)$ is used as a fertilizer in agriculture.

Deoxyribonucleic acid (DNA)  Bones  Fertilizer  Cell membrane

**Phosphorus Factoids**

- Chemical Symbol:    P
- Atomic Number:    15
- Phosphorus is non-metallic, and because it is highly reactive with other elements, it is never found in a free form in nature.
- Its name comes from the Greek words *phos* and *phoros*, meaning "light-bearer." The name is derived from the fact that phosphorus compounds glow faintly when exposed to oxygen.

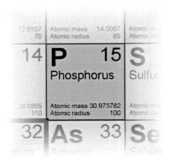

- Pure phosphorus is a colourless and transparent solid that ignites spontaneously when exposed to air.
- Phosphorus is not cycled through the atmosphere because it reacts too easily with other elements to form heavy, solid compounds.
- The average adult human body contains about 1 kg of phosphorus.
- Phosphorus is a regulating nutrient, particularly in aquatic environments. The growth rate of organisms is limited by the amount of phosphorus available in the environment. .

**Phosphorus Cycle Summary**
- Phosphate minerals in rock are weathered and eroded. These minerals either seep into soil or run off into aquatic ecosystems, where they are absorbed by plants and bacteria.
- The photosynthetic organisms absorb the inorganic phosphorus compounds and metabolize them into nucleic acids and ATP.
- Consumers feed on the producers, and decomposers feed upon the waste products and dead material of all three groups.
- Dead consumers, producers, and decomposers, as well as their waste products, leave phosphorus in the lithosphere in the form of sediments, which are compressed into sedimentary rock.

**Example 1**

Compare the phosphorus cycle to the nitrogen cycle.

*Solution*

The following is a list of some of the similarities between the phosphorus and nitrogen cycles.
- Both elements are essential for the formation of genetic materials. Nitrogen is necessary for nucleotides, and phosphorus is necessary for nucleic acids. DNA and RNA are composed of these building blocks.
- Both cycles are dependent on the activities of bacterial and microbial life. The nitrogen cycle requires bacteria and other microbes in order for fixation to occur. Nitrogen, therefore, migrates from the atmosphere to the lithosphere. The phosphorus cycle requires microbial life in order for phosphorous to escape from organic compounds and return to the lithosphere as an inorganic compound.

The following is a list of some of the differences between the phosphorus and nitrogen cycles.
- Nitrogen is predominantly found in nature in the atmosphere, while phosphorus is most commonly found in the lithosphere.
- Nitrogen tends toward a free elemental gaseous state, while phosphorus tends toward a compound solid state.
- The nitrogen cycle uses all three areas of the biosphere: the lithosphere, hydrosphere, and the atmosphere. The phosphorous cycle only uses two: the lithosphere and the hydrosphere.
- The phosphorous cycle involves a larger number of abiotic factors, such as soil, water, pressure, weather, erosion, and others.

## Example 2

How would a lack of phosphorus in a person's diet affect his or her health?

*Solution*

Because phosphorus is a crucial component to several body processes, a number of effects would be observed.

- A lack of calcium phosphate would lead to weaker bones and teeth.
- A deficiency in ATP would mean a loss of physical energy.

- A failure to produce nucleic acids would stunt a person's growth and inhibit his or her ability to reproduce.

## Example 3

Eutrophication accelerates all of the biogeochemical cycles, and it can eventually cause a loss of biodiversity within an ecosystem.
Why is biodiversity important?

*Solution*

Biodiversity includes all the different types of organisms within an ecosystem. As we can see through the processes of the carbon, nitrogen, and phosphorus cycles, many different guilds of life forms are required to cycle materials through the biosphere. The fewer the varieties of organisms, the more fragile the equilibrium becomes in terms of sustaining life. An ecosystem with a low degree of biodiversity is less able to withstand biotic or abiotic changes.

## Example 4

Debbie is going to her parents' cabin for the summer. A neighbour tells her that the fishing is very bad this year. Debbie suspects that phosphorus emissions from a nearby sewage treatment plant may be responsible.

What sort of experiments can Debbie conduct to verify whether or not she is right?

32

*Solution*

Debbie can do a number of things to prove her hypothesis.

- She can directly observe the surface of the lake to see if it is filled with green algae and a scummy-looking film.

- She can also examine the surface of the water. If the water is cloudy or if she cannot see the bottom at depths of more than three feet, the lake is probably eutrophic.

- She can look at a water sample from the lake under a microscope and observe the concentration of single-celled bacteria and algae.

- If she takes a sample of the lake water to a laboratory, a technician can use spectrophotometry or fluorometry to determine the concentration of chlorophyll in the water, which is an indicator of the presence of a primary producer.  Single-celled producers are likely to be cyanobacteria or algae.

## PRACTICE EXERCISE

1.  Which of the following processes is a biotic process within the phosphorus cycle?

    **a)** Erosion

    **c)** Respiration

    **b)** Fixation

    **d)** Decomposition

2.  Which of the following compounds does **not** contain phosphorus?

    **a)** DNA

    **c)** Nitroglycerin

    **b)** Nucleic acids

    **d)** Adenosine triphosphate

3.  What compound forms cellular membranes?

    **a)** DNA

    **c)** Phospholipids

    **b)** ATP

    **d)** Calcium phosphate

4.  Which of the following processes requires nucleic acids?

    **a)** Breathing

    **c)** Decomposition

    **b)** Reproduction

    **d)** Cellular respiration

5.  Which of the following is a product of ATP breaking down into ADP?

    **a)** Water

    **c)** Glucose

    **b)** Energy

    **d)** Chlorophyll

6.  Which of the following processes do animals use in order to assimilate phosphorous compounds?

    **a)** Digestion

    **c)** Decomposition

    **b)** Inhalation

    **d)** Perspiration

7.  Which abiotic factor is common to **all** producers in the process of intaking of phosphorus?

    **a)** Soil

    **c)** Water

    **b)** Rock

    **d)** Sediment

# *PRACTICE QUIZ*

1. Which compound comprises the largest percentage of the atmosphere by volume?

   **a)** $O_2$

   **b)** $N_2$

   **c)** $CO_2$

   **d)** $NH_3$

2. Which of the following terms describes a self-sustaining series of interactions where the properties of the system remain unchanged over time?

   **a)** Polymerism

   **b)** Equilibrium

   **c)** Oligotrophism

   **d)** Phosphorylation

3. What do hydrolysis, cellular respiration, digestion, combustion, and decomposition all have in common?

   **a)** They all produce heat.

   **b)** They all require oxygen.

   **c)** They all take place in producers.

   **d)** They all represent biotic processes.

4. Which of the following biogeochemical cycle does **not** directly involve the atmosphere?

   **a)** Water

   **b)** Carbon

   **c)** Nitrogen

   **d)** Phosphorus

5. Which of the following statements regarding the biosphere is **not true**?

   **a)** Heat escapes into space.

   **b)** Greenhouse gases retain heat.

   **c)** All life contains carbon molecules.

   **d)** The albedo of the polar ice caps creates $CO_2$.

6. Which of the following compounds does **not** act as a greenhouse gas?

   **a)** Methane

   **b)** Ammonia

   **c)** Water vapour

   **d)** Carbon dioxide

7. Which of the following terms **cannot** be used to define plants?

   **a)** Autotrophs

   **b)** Producers

   **c)** Consumers

   **d)** Photosynthesizers

8. In which organelle does photosynthesis take place?

   **a)** Chloroplast

   **b)** Chloroform

   **c)** Chemoplast

   **d)** Chloroglobin

9. Which of the following molecules can be found in every living cell?

   **a)** Fullerene

   **b)** Ammonia

   **c)** Phospholipid

   **d)** Sulphur dioxide

**10.** Which of the following molecules is produced by dehydration synthesis?

   **a)** Glucose

   **b)** Methane

   **c)** Carbon dioxide

   **d)** Macromolecules

**11.** Which of the following abiotic factors can fix free nitrogen?

   **a)** Wind

   **b)** Sunlight

   **c)** Lightning

   **d)** Ocean currents

**12.** Which of the following types of nutrients are generally found in fertilizers?

   **a)** Ammonia and methane

   **b)** Phosphates and nitrates

   **c)** Phospholipids and nucleotides

   **d)** Carbohydrates and nucleic acids

**13.** Which of the following processes is **not** a metabolic process?

   **a)** Digestion

   **b)** Combustion

   **c)** Photosynthesis

   **d)** Cellular respiration

**14.** Which of the following organisms are **not** classified as producers?

   **a)** Algae

   **b)** Fungi

   **c)** Cyanobacteria

   **d)** Phytoplankton

**15.** Which of the following pairings does **not** correctly match an element with its primary form of storage within the biosphere?

   **a)** Carbon/aqueous ions

   **b)** Oxygen/atmospheric gas

   **c)** Nitrogen/atmospheric gas

   **d)** Phosphorus/rocks and sediment

**16.** Which of the following human activities is a cause of eutrophication?

   **a)** Crop rotation

   **b)** Crop harvesting

   **c)** Crop fertilization

   **d)** Crop fermentation

**17.** Define a steady state equilibrium.

**18.** Give three examples of gas exchanges within the biosphere.

**19.** Define the greenhouse effect and its impact on the biosphere.

## Lesson 6  WATER

Water ($H_2O$) is a fundamental component of all living things. All living cells require water in order to transport nutrients, reproduce, and perform cellular respiration. A human being can live for approximately a month without any food, but they are only able to survive 3–4 days without water. Roughly 72% of the fat-free tissue in the human body is composed of water.

The biosphere as a whole does not contain large amounts fresh water. Of all the water found on Earth, 97% of it is salt water. Many living organisms, especially terrestrial plants and animals, require fresh water.

Water has a number of interesting chemical properties that are useful to biological systems. It also forms the basis of many measurement systems. For example, 1 litre of pure water has a mass of 1 kilogram.

### Water
(H₂O)

At first glance, water may seem like a fairly common and ordinary substance. It is colourless, odourless, and tasteless, but it has a number of characteristics that are unique. Water is a small molecule that contains one oxygen atom and two hydrogen atoms. In most cases, these atoms are bounded by a covalent bond that has an unequal sharing of electrons.

Because oxygen is about 16 times heavier than hydrogen, the shared electrons that form the covalent bond spend more time closer to the oxygen nucleus, which gives the molecule its distinctive v-shape. The shape is important because when water is in solid form, it crystallizes into snowflakes and ice lattices.

The other effect of the shape is that one side has a relatively positive (+) electromagnetic charge, while the other side is negatively (−) charged. The discrepancy between the two sides makes water a **polar molecule**. Because opposites attract each other electromagnetically, this means that water molecules can form **hydrogen molecular bonds** with one another. Hydrogen molecular bonds are very weak. However, the large number of bonds that can be formed helps groups of water molecules stick together.

The tendency for molecules of the same type to cluster is called **cohesion**. Water's cohesive qualities give it a very high **surface tension**. Water has the highest surface tension of all liquids except mercury, which is why water vapour that condenses into liquid can be seen as raindrops.

NOTES

Hydrogen molecular bonds are essentially weak, but can be formed in large numbers.

Cohesion is the tendency of molecules of the same type to cluster together.

The cohesiveness of water enables what is referred to as **capillary action**. This process can be observed as water is transported from the roots of tall trees upward to the leaves and branches. As water molecules evaporate from the leaves through the process of **transpiration**, the chain of water molecules in the vascular tissue of the tree pull one another up as they move into the space left behind.

In every quantity of water ($H_2O$), there is always a trace of hydrogen hydroxide (HOH). Hydrogen hydroxide molecules have the same number and type of atoms as water's more common form, dihydrogen oxide. The difference is that HOH is formed using an ionic bond between a positively charged hydrogen ion ($H^+$) and a negatively charged hydroxyl ion ($OH^-$), as opposed to the covalent bonds found in $H_2O$.

Essentially, hydrogen hydroxide is a water molecule where an electron has completely switched from one hydrogen atom to the other. This produces two ions, one negatively charged and one positively charged. The ions in water react with the hydrogen ions of acids and the hydroxyl ions of bases to form aqueous solutions.

The potential hydrogen value of a solution, or pH, varies according to the number of positive and negative ions present. Pure distilled water is neutral, which means it has a pH of exactly 7. However, most naturally occurring forms of water are actually solutions with dissolved minerals and gases in them. Seawater tends to be more basic, with a pH closer to 8, as a result of the salt content. Rainwater, on the other hand, is slightly acidic, with a pH closer to 6, as a result of the carbon dioxide it absorbs from the air.

Water's fascinating structure makes it one of the best solvents on Earth. More molecules dissolve in water than in any other substance known to science, which is why it is often called the universal solvent. For example, salt crystals are held together by strong ionic bonds, and yet salt dissolves rapidly in water. Nutrients such as nitrates also dissolve easily in water, which allows runoff and infiltration to carry important materials to plants and animals.

Gases also dissolve in water. Carbon dioxide dissolves more easily as the temperature of water decreases. This is an important part of the carbon cycle. Oxygen also dissolves in water, which is why aquariums have air pumps: to expose more gas to the water. Dissolved oxygen is critical to the survival of marine life.

NOTES

Capillary action occurs when a liquid is elevated or depressed by the contact of solid surfaces.

The pH of pure water is 7, which means that it is perfectly neutral.

NOTES

The diffusion of gases across living membranes also requires water. The bilayer membranes of polar phospholipids operate in conjunction with water to allow carbon dioxide and oxygen to travel between organelles and cell membranes. Gases can only diffuse across cell membranes after they are dissolved in water.

Because both carbon dioxide and oxygen are exchanged and must diffuse across cell membranes, photosynthesis and cellular respiration thus require water. Water is also a direct participant in both reactions, acting as an ingredient of photosynthesis and a product of cellular respiration.

Almost all important biochemical reactions have water as a key component. In certain reactions such as the release of energy from ATP molecules, water is used to break away a phosphate group from the rest of the molecule in a process known as hydrolysis. When biochemical macromolecules are formed or polymerized using dehydration synthesis, water is produced.

Water also experiences phase changes at relatively common temperatures within the biosphere. It is the only substance on Earth that naturally exists in all three states: solid, liquid, and gas. The temperature range necessary for the transition between solid (ice), liquid (water), and gas (vapour) is very narrow, spanning from 0°C to 100°C.

**The latent heat of fusion** is the amount of energy required to take a substance that is at its melting point and change its state.

The point that divides solid from liquid is called the **melting point**. Ice melts into a fluid and water freezes into a solid at 0°C. The heat needed to melt ice or the heat that needs to be removed from water to make it freeze is called the **latent heat of fusion**. Water has the highest heat of fusion of any other compound except ammonia.

The melting point of gold is 1 064°C. At that temperature, it does not take a lot of energy to make the hot gold change phase and become a liquid. It takes approximately 15.2 calories per gram to push gold over the threshold between solid and liquid. At that moment, the temperature of the gold does not increase, but its state shifts.

On the other hand, when water is at 0°C, it takes 80 calories per gram to make it shift from one phase to another. Considering that once water is a liquid and that it only takes one calorie per gram to increase the temperature each degree centigrade, the phase change comparatively consumes a lot of energy.

**The latent heat of vaporization** is the amount of energy required to take a substance that is at its boiling point and change its state.

The temperature at which water can make the phase change to become a gas or condense from a vapour into a liquid is known as the **boiling point**. The boiling point of water is 100°C. The energy needed to push water from a liquid to a gas is even greater than the amount necessary to go from a solid to a liquid. It takes 540 calories per gram to force water to make the phase shift and is known as water's **heat of vaporization**.

The heat of vaporization of gold is only 388 calories per gram. Of course, the gold would first have to be heated up to 2 856°C.

What can be concluded is that water is very stable in each one of its phases, and it takes a great deal of energy to make it change phase. That being said, the range between the melting point and the boiling point is very narrow. There are only 100°C between the two. Gold has 1 792°C between its melting and boiling points.

In addition to melting and boiling, water can also move from solid directly to gaseous form in a process known as **sublimation**. A wet blanket hung on a clothesline on a cold winter day will dry even as water molecules freeze. Some of the water will sublimate into the atmosphere. In this case, the energy needed for this phase change comes not from temperature, but from the action of the wind.

Another factor that affects phase change is pressure. Most of the values for points of phase change that are used for substances are based on the laboratory definition of standard temperature and pressure (STP). For example, at an elevation of 2 133 m, the atmospheric pressure is much lower, and in those conditions, the boiling point of water drops to 92°C.

Water is the only substance on the planet that becomes less dense when it makes the transition from liquid to solid. In the physical sciences, liquids tend to have less molecular energy than gases, and solids tend to have less molecular energy than liquids. As a material loses energy, its molecules tend to cluster closer together. Water defies this convention.

Placing a glass jar filled with water into a freezer will break the container because the water will expand as it freezes into ice. Ice occupies more volume and has less density than liquid water, which is why ice cubes float on top of cool water in a glass and why icebergs float atop the ocean. This property of water is of some importance to aquatic life forms. Ice forms on the tops, rather than the bottoms of lakes and rivers in winter, insulating and protecting the aquatic ecosystems below it.

The following diagram describes the relative densities of ice and water and shows why only 10% of the mass of an iceberg appears above the surface of the water.

$$\frac{920}{1\,025} \cong 90\,\%$$

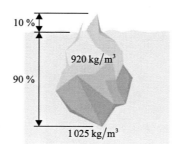

STP is 0°C and 101.325 kPa.

The comparatively narrow range of temperatures that separate the melting and boiling points of water allow for all three states of water to appear in the biosphere while still keeping an acceptable temperature range for organisms to function and survive. As an abiotic factor, water plays a part in almost every cycle and dynamic in all three subdivisions of the biosphere.

If there were no solid water in the form of ice, the amount of available land for terrestrial organisms would be greatly reduced, and the decreased albedo from the white snow and ice would mean that more solar energy would be accepted by the biosphere. Temperatures would therefore increase. Increased global temperature would mean more water vapour in the atmosphere and an intensification of the greenhouse effect. Ice and snow essentially prevent the planet from overheating.

If there were no gaseous water in the form of water vapour, on the other hand, the greenhouse effect would be significantly less, and global temperatures would drop to an unacceptably low level in terms of maintaining a biosphere. The three states of water help regulate the temperature of the planet. This is primarily a result of another of water's chemical characteristics: **specific heat capacity**.

Specific heat capacity is the measurement of how much energy it takes to heat up or cool down a substance. Water is a fairly stable substance, so it tends to stay the way it is. It takes a lot of energy to change the temperature of water, which means that when heated by the sun, water acts as a means of thermal storage.

Because of its specific heat capacity, water can act as a refrigerant or as a heating agent. It stays cooler or warmer longer than air, a phenomenon that can be observed by walking outside on a winter day at –25°C or by swimming in –25°C water. Walking in cold air can be very uncomfortable, but water at temperatures below zero can absorb a tremendous amount of body heat and possibly cool a person's core temperature to the point of hypothermia or even death. Air heats easily and thus does not draw heat from a person's body as quickly. Water can conduct heat out of or into another substance up to 100 times more efficiently than air. The specific heat capacities of several substances are listed below

Note that water has a relatively high specific heat capacity in all three phases.

42

| Substance | Specific Heat Capacity (calories/gram×degree) |
|---|---|
| Water (solid) | 0.506 |
| Water (liquid) | 1.000 |
| Water (gas) | 0.500 |
| Concrete | 0.211 |
| Iron | 0.108 |
| Wood | 0.100 |
| Copper | 0.092 |
| Mercury | 0.033 |
| Gold | 0.031 |

Finally, water in liquid form also has a low albedo and therefore reflects less radiant solar energy. The 90–95% absorption rate of solar radiation by 71% of Earth's surface that is covered in liquid water is crucial to the capture and use of the sun's energy by the biosphere

# PRACTICE EXERCISE

1.  Which of the following molecular bonds **cannot** be formed in or by water?

    **a)** Ionic                   **b)** Isotopic

    **c)** Covalent            **d)** Hydrogen

2.  Which of the following processes helps move water upward through the trunks of trees to reach the leaves?

    **a)** Capillary action      **b)** Photosynthesis

    **c)** Phosphorylation     **d)** Cellular respiration

3.  Which process is used to release energy from an ATP molecule in water?

    **a)** Fusion               **b)** Hydrolysis

    **c)** Vaporization       **d)** Dehydration synthesis

4.  Which of the following terms describes a substance dissolved in water?

    **a)** Aquatic solution      **b)** Aquarial solution

    **c)** Aqueous solution     **d)** Aquarius solution

5.  What is the pH of pure, distilled water?

    **a)** 6                    **b)** 7

    **c)** 8                    **d)** 15.2

6.  How much pure water is in a gram?

    **a)** 1 litre             **b)** 1 decilitre

    **c)** 1 millilitre        **d)** 10 cubic centimetres

7.  Which of the following changes to one gram of $H_2O$ requires the **most** energy?

    **a)** Melting from solid to liquid        **b)** Evaporating from liquid to gas

    **c)** Increasing the liquid temperature by 10°C        **d)** Increasing the gaseous temperature by 1°C

8.  The boiling point of water in Edmonton is approximately 98°C. Why is it not 100°C?

    **a)** Humidity            **b)** Pollution

    **c)** Hydrogen bonding     **d)** Atmospheric pressure

## *Lesson 7   THE HYDROLOGIC CYCLE*

Water, like all of the other materials and resources in the biosphere, needs to be recycled in order for organisms to maintain their life cycles and for other elements and compounds to be reused. Essentially, the quantity of water in the biosphere is static because it undergoes a balanced cycle that represents an equilibrium.

Because water is essential to the process of photosynthesis, it is an absolutely critical component of life. Without water, plants cannot grow or reproduce, and without plants, animals and other heterotrophs cannot survive. Water is also needed for the vast majority of metabolic activities necessary to maintain life.

**Distribution of Water in the Biosphere**

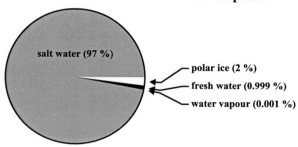

Because of the fact that a human being cannot survive for more than 96 hours without water and because humans and almost all terrestrial plants and animals cannot properly metabolize salt water, fresh water is very significant in the biosphere. However, 97% of all the water on the planet is salt water, and 2% is frozen in the polar ice caps. That leaves 1% for a tremendous number of plants and animals. Water needs to cycle very quickly to supply all of the demand.

The recycling of water through the biosphere is called the **water cycle** or the **hydrologic cycle**. The hydrologic cycle is able to operate very quickly and over great areas because of the narrow range of temperatures between the three states of water. Living beings require water as a liquid, but water is also stored as a solid and is transported as a gas. $H_2O$ only needs subtle changes in temperature and pressure to shift into a biologically usable form.

The most easily observable change of state in water is in precipitation. When gaseous water vapour runs into something cool and loses enough energy, it drops back into liquid state. This process is called **condensation**, and it can commonly be seen on the sides of cold bottles or cans when they 'sweat' or on the insides of windows in the winter when they frost over.

Condensation is the transition from gas to liquid.

NOTES

Convection is the rising of warmer gases or liquids above cooler gases or liquids.

The formation of a cloud is a good example of condensation. Clouds are composed of liquid water that was originally on the ground or in the ocean and that vaporized through the process of **evaporation.** The evaporated water then rises into the atmosphere as an unseen gas. A process known as **convection** causes warmer, expanding gases to rise above cooler, denser ones. The heat to power the convection process is almost exclusively provided by solar energy.

The warm water vapour can ascend as far as 3 kilometres into the sky before it encounters temperatures low enough to condense into liquid droplets or ice crystals. Basically, the water molecules rise until the surrounding conditions remove 540 calories per gram (the latent heat of vaporization) by absorbing their heat energy.

Water's cohesive property enables the droplets and crystals to cluster together until they are heavy enough to fall through any rising air below. Gravity then takes over and pulls the drops and flakes back to Earth in the form of **precipitation**, which includes rain, snow, sleet, and hail.

As water falls back down to Earth, solar energy and friction add energy to it. This leads to more evaporation, which sends it back upward. Rain that evaporates before it hits the ground is called **virga**. However, a lot of water still manages to make it to the lithosphere or hydrosphere. Some water falls back into large bodies of water, where it stays until it is evaporated from the surface.

Interception means that a plant's leaves or stem has caught the precipitation.

Some precipitation is **intercepted**. The falling precipitation releases energy when it hits the ground. This can result in things like erosion. Interception means that a plant's leaves or stem has caught the precipitation and has thus prevented the water form reaching the soil or surface. Trees and forests that catch rain and snow and gradually release the precipitation to the ground are called a **watershed**. Watersheds prevent flooding, erosion, and a rapid loss of water to the ocean.

Of the water that does make it to the surface, some immediately flows downhill and into a large body of water. This water is called **surface runoff**. The amount of precipitation that becomes surface runoff is determined to a large degree by the slope of the land. The steeper the land, the more likely it is that water will quickly return to the oceans and other large bodies of water.

Water in the aerated zone is known as **soil water**.
Water in the infiltration zone is known as **ground water**.
Water in the saturation zone is known as the **water table**.

If the slope of the land is less steep, water can either be absorbed by the soil or seep through rocks and clay. The water that stays in the aerated portion of the soil is called **soil water**. Some water seeps beneath the soil and reaches a level where it no longer interacts with the atmosphere. Water is absorbed by the lithosphere in this manner in a process known as **infiltration**. The water that collects underground after infiltration is called **ground water**. Quantities of water beneath the surface in a specific area called the zone of saturation are collectively known as that area's **water table**.

Most plants do not have root systems large enough to reach a water table and are therefore dependent upon the moisture that has been absorbed by the soil. Other plants that grow near lakes, rivers, and oceans may be able to draw water directly from the water table.

Waters that seep beneath a water table and collect inside porous rock or other enclosures deep underground are called **aquifers**. Aquifers are essentially removed from the hydrologic cycle because the water is trapped here unless it is released by geological activity or man-made pumps and drills.

Ground water eventually seeps and drains out into the ocean and thus rejoins the cycle. There are basically three ways in which water is then released back into the atmosphere in gaseous form: **sublimation**, **transpiration**, and **evaporation**. Sublimation is the transformation of water in its solid form (snow and ice) directly into its gaseous form. Water can use the energy from sunlight, low air pressure, and dry wind to change from solid to gas without first melting.

Sublimation is the state change of water that requires the most energy.

An example of good sublimation conditions can be found in southern Alberta, where dry winter Chinook winds that are rarely warmer than 15°C can blow across winter snow and ice and draw moisture from them.

Transpiration primarily occurs in the leaves of plants. As plants draw water from the soil, they need to transport the water upward and against the force of gravity to send nutrients to the leaves and the upper parts of the plant. Part of the pressure that pushes this water upward is called **osmotic pressure**. It involves the root pressure produced by the absorption of water from the soil. The other force comes from the evaporation of water from the leaves at the top of vascular plants.

Root pressure is a kind of osmotic pressure.

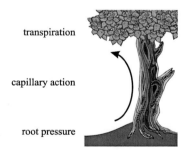

transpiration

capillary action

root pressure

The cohesive nature of water comes into play here as water evaporates and leaves a small vacuum that tugs water into the empty space.
Because water tends to stick together, particularly within solids, a capillary action pulls whole chains of water upward in what is known as the **transpiration-cohesion-tension mechanism**. By using this system, a large oak tree can release over 150 000 litres of water into the atmosphere in a single year.

There are other types of transpiration, including the perspiration from animals, but they are relatively insignificant. Water vapour from transpiration and the evaporation from oceans, rivers, lakes, and soils are sometimes collectively known as **evapotranspiration**.

Between sublimation and evapotranspiration, water is returned to the atmosphere, where it rises until the air around it is cold enough to condense it back into liquid form—and the cycle begins again.

The hydrologic cycle is interconnected with the other biogeochemical cycles. The connections are often indirect, but there are numerous examples of direct connections. In the case of the nitrogen cycle, the nitrates ($NO_3$) fixed by lightning require precipitation in order to reach the ground. In the carbon cycle, the water stored in the polar ice caps helps cool the ocean, which increases the rate at which carbon dioxide dissolves.

## Example 1

Compare and contrast soil water and ground water.

*Solution*

Soil water is at a level that can be reached by the roots of plants. It is near enough to the surface that it can dissolve nutrients such as nitrates and phosphates so that organisms can draw them into their cellular structure. Soil water is available for evaporation because it is still aerated.

Ground water is in a saturated zone and generally out of range for interactions with plant life or the atmosphere. Ground water is not aerated, which is to say that it will not evaporate into the atmosphere from its location, even if it is heated.

## Example 2

How do plants participate in the hydrologic cycle?

*Solution*

Plants extract moisture and dissolved nutrients from the soil and then transfer that water to the atmosphere through the process of transpiration. They form a major part of the cycle that changes water from a liquid to a gaseous form.

## Example 3

How do plants affect the amount of surface runoff?

*Solution*

The root systems of plants help absorb precipitation, while leaves, stalks, stems, trunks, and branches interfere with the progress of the ground precipitation toward. Overall, this has the effect of slowing the precipitation of water and thus reduces surface runoff.

## PRACTICE EXERCISE

1.  Which of the following processes is **not** a process within the hydrologic cycle?

    a) Runoff                        b) Erosion

    c) Evaporation                   d) Precipitation

2.  Which of the following processes absorbs heat from the sun and produces water vapour?

    a) Infiltration                  b) Interception

    c) Transpiration                 d) Condensation

3.  The density of ice is 920 kg/m$^3$, and the density of seawater is 1 025 kg/m$^3$. If these values are compared as a ratio, approximately what percentage of an iceberg should appear above the surface of the ocean?

    a) 10%                           b) 15%

    c) 25%                           d) 90%

4.  Which of the following features does **not** describe polar ice?

    a) Evaporates quickly            b) Cools ocean temperature

    c) Stores water in the biosphere d) Increases surface albedo of Earth

5.  Which of the following types of landscapes would **decrease** surface runoff in an area?

    a) Hard, rocky ground            b) Steeply sloped land

    c) Thickly wooded forest         d) Paved urban landscape

6.  In which of the following areas would you expect to find the **greatest amount** of transpiration?

    a) Polar ice field               b) Grassy meadow

    c) Tropical rain forest          d) Crowded city centre

7.  Which of the following terms describes a place where water is stored in the lithosphere?

    a) Geode                         b) Aquifer

    c) Aqualung                      d) Arctic seas

8.  Approximately how long can a human being survive without water?

    a) 2 days                        b) 4 days

    c) 28 days                       d) 96 days

## *Lesson 8  ENERGY AND MATTER*

The atmosphere has no definite boundary.  It extends outward from Earth and grows increasingly thinner as it approaches space.  Three quarters of the atmosphere's mass is within 11 km of the planetary surface in a layer known as the **troposphere**.  Although predominantly composed of nitrogen and oxygen, there are some important trace gases that cause significant effects within the biosphere.  The carbon-based gases and water vapour act as greenhouse gases, while ozone acts as a barrier to ultraviolet radiation from the sun.

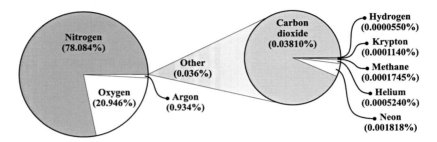

Living things greatly affect the composition of the atmosphere.
The carbon, nitrogen, phosphorus, and water cycles operate at different rates.  As they interact dynamically, they change the quantity of different gaseous molecules in the air.  Greenhouse gases and ozone are just two of the many compounds that change climate worldwide.  Atmospheric content can also drastically affect the balance of energy entering and leaving the biosphere as well as the health of plants and animals.

The northern lights, or *aurora borealis*, occur at altitudes of about 80–150 km.  To put this in perspective, the United States designates anyone who has been over 80 km high in the atmosphere to be an astronaut.  This illustrates is that even in what seems to be empty space, there are still atmospheric effects.  The biosphere is an open system because matter and energy are exchanged with parts of the lithosphere, hydrosphere, and atmosphere that are unable to support life.

Approximately 3.5 billion years ago, the atmosphere was mostly composed of carbon dioxide and water vapour, along with some ammonia, nitrogen, and . There was almost no oxygen present in the air. As the crust of Earth cooled over the course of two hundred million years, the water vapour condensed and formed lakes and oceans, which dissolved much of the carbon dioxide.

Around 3.3 billion years ago, the first cyanobacteria appeared and began to photosynthesize the carbon dioxide. The resulting oxygen reacted with the ammonia and released nitrogen gas. Eventually, the carbon in the atmosphere was stored in carbon sinks and biomass, and nitrogen and oxygen became the predominant compounds in the air.

The current biosphere is reliant on the same type of blue-green algae in the oceans to regulate the atmosphere. Oxygen does not tend to remain as a free gas in the atmosphere, but rather tends to be consumed by both plants and animals in cellular respiration and inorganic chemical reactions such as combustion. $CO_2$ is a more stable gas than $O_2$, and so all of the reactions that consume oxygen gas tend to produce aerial carbon dioxide.

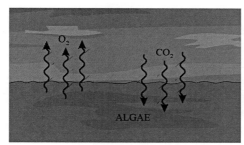

photosynthesis

What is important to note is that $CO_2$ dissolves in water, while $O_2$ tends not to. Therefore, as the carbon dioxide content in the air increases, more dissolves into the water, where blue-green algae consume it and expel oxygen back into the atmosphere. This creates a critically important equilibrium. Too much $CO_2$ will make the algae more active and thus begin a cycle that will drive the amount of $CO_2$ down. Too little $CO_2$ will make the algae less active, which will allow amounts to increase. Blue-green algae therefore act as the worldwide governors of carbon content in the atmosphere.

The biosphere began and continues to maintain itself with the fundamental process of photosynthesis. The use of solar energy to transform carbon dioxide and water into useful organic matter in the form of hydrocarbons is the basis for all biomass. The formation of oxygen gas as a waste product is also crucial, as it affects the composition of the atmosphere and thus facilitates the continued existence of all organisms, terrestrial organisms in particular.

The complementary metabolic process of photosynthesis is cellular respiration. Cellular respiration is required to extract the stored energy in glucose in order for that energy to be used for movement, reproduction, growth, and other metabolic processes such as decomposition. Even the earliest cyanobacteria would need to perform cellular respiration in order to reproduce and transport materials and nutrients through their cell membranes. Every living thing performs cellular respiration, but only producers perform photosynthesis.

The products of photosynthesis, glucose, and oxygen are the ingredients for cellular respiration. Cellular respiration, in turn, produces the water and carbon dioxide necessary to fuel the photosynthetic process. The chemical energy stored in glucose is transferred to molecules of ATP by adding phosphate groups to ADP and AMP. The solar energy that is stored as chemical energy in glucose by the process of photosynthesis is then made biologically usable by cellular respiration using the process of dehydration synthesis. The five elements necessary in these processes are hydrogen, carbon, oxygen, nitrogen, and phosphorus. By necessity, all of these elements have cycles that allow them to move through the different parts of the biosphere in order to maintain life.

The carbon cycle circulates the carbon atoms through biotic and abiotic forms and also through the lithosphere, hydrosphere, and atmosphere. As all organisms eventually die, the carbon that forms the core of all organic material needs to be returned to the atmosphere as carbon dioxide for further photosynthesis and hydrocarbon synthesis. It can then provide more biomass and nutrients for other living organisms.

The nitrogen cycle is primarily responsible for drawing stable nitrogen gas from the atmosphere and making it available for amino acid synthesis. Because the triple covalent bond of $N_2$ is so strong, it takes very specific processes to transform it into ammonia and ammonium and then transform those molecules into nitrates and nitrites, which are necessary for amino acids and other important organic compounds.

The phosphorus cycle is necessary because heavy phosphorus atoms are primarily found in rocks and sediment, and it requires a number of biotic and abiotic factors to transform phosphates into a usable biological form. Phosphorus is necessary for all living things because it is the key component of energy transfer.

Hydrogen and oxygen are circulated through the hydrologic cycle. Not only is water necessary for photosynthetic processes, but it is also a key abiotic factor in the other three major biogeochemical cycles. Water is stored as snow and ice and is primarily found within the biosphere in the form of seawater. In addition to being a catalyst for many metabolic functions, water is also the single most important substance in terms of its influence on weather and climate.

The four main biogeochemical cycles represent the biotic interactions between the biosphere and those areas found outside of the open system it represents.

One of the groups of abiotic interactions between the atmosphere and the lithosphere are known as **aeolian processes**. Because the air is constantly moving as a result of convection, uneven heating of Earth's surface creates wind currents. Wind not only moves moisture and different temperature cells of air around the biosphere, it also interacts with nutrients and other materials.

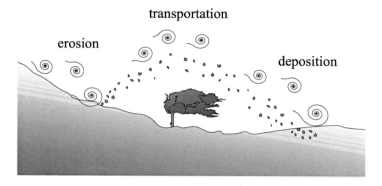

There are three aeolian processes: transportation, erosion, and deposition. Air can transport materials such as leaves and dust particles by lifting them off the ground and moving them to a different location hundreds of kilometres away. Erosion refers to the changing of the actual shape and composition of things within the lithosphere.

Erosion can shift the physical shape of a sand dune or carve interesting structures out of sedimentary rock, such as the hoodoos and canyons in the badlands near Drumheller. **Deposition** is the end result of transportation, where materials and nutrients are relocated to a different area.

**Example 1**

What are the three forms of energy found in the dynamic processes within the biosphere?

*Solution*

The primary energy source of the biosphere is **solar radiation**. This energy is transformed into **chemical energy** through photosynthesis and converted into metabolically usable chemical energy by cellular respiration. The ATP that stores chemical energy in organisms is then hydrolysed for all metabolic processes.

Every stage of this process releases energy in the form of **heat**, which is also known as **long-wave radiation**. Heat eventually bleeds out of the atmosphere and into space, thus maintaining the balance of energy exchange in the biosphere.

NOTES

**Example 2**

In what form is nitrogen most commonly found in nature and why?

*Solution*

Nitrogen is most often found in its free, gaseous state as $N_2$.
The reason that nitrogen tends to form this particular compound is because a nitrogen atom can form a triple covalent bond with another nitrogen atom. This bond is very strong and more stable than the vast majority of bonds with other atoms.

**Example 3**

Define an open system in reference to the biosphere.

*Solution*

An open system has interactive exchanges of matter and energy with other systems around it. The biosphere interacts with Earth's core through volcanoes, geysers, and seismic activity. It also interacts with the outer layers of the atmosphere by radiating heat and absorbing energy and material from outer space.

## PRACTICE EXERCISE

1. Which of the following processes is **not** an aeolian process?

   **a)** Erosion                                  **b)** Deposition

   **c)** Precipitation                             **d)** Transportation

2. Which of the following terms can be used to describe the bonds within carbon dioxide?

   **a)** Ionic                                     **b)** Covalent

   **c)** Metalloid                                 **d)** Atmospheric

3. Which layer of the atmosphere is has the **greatest** mass?

   **a)** Ionosphere                                **b)** Troposphere

   **c)** Stratosphere                              **d)** Thermosphere

4. The **greatest** impact on carbon dioxide content in the atmosphere is caused by

   **a)** Convection          **b)** Aurora borealis   **c)** Blue-green algae   **d)** Adenosine triphosphate

5. Which of the following processes would cause the formation of water molecules?

   **a)** Freezing                                  **b)** Photosynthesis

   **c)** Aeolian deposition                        **d)** Cellular respiration

6. Which of the following compounds comprises the **greatest** percentage of the atmosphere?

   **a)** $O_2$                                     **b)** $CO_2$

   **c)** $CH_4$                                     **d)** $NH_3$

7. In which of the following areas is nitrogen **most likely** found?

   **a)** Exosphere                                 **b)** Lithosphere

   **c)** Hydrosphere                               **d)** Atmosphere

8. Which of the following compounds is least likely to be found in the atmosphere?

   **a)** Argon                                     **b)** Methane

   **c)** Carbon dioxide                            **d)** Calcium carbonate

## *Lesson 9  MAINTAINING THE BALANCE*

NOTES

The four main biogeochemical cycles function as a series of checks and balances  in order to maintain a steady-state equilibrium within the biosphere.  Any significant variation within one of these cycles could create an imbalance that would upset the entire structure of life on Earth.  Generally, there are compensatory structures within each biogeochemical cycle that help prevent any extreme changes, but human activities are currently having a greater impact on natural processes than at any other point in history.

Human industrial activities, such as the burning of fossil fuels or the refrigeration of foods, can add carbon dioxide ($CO_2$), carbon monoxide (CO), methane ($CH_4$), nitrous oxide ($N_2O$), ozone ($O_3$), chlorofluorocarbons (CFCs), and water vapour into the troposphere.  Even small concentrations of these molecules can greatly alter the balance of energy entering and leaving the biosphere and affect the health of plants and animals.

These gases—carbon dioxide, methane, and water vapour in particular,— act as greenhouse gases (GHGs).  GHGs absorb long-wave infrared radiation.  This contributes to the warming of the atmosphere.  These gases are necessary to keep the average global temperature near 14°C.  Without greenhouse gases, the average global temperature would be close to −18°C, which is too cold to support much of the life on this planet.

The greenhouse effect, in addition to being an essential part of the operation of the biosphere, is also a precariously balanced phenomenon.  If there are too many greenhouse gases in the atmosphere, there exists a danger that global warming might lead to higher sea levels and a decrease in the size of the polar caps.  Below is a list of these some greenhouse gases.

Water vapour is expressed chemically as $H_2O_{(g)}$.

### Water Vapour

As a chemical formula, water vapour is expressed as $H_2O_{(g)}$.  It is the most important GHG in the atmosphere because it has the highest specific heat capacity and thus can store the most energy.
Water vapour is generally transported into the atmosphere through evaporation and transpiration, although over-irrigation can play a part in terms of human agricultural practices.

Nitrous Oxide is expressed chemically as $N_2O_{(g)}$.

### Nitrous Oxide

$N_2O_{(g)}$ is also known as laughing gas and can be used as an anaesthetic.  It is naturally emitted by soil and oceans, usually as nitrates and nitrites decompose, but can also be found in the combustion of coal and the decomposition of excessive fertilizers in the soil.  Nitrous oxide is important in the production of ozone in the atmosphere, but prolonged human exposure to it leads to irreversible brain damage and blood hypoxia (low blood oxygen levels).

## Carbon Dioxide

Carbon dioxide, or $CO_{2(g)}$, acts as the largest GHG component of the atmosphere by volume, with the exception of water vapour. It is produced naturally in the cellular respiration of plants and animals, as well as any hydrocarbon combustion, such as a volcano or a forest fire. Humans produce excess carbon dioxide in industrial processes such as the making of commercial cement and by burning fossil fuels for heat and energy.

Carbon dioxide is expressed chemically as $CO_{2(g)}$.

## Methane

Methane, or $CH_{4(g)}$, is generally produced as a by-product of anaerobic decomposition and digestion in grazing animals such as cows and sheep. Swamps, marshes, landfills, rice patties, and sewage treatment plants are all sources of methane. The Intergovernmental Panel on Climate Change (IPCC) has suggested that methane may be 23–30 times more powerful than carbon dioxide in terms of the net global warming effect.

Methane is expressed chemically as $CH_{4(g)}$.

## Ozone

Also written as $O_{3(g)}$, ozone occurs naturally in the stratosphere, but not in the troposphere. Ozone is critically important in filtering out harmful ultraviolet radiation from the sun, but it can be very dangerous when found at lower elevations. It forms a major component of urban smog and aerial pollution and is very corrosive when it reacts with the water molecules inside lungs.

Ozone is expressed chemically as $O_{3(g)}$.

## Chloroflourocarbons (CFCs)

Representing a variety of different gases, chloroflourocarbons do not occur naturally inside the biosphere and act as carcinogens (cancer-causing agents). These compunds also damage the ozone layer. CFCs are produced as a result of manufacturing plastics. They are also used in refrigeration units and aerosol cans. Many industries are trying to move away from CFC-intensive activities.

There are a number of different CFCs that act as CFCs. They all have chemical expressions that include carbon (C), chlorine (Cl), and flourine (F).

The atmosphere is not the only place where human activity is having an impact. The use of nitrites, nitrates, and phosphates as fertilizers has had a significant effect on the hydrosphere. Algae and photosynthesizing bacteria experience super-saturations of nutrients from groundwater runoff. These nutrients create eutrophic conditions, such as algal blooms and hypoxia. The illustration below shows the different states of a lake.

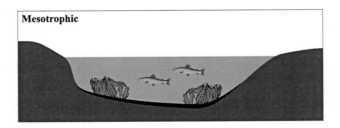

A lake can be classified as: oligotrophic, mesotrophic, eutrophic, or hypereutrophic, depending on the rate of biological cycles and the amount of phosphate and nitrogenous nutrients in the ecosystem.

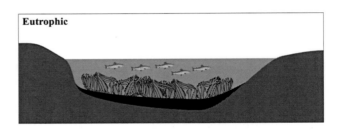

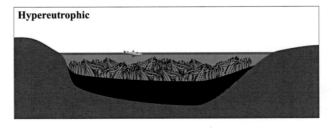

An oligotrophic lake has a very slow rate of biogeochemical change. There are generally fewer life forms, and the water has less nutritive value. As the levels of phosphates and nitrates increase, the lake becomes mesotrophic. The biodiversity also increases because these conditions provide more nutrition for a larger number of species. As the lake becomes increasingly filled with nutrients, the growth of algae begins to reduce the number of other species. Finally, by blocking the sunlight and consuming the dissolved oxygen in the water, the algae starve the other life forms in the lake.

The lithosphere has also been experiencing a change in composition as carbon sinks are excavated and the combustion of the hydrocarbon molecules migrate carbon into the atmosphere. The ocean-dwelling blue-green algae that regulate the quantity of carbon in the atmosphere will probably accelerate their life cycles in order to cope with the corresponding increase in carbon dioxide content dissolved in the seawater. This in turn will generate more dead materials, which will sink even more carbon to the bottom of the hydrosphere.

The problem with this equilibrium compensation is the activity of humans. Human society has been using non-renewable resources for nearly two centuries. Carbon may be slowly returning to the lithosphere to form more carbon sinks, but at a rate that will not match the amount of fossil fuels that society consumes through combustion.

Living things greatly affect the composition of the biosphere. The carbon, nitrogen, phosphorus, and hydrologic cycles all contain both biotic and abiotic factors, since all four substances are necessary for respiration and photosynthesis.

The most recent attempt by humanity to emulate natural equilibriums was when an initiative to develop a man-made biosphere was developed in Oracle, Arizona in 1987. It was called the Biosphere II project and was designed to create an artificial environment that cycles materials and nutrients within a small, enclosed area. Unfortunately, the project met with limited success as designers struggled to maintain a balance of oxygen within the ecosystem. In 2006, the site was sold to private contractors, who intend to make it into a planned community.

**Example 1**

Describe the effect of ozone on global climate.

*Solution*

Ozone is a very light gas that expands rapidly and so pushes itself to a higher altitude. When ozone is at the stratospheric level of the atmosphere, it intercepts and blocks some potentially harmful types of solar radiation.

At lower levels, ozone is harmful to humans and can sometimes be found after lightning storms. It also functions as a greenhouse gas, which keeps long-wave radiation in the form of heat close to the surface of Earth.

**Example 2**

Discuss some of the ways in which agriculture can affect the different cycles of the biosphere.

*Solution*

Essentially, agriculture encompasses two groups of activities: ranching and farming.

Fertilizers and pesticides from croplands are often washed into bodies of water as runoff, and if the concentration of these materials reaches a certain critical point, the aquatic ecosystem could be put at risk.

In addition, the feed for plants and animals also contains nitrates and phosphates that could migrate to another ecosystem and increase the amount of available nutrients disproportionately.

Finally, livestock such as cattle and sheep are ruminants, and one of the products of a ruminant's digestive process is methane gas. As a greenhouse gas, methane could change the amount of the sun's energy that is retained by the biosphere and lead to a net increase in average temperature.

**Example 3**

Discuss the role of humans have on the level of carbon dioxide in the atmosphere.

*Solution*

As a result of cellular respiration, humans naturally breathe carbon dioxide into the air and inhale oxygen from the air.

Perhaps even more significantly, after the dawn of the Industrial Revolution, human activities have become more dependent on the combustion of fossil fuels, such as coal, petroleum, and natural gas. The usage of fossil fuels from previously biologically inert carbon sinks increases the amount of carbon in the atmosphere and decreases the amount in the lithosphere.

## PRACTICE EXERCISE

1. Which of the following compounds does **not** act as a greenhouse gas?

   **a)** Ammonia

   **b)** Nitrous oxide

   **c)** Water vapour

   **d)** Carbon dioxide

2. Which of the following gases is **not** harmful to humans when inhaled for prolonged periods?

   **a)** $O_3$

   **b)** $N_2$

   **c)** CO

   **d)** $N_2O$

3. Which of the following events would **not** result from an increase of greenhouse gases in the air?

   **a)** Sea levels would rise

   **b)** Polar ice caps would shrink

   **c)** Planetary albedo would increase

   **d)** Average global temperature would rise

4. Which of the following compounds is **not** a nutrient that affects eutrophication?

   **a)** Nitrite

   **b)** Nitrate

   **c)** Phosphate

   **d)** Hydrocarbon

5. Which GHG has the **greatest** specific heat capacity?

   **a)** Ozone

   **b)** Methane

   **c)** Water vapour

   **d)** Nitrogen oxide

6. Which of the following variables has the greatest effect on nitrogen content in the atmosphere?

   **a)** Bacteria

   **b)** Fertilizers

   **c)** Blue-green algae

   **d)** Anaerobic decomposition

7. Which of the following natural phenomena would produce the **most** atmospheric methane?

   **a)** Desert

   **b)** Swamp **c)** Forest fire

   **d)** Freshwater lake

8. Which of the following gases is **not** produced naturally in the biosphere?

   **a)** Methane

   **b)** Ammonia

   **c)** Nitrous oxide

   **d)** Chloroflourocarbons

# *REVIEW SUMMARY*

- The majority of energy that powers the dynamics of the biosphere comes from solar radiation.
- The process of photosynthesis transforms light and heat energy from the sun into a usable chemical form: glucose, or $C_6H_{12}O_6$.
- Glucose can be joined together into chains called polymers using dehydration synthesis.
- Cellular respiration can take the chemical energy in glucose and attach high-energy phosphate groups to an amino acid and a sugar group to form adenosine triphosphate, or ATP.
- The ATP molecule can lose a phosphate group in a hydrolytic process called dephosphorylation, which releases energy for other metabolic processes.
- The end product of all the energy exchanges in the biosphere is eventually lost as heat.
- Greenhouse gases, such as water vapour and carbon dioxide, keep some heat near Earth's surface in a part of the atmosphere called the troposphere.
- There are four basic matter cycles in the biosphere. These cycles are perpetuated by complementary reactions that are perfectly balanced so that the ingredients of one are the product of another.
- The four matter cycles in the biosphere are the carbon, nitrogen, phosphorus, and hydrologic cycles.
- Water has a number of unique qualities that facilitate life within the biosphere.
- Because water's melting point and boiling point are relatively close together, it is the only compound that appears in all three states of matter in the biosphere.
- Hydrogen bonding between water atoms is an important feature and gives water greater cohesion.
- The specific heat of water allows it to retain energy from long-wave radiation in the form of heat.
- Water is the only liquid that becomes less dense when it freezes.
- Earth loses energy in the form of heat from the atmosphere into outer space, which conserves both matter and energy within the biosphere.
- The dynamic relationship between photosynthesis and cellular respiration allow the products of one reaction to form the ingredients of the other, provided that there is sufficient solar energy in the system and that heat is lost as a result of each reaction.
- In particular, photosynthesis produces oxygen, while cellular respiration produces carbon dioxide. If there is an imbalance in the number of reactions, the atmospheric content of the system may be disrupted.
- Human activities such as respiration, combustion of fossil fuels, and industrial production also change the atmospheric composition. The predominant pattern for human activity is to produce more carbon in the atmosphere.
- The use of fertilizers, pesticides, and livestock feed can lead to runoff into water bodies, where an imbalance in nutrients can cause eutrophication and hypereutrophication.
- Hypereutrophication can cause the loss of biodiversity in an ecosystem and a complete predominance of cyanobacteria and algae.
- Carbon sinks in the lithosphere are often excavated, and the hydrocarbons there are used as fuel. This process then transfers carbon from the ground into the air. Carbon sinks can still form, but they are generated at such a slow rate that subterranean hydrocarbon deposits are considered non-renewable.
- Activities like deforestation and clear-cut logging increase erosion and affect watersheds.

# *PRACTICE TEST*

1. Which of the following processes is **not** involved in water and nutrient movement inside vascular plants?

   **a)** Transpiration

   **b)** Fermentation

   **c)** Capillary action

   **d)** Root pressurization

2. Which of the following is a product of cellular respiration?

   **a)** $O_2$

   **b)** $CO_2$

   **c)** $CH_4$

   **d)** Glucose

3. What types of plants aid in nitrogen fixation?

   **a)** Mosses

   **b)** Legumes

   **c)** Vascular plants

   **d)** Single-cell producers

4. What is the prime characteristic of aeolian abiotic factors?

   **a)** Wind movement

   **b)** Cloud formation

   **c)** Precipitation interception

   **d)** Water seeping into aquifers

5. In which zone is the water table located?

   **a)** Aeration

   **b)** Hydration

   **c)** Saturation

   **d)** Infiltration

6. Which of the following statements regarding rivers is **true**?

   **a)** They primarily store water.

   **b)** They are primarily made of overland flow.

   **c)** They have a significant percentage of surface water.

   **d)** They are key elements in the evapotranspiration cycle.

7. Which of the following processes requires the **most** energy?

   **a)** Boiling

   **b)** Sublimation

   **c)** Evaporation

   **d)** Condensation

8. What is water vapour in the atmosphere called?

   **a)** Fog

   **b)** Rain

   **c)** Steam

   **d)** Clouds

9. Which of the following statements about soil at the base of a hill slope compared with soil at the hilltop is **true**?

   **a)** It is thicker.
   **b)** It is wetter.
   **c)** It is more nutrient-rich.
   **d)** all of the above

10. Which of the following terms describes the reflective ability of a substance?

   **a)** Albedo
   **b)** Saturation
   **c)** Deposition
   **d)** Phosphorescence

11. What percentage of the atmosphere is **not** composed of free oxygen or free nitrogen?

   **a)** 21%
   **b)** 78%
   **c)** 99%
   **d)** less than 1%

12. Which of the following processes is a nitrogen-fixing process?

   **a)** Acidification
   **b)** Nucleification
   **c)** Legumification
   **d)** Ammonification

13. Which of the following compounds does **not** contain oxygen?

   **a)** Nitrate
   **b)** Ammonia
   **c)** Nitric acid
   **d)** Nitrous oxide

14. What type of molecule forms cell membranes?

   **a)** Nucleotide
   **b)** Nucleic acid
   **c)** Phospholipid
   **d)** Adenosine triphosphate

15. Which type of pressure is root pressure an example of?

   **a)** Air pressure
   **b)** Ionic pressure
   **c)** Osmotic pressure
   **d)** Cohesive pressure

16. What is added to ADP to make high-energy ATP using dehydration synthesis?

   **a)** Nitrite
   **b)** Nitrate
   **c)** Phosphate
   **d)** Phosphorus

**17.** Which features define the biosphere as an open system?

**18.** List three ways in which human activities affect the carbon cycle.

**19.** Discuss the effects of a massive increase in the greenhouse effect. Also, discuss the ways in which matter cycles in the biosphere can help maintain the equilibrium of the system.

# NOTES

# ECOSYSTEMS AND POPULATIONS

When you are finished this unit, you will be able to…

- identify and describe the characteristics of ecosystems
- identify and describe the characteristics of biomes
- describe the characteristics of the world's major biomes
- describe the biotic and abiotic factors that act on ecosystems
- use food chains or food webs to describe the relationship between trophic levels
- explain the fundamental principles of taxonomy and binomial nomenclature
- use energy and biomass pyramids to describe the movement of energy and matter within ecosystems
- describe the nature and origin of variation within populations
- describe how populations adapt to their environment
- evaluate evidence that supports evolutionary theory
- describe how natural selection influences future populations and leads to evolutionary change
- evaluate the impact of human activities on the equilibrium of the biosphere

## PREREQUISITE SKILLS AND KNOWLEDGE

Prior to starting this unit, you should be able to…
- describe some terrestrial and aquatic ecosystems
- understand the relationship between mathematics, notation, and scientific methodology
- compare and contrast freshwater and saltwater habitats
- list the advantages of biological diversity
- apply mathematical and conceptual models to assess field studies

## *Lesson 1  ECOSYSTEMS*

Biotic: living
Abiotic: non-living

An ecosystem is the combination of all the biotic (living) and abiotic (non-living) components in a given area.  It can be virtually any size: a continent, a lake, a fish tank, or the forgotten bit of cheese at the back of the fridge.  The principles of ecosystems can be applied at any scale.  These principles deal primarily with the composition of the ecosystem and the interaction among the various elements.

### ABIOTIC COMPONENTS OF AN ECOSYSTEM

Abiotic components of the biosphere are the nonliving chemical and physical factors of the biosphere.  They interact with each other and with the living beings in the ecosystem in order to determine the nature of the ecosystem itself.  There are many abiotic factors to consider when studying an ecosystem.  Some are listed below.

**Terrestrial**
*Physiographic*
- Water: In order to support life, the availability of water is critical in any given ecosystem.
- Latitude: The north/south position of the ecosystem determines many of the climatic factors that influence an ecosystem.
- Slope: Sloping terrain may affect soil erosion, water retention, and other physiographic and climatic factors.
- Altitude: The altitude of the ecosystem affects many climatic factors, such as atmospheric composition and pressure.

*Climatic*
- Temperature: Living things need to be able to maintain healthy temperatures in order to ensure their survival.  Temperature extremes can interfere with this.
- Clouds: Clouds can contribute to the humidity in the atmosphere and can also limit the amount of sunlight that an ecosystem receives.
- Atmospheric Composition: Living things require the correct atmospheric gases to survive.  Animals tend to thrive in oxygen-rich environments.
- Sunlight: Because photosynthesis requires sunlight, the level of sunlight that an ecosystem receives is critical to its composition.
- Wind: Winds are particularly important factors in temperature, soil erosion, and plant pollination.
- Humidity: Humidity affects temperature, oxygenation, and decomposition.

*Edaphic* (soil and its effect on living things)
- Soil Composition: Affects the materials available to root plants, including water.
- Soil pH: Affects the type of plants that can grow in soil.  Phosphorus availability is higher in acidic soil.
- Rocks and Minerals: Very few life forms can survive on bare rock.

**Edaphic factors** are those relating to soil and its effect on living things.

68

## Aquatic

*Physical*

- Water Currents: In oceans, the strength and direction of currents can affect water temperature and the dispersal of organisms.
- Tides: Tides redistribute sediment, create and refresh tidal pools, and affect currents.
- Turbidity: Turbidity refers to the amount of material in suspension in water. Increased turbidity reduces water oxygenation and the depth to which sunlight can penetrate.
- Depth: Increased depth leads to increased pressure and reduced sunlight exposure.
- Pressure: Pressure affects current. In order to survive at significant depths, organisms must be adapted to endure great pressure.
- Temperature: Water density varies with temperature, and freezes when the temperature falls low enough.

*Chemical*

- Acidity or Alkalinity (pH): Most aquatic life forms are adapted to survive in a particular range of pH. Fish, for example, generally require a pH close to neutral, whereas algae thrive in a slightly basic environment.
- Salinity (saltiness): Aquatic organisms are adapted to survive in a particular range of salinity. For example, placing a saltwater fish in fresh water will cause fatal cellular damage to the fish. This is caused by passive transport (osmosis).

In addition to the above, natural disasters (earthquakes, hurricanes, etc.) can be considered abiotic factors.

## BIOTIC COMPONENTS OF AN ECOSYSTEM

Biotic factors are the living interactions and components of the biosphere. There are hundreds of biotic components. A few important ones are listed below.

- Migration/Dispersal: The movement within and between ecosystems.
- Population Density: Dense populations can lead to increased variation, but they may also cause increased competition.
- Competition: When food or other resources are scarce, individuals or populations must compete for them.
- Predation: Predators are organisms that consume other organisms for sustenance.
- Parasitism: An interaction between organisms where one organism (the parasite) benefits while another (the host) is harmed.
- Mutualism: An interaction between organisms where both organisms benefit.
- Commensalism: An interaction between organisms where one organism benefits while another is neither helped nor harmed.

- Disease: Infectious agents or malnutrition can cause diseases in individuals or populations
- Variation: Populations with a high degree of variation tend to be more robust.

Most of these factors will be discussed in detail later on.

**LEVELS OF ORGANIZATION IN THE ECOLOGY**

*Ecology* is the study of the relationships between organisms and the environment they inhabit. Biological activities in the biosphere and ecosystems can be organized in order of all-inclusive categories to very specific and exclusive categories. The biosphere also has levels of organization. The levels can be organized from the all-inclusive to a more narrow and specific area of study. The following diagrams outline the levels of organization found in ecology.

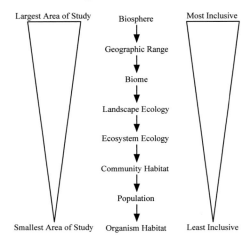

# Ecology
Levels of Organization

| Largest Area of Study | Biosphere | Most Inclusive |
| --- | --- | --- |
| | Geographic Range | |
| | Biome | |
| | Landscape Ecology | |
| | Ecosystem Ecology | |
| | Community Habitat | |
| | Population | |
| Smallest Area of Study | Organism Habitat | Least Inclusive |

**Organism Habitat**

An organism habitat is a specific area within a given area for a particular animal or plant. The habitat of a plant or animal normally provides what is needed to survive. A habitat includes all the factors found where an animal lives. A habitat includes considerations of climate, moisture, edaphic (soil) conditions, food availability, predators, and competition. Animals and plants adjust to all of the conditions of the habitat in which they find themselves. Habitats help shape specific animal and plant behaviours. An ecologist would study the special adaptations and behavioural strategies that a particular organism possesses in order to meet the challenges of its environment. The morphology (shape and structure) and the physiology (function) of the organism are also studied.

70

## Population

A population refers to the total number of a particular species that occupy a specific area at a specific time. It is a count of the organisms and how they relate and compete with each other. Population size, density, distribution, and growth are measured and calculated to better understand ecological relationships. Members of a population must be able to interbreed with one another. The area may be a small pond in the case of a special type of frog. In the case of humans, the population is spread over a much larger area. The area is generally confined to the limits where individuals will likely find mates. The group of breeding individuals that is contained in a specific area is called a local population, or a **deme**.

Two types of factors limit population sizes. The first type includes density-dependent factors. These are the types of conditions that limit population growth based on the size of the group. Certain factors that affect a population are related to the density of the population. Density-dependent factors tend to be biotic. Generally, factors that are related to the density of the population are biotic (food supply, waste production, predators, disease, parasites, hormones, etc). For example, mice that are over-crowded produce different hormones. Hormone production would thus be a density-dependent factor. Most diseases spread more rapidly through densely populated areas. Shortages of food are more critical in high-density populations. Also, waste produced by a dense population often poisons the same population.

The second factor type that controls population sizes is comprised of density-independent factors. These are factors that act on a population and are unrelated to density of the population. Density-independent factors tend to be abiotic. These factors also naturally control populations from getting out of hand. Generally, the factors that are unrelated to the density of the population are abiotic (weather, inorganic chemicals, fire, landslides, volcanic eruptions, etc.). The cyclic nature of the seasons can control population sizes of plants and animals. Populations are often cut back by seasonal changes before they ever suffer the effects of over-crowding. For example, regardless of how many cucumber plants there are, an early frost may kill them all. Eventually the winter frost kills all the plants before the weeds in the garden choke each other out. Factors such as frost, which are unrelated to density, are called density-independent factors. A drought, cold-snap, or a flood affects a population regardless of the number of individuals in the population.

## Community Habitat

A community consists of a variety of species that occupy a specific area. Several populations sharing the same habitat make up a community. Thousands of interactions occur within communities. When one population exists in the same area as another population, many different interactions occur. For example, the dead leaves from a tree or the digestive waste from an animal (urine and dung) cause many interactions. They may fertilize the soil or provide food for another population. One population can provide many resources to another population.

NOTES

Communities change when the conditions or the environment in which its organisms live also change. Examples of environmental changes include a river changing its course, a drought drying up a pond, or a fire burning down a forest. Communities may also change as population sizes and densities change. A population that grows too fast or becomes extinct changes the community.

**Ecosystem Ecology**

Ecosystem ecology involves the study of several communities that are found around specific areas. It is primarily concerned with the flow of energy and the cycling of matter between communities. An ecosystem such as pond or a lake may have several communities in it. If these communities interact or influence each other, then they are related because of these interactions. The study of these interactions is called ecosystem ecology.

**Landscape or Seascape Ecology**

Landscape ecology is the study of how land formations interact with the communities found on or near a particular landscape. It is concerned with how one ecosystem may affect a nearby ecosystem. For example, landscape ecology may look at the ecosystems found on the windward (upwind) and leeward sides of a mountain. The windward side of a mountain faces the wind and is more likely to have heavier rains. The ecosystem of the windward side is vastly different than the leeward side. In another example, a landscape ecologist may look at the ecosystems found at the edge of an area where human activity such as farming interacts with the ecosystem in the natural area.

## ECOSYSTEM INTERACTIONS

*Terrestrial Ecosystems*

The interaction of the factors above, both abiotic and biotic, determines how energy and matter move through an ecosystem. As an example, let us consider a small stand of aspen trees in Elk Island National Park in Alberta. The aspen trees absorb sunlight through their leaves and water and nutrients through the soil. During autumn, the aspen sheds its leaves. The decomposing leaves renew the nutrients in the soil. The trees also shelter the soil from erosion by wind and water.

A stand of aspen trees

The trees may also act as host parasitic beetles, which survive by consuming tree bark and living wood. These insects, in turn, are consumed by birds that use the trees as shelter.

These relationships help keep the ecosystem in balance. The trees are kept in check by the beetles, which prevent the trees from removing too many nutrients from the soil. Similarly, the birds keep the beetle population from becoming too large for the trees to support.

Ecosystem equilibriums tend to be dynamic; that is, they can respond to change. For example, imagine that the local bird population is hit with a disease that reduces their numbers by half. The number of beetles will increase as a result of a decrease in predators. The increased beetle population is a threat to the survival of the aspen stand.

However, the surviving birds now have an abundance of food; there is more prey and less competition for it. This increases their chances of surviving and producing offspring. The bird population will increase, and the equilibrium will eventually be restored.

This is an oversimplification. There are thousands of distinct plant, insect, bird, reptile, amphibian, fungus, and mammal species in Elk Island National Park, and the interactions between them are extremely complex. This example simply serves to illustrate how ecosystems maintain equilibrium.

### Aquatic Ecosystems

Canada contains well over half of the world's lakes. Most lakes in Canada were formed when glaciers retreated at the end of the last ice age; in geological terms, they are quite young. In biological terms, however, many lakes are already nutrient-rich and thriving. A good example is Nakamun Lake, Alberta.

Nakamun Lake is incredibly fertile. Runoff from the nearby forests and plains carries nutrients into the lakebed. Animal waste and decomposing organisms also add nutrients. The lake's surface receives plenty of sunlight throughout the summer months.

The most prevalent life forms in Nakamun Lake are micro-organisms: algae and cyanobacteria (blue-green algae). These organisms float on the surface of the lake. The lakebed is home to larger plants, such as pondweed and watermilfoil. The sediment in the lakebed is where the nutrients eventually settle, unless disturbed by currents or waves.
The lake is also home to fish: minnows, yellow perch, and northern pike. These fish feed on phytoplankton, insects, insect larvae, and each other.

During the summer months, the sun warms the nutrient-rich water. Blue-green algae thrive in these conditions, and reproduce rapidly, which creates an algal bloom. Algal blooms are visible patches of algae that float on the surface of a body of water and are often called 'pond scum.'

An algal bloom forming

These blooms affect the lake ecosystem in a number of ways. First, they reduce the amount of sunlight that penetrates the water. This means that the plants rooted in the lakebed receive less sunlight for photosynthesis. Only the plants at the water's edge will remain unaffected. Second, the algae are very toxic. Animals who are exposed to too much of the algae may be fatally poisoned. Algal blooms normally disappear within a matter of days, sometimes weeks, but this presents a third problem. Dead algae are broken down by aerobic (oxygen-using) decomposers. This removes oxygen from the water, which can have a deadly effect on fish populations.

**Human Impact–Farming Practices**

We know that ecosystem interactions determine the nature of the ecosystem itself. Humans can use this knowledge to influence the development of ecosystem. This is the principle behind farming. Humans alter the ecosystem so that it supports crops—not only food crops, but also fibres (cotton, flax, and hemp) and chemicals (sugar, alcohol, tobacco, and other legal and illegal drugs).

Farming is a cornerstone of our civilization. It frees most of us from the need to hunt or gather our own food, which means that we are able to spend our time on other pursuits. Advances in technology have meant that farming has become more efficient and more productive. Modern agriculture uses several methods to ensure a good crop. Fertilizers provide crops with the nutrients they need. Insecticides and fungicides keep pests from destroying plants. Selective plant breeding produces offspring that can adapt to a variety of climatic conditions.

Farmers must use proper practices to ensure they do not do any environmental harm. Improper practices may harm the farmer's own landor influence other ecosystems.

One way in which environmental harm can be done is through the overuse of chemicals. Rain and wind can transport fertilizers and pesticides to other ecosystems. In the case of fertilizers, the nutrient balance may be altered. For example, if fertilizers are washed into a lake, it may result in algal blooms, reduced oxygen saturation, and reduced fish populations. Pesticides can poison wildlife or reduce the food supply for insectivores (insect-eating creatures).

Slash-and-burn agriculture is another damaging agricultural practice and is normally used in poorer regions. In the first part of slash-and-burn, all the vegetation in the area is cut down and left to dry. The vegetation is then burned. This provides an immediate boost in the productivity of the soil. Nitrates are returned to the soil through the ash, and the increased acidity (again due to the ash) facilitates phosphorus absorption. However, the nutrients in the soil are rapidly depleted, and there is no way to replace them. Slash-and-burn agriculture eventually leaves the soil completely barren.

Slashing-and-burning in Finland, 1892

## PRACTICE EXERCISE

1. Which of the following variables is **not** a climatic component of an ecosystem?
   a) Wind
   b) Latitude
   c) Sunlight
   d) Humidity

2. Edaphic conditions are those relating to
   a) Atmosphere
   b) Acidity
   c) Tides
   d) Soil

3. Which of the following factors is a biotic component of an ecosystem?
   a) Commensalism
   b) Structuralism
   c) Turbidity
   d) Salinity

4. Which of the following terms refers to an interaction between organisms where both organisms benefit?
   a) epiphysis
   b) predation
   c) parasitism
   d) mutualism

5. How do trees help renew nutrients in the soil?
   a) Trees shelter the soil from sunlight.
   b) Animals living in a tree excrete wastes.
   c) Trees release nutrients from their roots.
   d) Decomposers break down dropped leaves.

6. Which of the following products is not in some way produced as a result of farming?
   a) Feather pillow
   b) Loaf of bread
   c) Glass of beer
   d) Cigarette

7. Which of **the** following disciplines is the study of relationships between organisms and the environment they inhabit?
   a) Ecology
   b) Biology
   c) Chemistry
   d) Ergonomics

8. Which of **the** following statements is **true**?
   a) Biotic components are the living parts of an ecosystem and an example of one is a plant
   b) Biotic components are the living parts of an ecosystem and an example of one is glucose.
   c) Biotic components are the non-living parts of an ecosystem and an example of one is a plant.
   d) Biotic components are the non-living parts of an ecosystem and an example of one is temperature.

9. Which of the following arrangements is in the correct order from smallest to largest?
   a) Habitat, biome, biosphere
   b) Biosphere, biome, habitat
   c) Biosphere, habitat, biome
   d) Habitat, biosphere, biome

**10.** Which of the following terms correctly correspond to land, water, and air, respectively?
   **a)** Hydrosphere, lithosphere, atmosphere
   **b)** Lithosphere, hydrosphere, atmosphere
   **c)** Atmosphere, lithosphere, hydrosphere
   **d)** Lithosphere, atmosphere, hydrosphere

**11.** Which of the following terms describes a specific area within a given region that is home to a particular animal or plant?
   **a)** Biome
   **b)** Habitat
   **c)** Biosphere
   **d)** Ecosystem

**12.** For a group of animals to be defined as a population, they must share an area and
   **a)** have similar features
   **b)** have fertile offspring
   **c)** have similar social behaviour
   **d)** have at least 10 members within a group

**13.** Which of the following scenarios would be a density-dependent limiting factor on a bird population?
   **a)** A fire that destroys nesting sites
   **b)** A large mudslide that destroys habitat
   **c)** A pesticide that is sprayed on feed grain
   **d)** A virus that is transferred through the air

**14.** Which of the following terms describes a variety of species that occupy a specific area?
   **a)** Community
   **b)** Ecosystem
   **c)** Habitat
   **d)** Biome

## Lesson 2  TERRESTRIAL BIOMES

### BIOMES

Biomes are large areas with many landscapes or seascapes. A terrestrial biome is a large ecological region of land where populations of plants and animals may coexist, such as a forest, desert, or savanna. A biome has a distinct climate. Temperature, water, sunlight, and wind play the most important roles in regards to climate and biomes.

It is difficult to map biomes because they usually do not have distinct borders. One biome merges into another with gradual changes in the climate and flora. They usually have many distinct populations and communities.
The vegetation found in the region helps classify most biomes. Biomes are generally arranged by latitude and are greatly affected by air currents, ocean currents, and the intensity of the sun's radiation. Earth has a wide diversity of biomes. Some of the common biomes include the grasslands, the boreal forests (Taiga), and the tropical rainforests.

### GEOGRAPHIC RANGE

A geographic range includes activities and living interactions across several biomes. The geographic range refers to the areas of the world where a certain species may be found. Most species occupy a large range that involves more than one biome. Migratory birds, for example, inhabit a large geographic range and live in many different biomes. A certain species may be found in a variety of locations around the world, especially humans. However, most species are found only in specific areas. Some animals live in a small geographic range. Giant pandas, for example, can only be found in a small area of western China. The lowland gorilla is only found in Cameroon and in the Central African Republic. Kangaroos and koala bears are found in narrow geographic ranges of Australia.

Animals such as the bottlenose dolphin have a large geographic range, as they are found in warm waters all over the world. Various species of foxes live all over the world except in South America, Australia, and some islands. Rats also have a large geographic range; one or two species of rats can be found anywhere human beings live.

### BIOSPHERE

The biosphere is the broadest geophysiological (geo = earth + physiology = the study of living functions) area of study in ecology. The biosphere is all-inclusive, as it involves the water (hydrosphere), the air (atmosphere), and the ground (lithosphere) where life exists. It includes all the ecosystems and the global climate. The biosphere ranges from more than 5 000 meters above sea level to at least 9 000 meters below sea level. Occasionally, the extremes of the biosphere have been tested. Ruppell's Vultures have been spotted at 11 300 meters above sea level, and Barhead Geese have been spotted at 8 300 meters over Mount Everest. In the deep waters near the Caribbean, fish have been found as low as 8 372 meters below sea level.

There are six major terrestrial biomes:
- rainforest
- deciduous forest
- coniferous forest
- desert
- grassland
- tundra

It is difficult to map biomes because they usually do not have distinct borders. One biome merges into another with gradual changes in the climate and flora. They may also expand or shrink over time, given climatic changes, human activity, and so forth.

Biomes can generally be subdivided further according to geographic location, annual precipitation, and other factors that impact living conditions. The Great Plains of North America, Africa's Serengeti region, and the steppes of Central Asia are all considered grassland biomes.

The *specific* plant and animal life will differ between biomes of the same type, but they will be *generally* similar. For example, bison are only found on the North American prairie, while the Cape Buffalo lives in the grasslands of Africa. However, both species are large herbivorous mammals. They occupy a similar ecological niche in their respective regions.

**Rainforests**

Rainforests are areas of high annual precipitation (more than 200 cm per year) that have high humidity and lush tree and plant populations. Tropical forests have a rich diversity of insects, birds, reptiles, amphibians, and mammals. In some cases, biologists estimate that there are over 250 000 different species in one hectare of rainforest. The diversity is so complex that many species of plants and animals have yet to be discovered.

A Chestnut-mandibled Toucan in the Amazon Rainforest

The temperatures in rainforests do not vary much during the year. Depending on the altitude, the temperatures range between 25°C and 31°C. Rather than going through a cycle of hot and cold seasons, tropical forests go through wet and dry seasons. Of course, as the name suggests, rainforests do not endure long dry spells.

79

NOTES

The vegetation in tropical forests is stratified, which means it exhibits distinct layers of plants at different heights. The tallest trees, or **emergents**, can reach 60 meters in height. Below them, at around 40 meters high, other trees form a high and dense **canopy** that provides shade for the lower levels. This protects the forest floor from solar radiation, which could kill the detritivores and decomposers. These organisms are needed to quickly return nutrients to the ground.

At the lower level, there are trees with vines that compete for the sunlight. This level is composed of **understory trees**. These trees rarely grow above three or four meters. Plants in the tropical rain forest have special adaptations to compete for light.

The **rainforest floor** is dark, cool, and damp because most sunlight is blocked by the canopy and understory. The warm temperature, shade, and humidity are excellent conditions for soil bacteria, fungi, lichens, ferns, and moss. Decay occurs quickly on the rainforest floor, as the top layer of soil is rich in microbial life. A leaf that takes one year to decompose in the grasslands will completely decompose in two to six weeks on the rainforest floor. The minerals and nutrients released from the decomposition are quickly absorbed by the fast-growing plant life.

Because of this rapid cycling of nutrients, the soil conditions are poor. Good soil may only be found on the thin top layer. Heavy rainfall washes many of the nutrients out of the soil. Good farmland (see the grasslands) can have a depth of as much as 50 or 60 centimetres of good soil; in the rainforest, there are only five to 30 centimetres of good soil.

This is why slash-and-burn agriculture is not sustainable: once all the trees are cut down and removed, there is not enough good soil and nitrogen to support the growth of crops or new plants. The nutrients in the thin layer of good soil are soon depleted. To make matters worse, with the shade (canopy) removed, many of the decomposers become exposed to the sun and die. This leaves the soil void of the microbial activity needed to keep the soil fertile.

**Deciduous Forests**

Temperate forest areas have adequate rainfall (more than 150 cm per year), which allows the growth of deciduous forests. Deciduous trees are those that shed their leaves in winter. Such trees include maple, walnut, birch, elm, oak, and beech. Temperate forests are also rich in natural herbs and ferns. Lichen and mosses are found on the forest floor.

Deciduous trees in Québec's Charlevoix region

The forests contain raccoons, deer, rabbits, squirrels, skunks, and foxes. Larger predators include bears, wolves, and mountain lions.

These forests are subject to the cycle of warm and cold seasons. Temperatures vary greatly over the course of a year, from –30°C in the winter to +30°C in the summer. The rain falls evenly throughout the year. This is in contrast to the type of rainfall in the grasslands and the savannas. Because of the abundant rainfall and fallen leaves, the soil is rich in organic material.

### Boreal Forest

Boreal forest, or taiga, consists of northern forests of coniferous (cone-bearing) trees such as fir, spruce, hemlock, and tamarack. These areas have four seasons characterized with long, cold, and dry winters. Winters have an average temperature of around – 10°C, and the short summers average

Banff National Park, Alberta

around 20°C. The amount of daylight is very short in the winter and very long in the summer.

These forests receive about 76 cm of precipitation per year. However, most of this precipitation comes in the form of snow in the winter and remains frozen.
As a result, there is very little water available for plants. Plants in this region thus have special adaptations to conserve water.

Wildlife of the boreal forest includes moose, elk, bear, wolf, lynx, squirrel, and many other rodents.

The variety of species is very limited in these forests, with spruce, fir, and tamarack trees being most abundant. Pine needle leaves are very narrow and wax-coated to prevent water loss. The tapered shape of these trees prevents snow from accumulating on the branches, which reduces the weight on the branches and improves the leaves' access to sunlight. Conifers also prevent competitors from taking all the limited water by dropping leaves that make the soil acidic.

The soil of these forests is very thin and very poor because the dry cold conditions slow down the organic decomposition. The soil is also acidic as a result of the pine needles that are dropped.

NOTES

## Deserts

Saguaro cacti in the Sonoran Desert

Deserts are areas of low annual precipitation (less than 25 cm) and sparse vegetation. They generally thrive in tropical and subtropical regions. Desert plants are adapted to conserve water. For example, cacti have developed spine-like leaves that limit water loss and protect them from animals. Oleanders have deep and extensive root systems. Other desert plants include yuccas, buckwheat bushes, foojum, and ocotillo. Small trees and shrubs have deep roots that help them survive. Plants in the desert have special adaptations to compete for water.

Most animals in the desert are nocturnal. During the day, they protect themselves in burrows or other sheltered areas. They tend to be small carnivores and insectivores: rodents, reptiles, scorpions, spiders, birds, etc.

Deserts are also characterized by extreme daily temperature variation. Daytime temperatures can exceed 40°C. At night, temperatures can drop to below –10°C. Deserts experience some seasonal variation, but remain hot even in winter.

The soil quality in deserts is very poor. Although the soil has plenty of nutrients, it is dry, loose, and contains almost no organic matter. This makes any sustained agriculture in deserts impractical, except in areas near rivers. The Nile River in North Africa is an excellent example of this. For millennia, farmers in Egypt awaited the annual flooding of the Nile, which would deliver water and organic matter to formerly barren desert. The Nile River flood plain became extremely fertile.

## Grasslands

Grasslands, as the name suggests, are dominated by grasses. Trees and shrubs are generally limited to areas near lakes and rivers. The grasslands biome is incredibly varied and has two major subtypes: temperate and tropical.

### Temperate grasslands

Temperate grasslands include the North American Prairie, the South American *pampas*, and the African veldt. While grasses are the dominant vegetation, flowers, clover, and other small plants are also relatively common. There are few naturally growing trees and bushes because of the low precipitation and the cooler temperatures. Trees and bushes are only found in valleys near rivers or creeks.

Grasslands are home to a wide variety of species: rodents, insects, large herbivores such as birds, and a variety of small carnivores. Larger carnivores, such as lions and wolves, prey on the other animals.

Temperate grasslands are subject to seasonal variations in temperature.

Beargrass on the Argentinean *pampas*

In the summer, temperatures can exceed 30°C and can drop below –30°C in the winter. Grasslands receive a moderate amount of rain each year (approximately 25–76 cm). Most of the rain comes in the spring and early summer. To protect themselves from long winters and grazing herbivores, the biome's grasses develop deep, extensive roots. When the grasses die, the decaying roots release their nutrients back into the soil, which makes them available to new plants. This means that temperate grassland soil is exceptionally fertile, even at depths of up to 60 cm. The fertility of the temperate grasslands has resulted in much of it being used for agricultural purposes.

*Tropical grasslands*

Tropical grasslands, or savannas, are open grasslands with long, dry seasons. The African Serengeti and Brazilian *cerrado* are savannas. Unlike temperate grasslands, savannas typically support widely-spaced trees and bushes. Plants in these regions have adaptations that allow them endure long dry periods.

Savannas are characterized by extraordinary biodiversity. As with temperate grasslands, large herbivores are common. For example, wildebeests, zebras, and elephants are popular tourist attractions of the Serengeti in Eastern Africa. There are also numerous smaller herbivores and carnivores: rodents, insects, birds, etc.

Savannas have a wet season and a dry season. The dry season can be very long; a savannah can receive the bulk of its rainfall in the space of a few weeks (between 50 and 150 cm annually). The temperatures range from 20°C to 30°C.

The soil in savannas is poor in comparison to temperate grasslands. The long, dry seasons reduce the action of decomposers and detritivores in the soil. Occasional fires help renew the soil. Grasses recover quickly once the fire passes. Agriculture is possible, but the inconsistent rainfall and nutrient-poor soil makes it more difficult and expensive.

## Tundra

Tundra near Cape Churchill, AB

Tundra is made up of boggy open grasslands, permafrost, and few small trees. This region is cold most of the year, with harsh winter temperatures of below – 35°C, on average. Occasionally, the temperature drops to –50°C. There are very few hours of light during the winter. In the summer, temperatures average around 10°C. There is very little precipitation in the tundra (less than 15 cm annually).

Tundra is treeless: the permanently frozen ground, or **permafrost**, prevents plants with deep roots from growing. The condition of the soil is very poor. It is dry, and the cold limits the action of decomposers. Nevertheless, tundra has a wide variety of life, particularly during the summer season. Lichens, mosses, sedges, flowers, and dwarfed shrubs are able to grow.

There is very poor drainage in this region because of the permafrost. This results in the collection of water on the land during the summer. These pools of water thus become good breeding grounds for flies, mosquitoes, and insects, which attracts migratory birds. Reindeer, lemmings, caribou, Arctic wolves, foxes, and hares are common to this biome. Polar bears are also found near the coast of the tundra.

## ECOLOGICAL NICHE

All the factors of a habitat contribute to the species' **ecological niche**. An ecological niche refers to specific interactions between an organism and its environment. A niche is a complex concept that involves more than a specific location. It includes how an organism lives in relation to its biotic and abiotic environment. In an ecological niche, attention is given to how an organism behaves in that particular location. There are two types of ecological niches. One is called a **fundamental niche** and refers to an organism's existence in a certain area without competition. This generally does not occur in nature.

Two types of niche: fundamental and realized.

A fundamental niche is theoretical and may only occur in laboratory or zoo conditions. A realized niche describes organisms in natural conditions where competition exists.

## SUCCESSION IN COMMUNITIES

Community changes often lead to a stable biological environment. The interactions between organisms and the environment follow a pattern of moving from simple to complex interactions. This directional change in complexity is referred to as **succession**. A complex community that finally becomes balanced is referred to as a **climax community**. Climax communities have a high biomass, a broad variety of species, and many heterotrophic plant species (plants that live off dead plant life). Climax communities tend to be stable with complex food webs. The intermediate stages that lead up to the climax community are called the **seral communities**. There may be many seral communities before the climax community is established.

Succession is very slow, but it occurs all the time in many different forms. Cleared woodlands that are left alone over a span of a decade or two re-develop into woodlands. Land ravaged by forest fires quickly reclaims plant life and rebuilds the forest through natural biological interactions. Cultivated fields that are no longer used eventually become grasslands again. Flooded land can return to original conditions. An oligotrophic lake (poor in nutrients) can naturally become a eutrophic lake (rich in nutrients). Land damaged by volcanic activity or chemical spills will eventually repair itself as vegetation gradually reclaims the area. This gradual reclamation, known as **biological succession**, allows damaged ecological niches to return to their earlier state.

Dr. Ellie E. Prepas, from the University of Alberta, researches eutrophic systems. In particular, she studies the natural blue-green algae or cyanobacterial toxins (poisons) that are produced in eutrophic lakes. These toxins could have a negative impact on the aquatic food chain and human health. Eutrophic waters have reduced dissolved oxygen. Less oxygen in the water produces an environment that favours floating plant life over animals that require dissolved oxygen. Dr. Prepas studies methods to control eutrophication.

## SECONDARY SUCCESSION

The gradual changes that reclaim land or water that once supported life are called **secondary succession**. This type of succession involves the rebuilding of a certain area that may have at one time supported a well-developed and stable community. Secondary succession implies that good soil already exists in the damaged area.

The rebuilding of the area always begins with simple, hardy life forms and moves to more complex communities. This occurs until the land is completely reclaimed by the plants and animals that originally inhabited the area. The species that first moves into a damaged area is called a **fugitive species**. A fugitive species does well as long as there is little competition. After a fire, fugitive plants spread quickly over the nutrient-rich soil, but disappear as soon as other plants move into the same area. Weeds, grasses, and a plant called foxglove often serve as fugitive species. These plants prepare the soil conditions and a seedbed for larger and more permanent plants.

A seral community is an intermediate stage in the development of a climax community.

Shrubs that are resistant to long hours of solar radiation and that require less water and nutrition take over from fugitive species. As the community progresses and trees take over from shrubs, a canopy develops. A canopy is a covering developed by the leaves and branches of many trees that shades the ground, which protects it from direct sunlight. Larger trees also provide a canopy. This will impede the survival of certain fugitive species or shrubs that require direct sunlight.

## PRIMARY SUCCESSION

Biological communities sometimes do not exist in certain places such as mountain slopes, volcanic slopes, and glacial areas. Certain sturdy life forms may move into areas like this, where no life exists, and make the conditions right to support life.

Areas with no life generally have no soil and poor water conditions. The first organisms that are able to live in this area have the special ability to prepare a life-supporting environment from abiotic factors (non-living things). Succession that starts with barren-rock terrain is referred to as **xerarch succession**. Succession that begins on the surface of nutrient-poor water is called **hydrarch primary succession**.

A xerophyte is a plant that can grow in barren rock conditions. *Xero-* is from the Greek, meaning "dry."

Organisms such as lichens and moss are able to survive in harsh living environments. They are able to endure long hours of solar radiation. Lichens live on rocks and secrete acids that break the rock down into tiny pockets of dust and dead lichens. Moss can live on tiny pockets of dust and help retain water. Eventually, tiny pockets of soil are formed.

The algae, lichens, and moss are sturdy plants that develop or pave the way for more complex life forms. Their ability to move into a new environment that normally does not support life earns them the title of **pioneer species**. Pioneer plants eventually form a pioneer community. Pioneer communities overall have a low biomass, therefore vast amounts of solar energy that reaches the community goes uncaptured and is wasted.

After a long period of time, enough soil, water, and organic material are available to give rise to decayed material called **humus**. Humus changes the characteristics of the soil to such a degree that the original pioneer plants no longer flourish. Other small plants and eventually larger plants take over the area. The process of creating a complex community from an environment that never supported life is referred to as **primary succession**.

## CHARACTERISTICS OF AQUATIC ENVIRONMENTS

Ecosystems exist in water as well as on land. Water ecosystems interact with terrestrial ecosystems in many ways. Birds, some mammals, and humans interact with these ecosystems as they capture food from lakes, rivers and oceans. Not all the interactions, however, are beneficial: pollutants from the land often end up in waterways.

Aquatic environments are classified by fresh water or saltwater (marine) environments. Tides, waves, dissolved oxygen, organic material, salinity, run-off, turbidity (cloudiness of the water), and currents make up some of the important abiotic factors that influence life in ocean waters.
There is less movement in fresh water environments such as lakes, ponds, and swamps. Springs, rivers, and creeks, however, have considerable current.

Viscosity, pressure, buoyancy, temperature variation, availability of gases, and light penetrations are very different in water than on land. Therefore, plants and animals have special adaptations to survive in aquatic habitats.

## WATER PLANTS ADAPTATIONS

Plants in ponds or lakes can float on water. This allows them to have direct contact with sunlight and the carbon dioxide they require to produce food. Some water plants even have little air bladders that help them float. Such is the case of algae.

Other plants, like water lilies, have large air spaces in their leaves or have spines or projections to increase their surface area. These physical traits increase their buoyancy, or their ability to float. A larger surface area also makes it easier to absorb sunlight.

Plants in a river or creek also need special adaptation. Floating might not be an option in a fast-moving stream. Plants near a river have thin, ribbon-shaped leaves that do not provide resistance to the moving water.
Some plants, like algae, have a *holdfast* that is anchored onto rocks.

NOTES

Turbidity is a measure of a liquid's ability to block or obscure light. It has the same root word as "disturb." In terms of a liquid, it means there are unsettled materials floating throughout it.

## PRACTICE EXERCISE

1. Which of the following terms describes distinctive plants, animals, and climatein a given region?
   a) Biome
   b) Habitat
   c) Community
   d) Population

2. Which of the following variables is the **least** important factor in determining the climate of a given area?
   a) Soil
   b) Wind
   c) Sunlight
   d) Temperature

3. Which biome has the **greatest** diversity of life and the **highest** biomass?
   a) Taiga
   b) Tundra
   c) Grassland
   d) Tropical rainforest

4. Which of the following biomes has poor soil quality and contains numerous organisms that are nocturnal as well as plants that are leafless, but have good root systems?.
   a) Taiga
   b) Desert
   c) Grassland
   d) Tropical rainforest

5. Which of the following biomes is characterized by large ungulates, four seasons, and deep rich soil?
   a) Taiga
   b) Desert
   c) Grassland
   d) Tropical rainforest

6. Which of the following biomes has soil that is thin, acidic, and receives very little useable precipitation?
   a) Taiga
   b) Tundra
   c) Grassland
   d) Tropical rainforest

7. Which of the following biomes have bogs that are a result of poor drainage in a permafrost environment?
   a) Taiga
   b) Tundra
   c) Grassland
   d) Tropical rainforest

8. An example of primary succession would be
   a) a valley that is temporarily flooded
   b) farmland with crops that are removed
   c) a new island created through volcanic activity
   d) a forest completely that is burned to the ground

## *Lesson 3   FOOD CHAINS, WEBS, AND PYRAMIDS*

We have already looked at the biogeochemical cycling in the first unit. We will now look at the energy flow through an ecosystem.   Studying the flow of energy in an ecosystem involves the study of food chains and food webs.

### FOOD CHAINS

A food chain is a linked series of organisms.  Each organism is consumed by the next organism on the chain.  For example, a hazel tree is an autotroph.  It begins the chain because it doesn't consume any other creature.  The next link in this example might be a moth, as it consumes the leaves of the hazel tree.  The moth is then eaten by a wood frog, which in turn is consumed by a skunk.

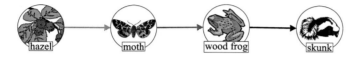

There are usually only four or five links in a food chain.  This has to do with the fact that a great deal of energy is lost at each link.  Organisms use energy to grow, reproduce, move,etc.  This energy is generally expended as heat and is not available to the next consumer in the chain.

Organisms can be classified according to their position in the flow of energy.  These classifications are called **trophic levels**.  Trophic means "nutrition-related."  In this particular case, it applies to an organism's source of nutrients.  There are five trophic levels.
- Primary producers: (autotrophs)
- Primary consumers: (herbivores)
- Secondary consumers: (carnivores or omnivores)
- Tertiary consumers:  (carnivores or omnivores)
- Decomposers/detritivores

Primary producers are **autotrophs** (self-feeding).  Consumers, decomposers, and detritivores are all **heterotrophs** (feed on others).

### Primary Producers

Primary producers are mostly plants that use sunlight and generate food via photosynthesis.  They are the only organisms that directly capture and use solar energy.  Therefore, producers determine the entire energy budget for an ecosystem.  They are also the most efficient in terms of energy retention.

There are, however, primary producers that do not require sunlight. For example, there is a species of bacteria that can synthesize light from deep-sea hydrothermal vents.  Others can use heat and chemical compounds from these vents to make energy in a process called *chemosynthesis*.

Examples:  phytoplankton, trees, grasses, algae, grains, and vegetables.

### Primary Consumers

Primary consumers are animals that feed off of primary producers. They are strictly herbivorous animals.

Examples: seed-eating birds, zooplankton, krill, turtles, most insects, some fish, snails, mice, all grazing mammals, and most invertebrates.

### Secondary Consumers

Secondary consumers are animals that consume herbivores (i.e., primary consumers). Some secondary consumers may also consume plants.

Examples: spiders, squid, carnivorous zooplankton, frogs, insect-eating birds, and most fish.

### Tertiary Consumers

Tertiary consumers are animals that consume smaller carnivores and herbivores. They may also consume plants.

Examples: foxes, wolves, whales, sharks, seals, owls, goshawks, and cats.

### Decomposers/Detritivores

Decomposers and detritivores are animals that feed on organic wastes: droppings, dead organisms, fallen leaves, and so forth.

Detritivores survive by consuming organic wastes, thereby reintroducing the material into the food chain.

Examples: earthworms, blowflies, maggots, and dung beetles.

Decomposers break down organic wastes into simpler forms that can be used by plants.

Examples: bacteria, fungi, and some protozoa.

### Classification of Food chains

There are two basic types of food chain.

**Grazing food chain:** In a grazing food chain, energy is initially derived from an autotroph. An example of a grazing food chain would be a rabbit that eats grass, and then a fox that eats the rabbit.

**Detrital food chain:** In a detrital food chain, energy is initially derived from dead organic matter (dead organisms, wastes, etc.). Decomposers feed on the detritus and are in turn consumed by more complex organisms. An example of a detrital food-chain would be bacteria breaking down dead grass, a roundworm eating the bacteria, and a porcupine eating the roundworm.

As the energy moves through the chain, both matter and energy are lost to the chain. First, carbon is lost at each level as a result of cellular respiration. It is alsoexcreted as undigested food and waste. Carbon is needed to make biomass (glucose, cellulose, proteins, nucleic acids, etc). As a result, each trophic level has less biomass. Energy is lost at each level, usually in the form of heat. This means that less energy is available, which results in less construction of biomass and fewer organisms at each successive level in the chain. Approximately ten percent of the biomass is transferred from one living organism to the organism that consumes it.

## ENVIRONMENTAL MATTER MOVES THROUGH THE FOOD CHAIN

When grass grows, it captures trace elements such as iron from the soil. A cow that grazes on the grass will obtain iron from the grass. When humans eat cow meat, they likewise take in iron. Such trace elements are important components of our diet. Iron, for example, is essential for the circulation of oxygen through our bodies. Sometimes, however, dangerous elements can be distributed throughout the food chain. Those dangerous elements can then collect in the bodies of tertiary consumers by virtue of the fact that they tend to live longer and thus consume more food over a longer period of time.

In the earlier 1960s, an insecticide called DDT (Dichlorodiphenyl-trichloroethane) was used to kill mosquitoes. It is an extremely effective insecticide, but it collects in the fats of animals. Animals that consumed dead or dying mosquitoes were exposed to only a tiny amount of DDT, but over time, they began to accumulate DDT in their tissues. When those same animals were consumed by other animals in the chain, the DDT was passed along.

The use of DDT in the United States nearly caused the extinction of the bald eagle. DDT can harm bird embryos and cause eggshells to become brittle. DDT is also highly toxic to many aquatic animals.

Further research revealed DDT in the milk of polar bears and seals. DDT had washed into rivers and was consumed by plankton, which allowed it to move up a completely different food chain that was many kilometres away from the original source.

Even though DDT has been made illegal, there are other toxic pollutants such as mercury and PCBs (polychlorinated biphenyls) that still find their way into global ecosystems. These pollutants move up the food chain as predators and tertiary consumers (including humans) consume animals and organisms that are so called 'bottom-feeders'.

## FOOD WEBS

Food webs show more complex interactions between organisms in an ecosystem. Most organisms have multiple food sources. Some even feed at more than one trophic level. For example, a black bear might eat blackberries (primary producer), a rabbit (primary consumer), or salmon (secondary consumer).

Food webs usually represent only a portion of the creatures in an ecosystem. This is due to the fact that so many different creatures can inhabit an area, even a small one. For example, in order to include every single organism in an acre of rainforest would require a chart of such complexity that it would be virtually impossible to create. Food webs also tend not to include decomposers and detritivores. Doing so would cause the web to loop back on itself infinitely.

The food web is useful when tracking relationships between apparently unrelated organisms. A sample food web is given below.

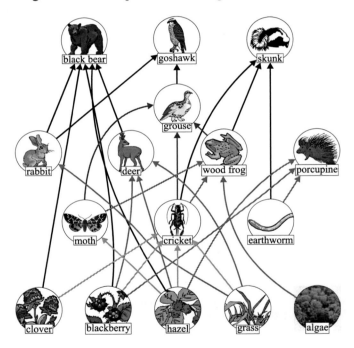

To get an idea of how the food web works, consider the following example. Let us say that, conditions are ideal for the growth of algae during one particular spring. Wood frog tadpoles consume algae; more algae means more tadpoles will survive to adulthood. If this is the case, there will be more frogs available to such predators as the grouse. The grouse population will thus increase as a result. Some may even migrate into the ecosystem in search of the abundant food.

All of this is good news for the goshawks, which will have plenty of grouses to prey upon. Because there are more grouses, the goshawks will have less need to consume rabbits. This, in turn, will leave more rabbits available for other predators, such as the black bear.

**ENERGY AND NUMBER PYRAMIDS**

Producers capture more energy for their body weight than any other organisms. They also use that energy very efficiently. Plants lose very little heat as they carry out their many functions.

When the plant is eaten by a primary consumer there is a big change in efficiency. Only 5–20% of the energy stored in the plant is captured. What happens to the rest of the energy? The rest of the energy is lost in the form of heat, muscular movement, movement of molecules, anabolic activities, neuron activity, and other physiological activities of the primary consumer. This means that 80–95% of the energy is lost in activities such as keeping warm, hunting, moving, thinking, and so on. When primary consumers are eaten by secondary consumers, only 5–20% of the energy is retained.

As a result of this great energy lost, most ecosystems have more plants than herbivores, more herbivores than carnivores, and more small carnivores than larger ones. This can be diagrammed in the form of a pyramid shape, with producers at the base of the pyramid. This *pyramid of numbers* is a generalization and does not always apply to every ecosystem.

Pyramid of Mass and Numbers

Note that as the trophic level increases, the mass or number decreases. Consider the following example. Imagine that 10 000 hazel trees can support 1 000 moths. 1 000 moths can in turn support 100 frogs, which is enough to feed 10 skunks.

NOTES

A *plankter* is an individual plankton.

Body size has to be taken into account. As you move up the trophic levels, body size tends to increase. A blue whale certainly weighs more than a single phytoplankter. However, this is not always the case in every ecosystem. Pack animals like wolves hunt and consume larger herbivores.

If all of the organisms at each trophic level are counted and converted into dry weight or kilojoules per gram, a more reliable pyramid of biomass (grams of dry organic material/m$^2$) or pyramid of energy results (kJ/gram).

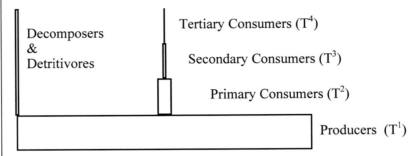

Decomposers & Detritivores

Tertiary Consumers (T$^4$)

Secondary Consumers (T$^3$)

Primary Consumers (T$^2$)

Producers (T$^1$)

Grams of dry biomass per square metre

The biomass of each trophic level is less because of lost carbon dioxide, undigested food (organic waste), and energy lost as heat.

The biomass of detritivores and decomposers remains constant.

**EFFICIENCY**

It is important to distinguish between the amount of energy available at each trophic level and the amount of energy each individual contributes. For example, a field of grass contains a great deal of energy, but an individual blade of grass does not. A single cow obviously contains more energy than a blade of grass; it takes a great number of blades of grass to provide a cow with what it needs to live and grow. Therefore, despite the energy lost between trophic levels, a consumer will derive more energy from eating a kilogram of cow meat than it will from eating a blade of grass. In short, the loss of energy is a factor of the ecosystem, not of the individuals within it. This is especially important where sources of food energy are limited.

Efficiency is important where sources of food energy are limited. Human populations across the globe face food shortages and famine. It is more efficient for humans to feed on agricultural crops directly rather than feeding the crops to animals and eating them. If you were stranded on an island with nothing but an apple tree and a pig, you would not want the pig to eat the apples (and then eat the pig yourself). Even though a kilogram of pork contains more energy than a kilogram of apples, you would lose 80–95% of the total food energy available by eating meat rather than plants.

# PRACTICE EXERCISE

1.  A food chain is normally characterized by _____ organisms. Each organism eats _____.
    a) 6 or more, only one other organism
    b) 6 or more, many other organisms
    c) up to 5, only one other organism
    d) up to 5, many other organisms

2.  Which of the following variables is an important factor that limits the length of a food chain?
    a) Size of each organism
    b) Cycling of food chain energy
    c) Heat loss and an organism's functions
    d) Number of organisms within each trophic level

3.  An organism obtains its energy by virtue of its
    a) Niche                           b) Population
    c) Community                       d) Trophic level

4.  Primary consumers consume
    a) only plants                     b) only animals
    c) organic waste                   d) both plants and animals

5.  Which of the following creatures are examples of detritivores?
    a) sharks and wolves               b) earthworms and maggots
    c) deer and seed eating birds      d) frogs and insect eating birds

6.  A food chain diagram
    a) requires an autotroph, not the sun      b) requires the sun, not an autotroph
    c) requires an autotroph and the sun       d) does not require the sun or an autotroph

7.  Which of the flowing statements is **true**?.
    a) A food web simpler than a food chain.
    b) A food web is more complex than a food chain.
    c) A food web contains fewer organisms than a food chain.
    d) A food web shows more trophic levels than a food chain.

8.  As one moves up a pyramid of mass
    a) each individual organism increases in biomass
    b) each individual organism decreases in biomass
    c) the overall biomass of the trophic level increases
    d) the overall biomass of the trophic level decreases

# PRACTICE QUIZ

1. Which of the following variables would be considered an abiotic component of an ecosystem?
   a) Plants
   b) Water
   c) Bacteria
   d) Detritivores

2. Energy is described as _____ through an ecosystem.  Matter is described as _____.
   a) cycled; cycled
   b) flowing; cycled
   c) cycled; flowing
   d) flowing; flowing

3. A habitat could be described as the
   a) food an organism consumes
   b) continent a population inhabits
   c) behaviour an organism exhibits
   d) specific area an organism occupies

4. Which of the following scenarios is the **best** example of a population?
   a) A pack of roaming male wolves
   b) Two different ant species that occupy the same area
   c) A lion pride that consists of only a few dominant males and numerous breeding females
   d) Two large groups of birds of the same species that occupy the same feeding area but nest apart

5. Which of the following terms could be used to describe interacting plants, insects, birds, and small rodents that occupy the same area?
   a) Biome
   b) Habitat
   c) Ecosystem
   d) Community

6. What determines the boundaries of a biome?
   a) Distinctive organisms and climate
   b) Large bodies of water (such as oceans)
   c) The movement of individual populations
   d) The area that provides food and shelter to a community

7. Stratification is a term that describes the layering of organisms within a
   a) taiga biome
   b) tundra biome
   c) a grassland
   d) tropical rainforest biome

8. Plants that use a waxy coating and stems (spikes) to conserve water would most likely be found in a
   a) taiga biome
   b) desert biome
   c) grassland biome
   d) tropical rainforest biome

9. Large producers adapted to cool temperatures and acidic soil conditions would be found in the
   a) taiga biome
   b) tundra biome
   c) grassland biome
   d) tropical rainforest biome

10. Which of the following biomes is characterized by poor soil drainage as a result of a permanent layer of underlying ice?
    a) Taiga
    b) Tundra
    c) Grassland
    d) Tropical rainforest

**11.** Secondary succession
   **a)** requires land with no life on it
   **b)** would most likely require humus
   **c)** occurs on recently solidified lava
   **d)** could not happen on land affected by an intense forest fire

**12.** A food chain is a _____ diagram of energy flow. Approximately _____ % of energy is not available to the next organism.
   **a)** complex, 90           **b)** complex, 10
   **c)** simplified, 90        **d)** simplified, 10

**13.** The trophic level of an organism is used to categorize
   **a)** an organism's habitat           **b)** an organism's social behaviour
   **c)** how an organism obtains energy   **d)** the biome in which an organism inhabits

**14.** In a food chain, the role of an autotroph could be carried out by
   **a)** fungi                **b)** a herbivore
   **c)** an omnivore          **d)** chemosynthetic bacteria near deep-sea vents

**15.** A food web is
   **a)** a series of interacting food chains
   **b)** limited to approximately five organisms
   **c)** a diagram that does not require autotrophs
   **d)** a diagram of one organism eating another organism

**16.** Explain why energy is described as flowing while matter is said to cycle.

**17.** Food chains and webs share a number of characteristics with energy/biomass/number pyramids. Explain two similarities and two differences

**18.** With increasing human populations and decreasing availability of land, it has been proposed that humans alter their eating habits. Specifically, it has been suggested that diets move from the consumption of animal proteins to plant proteins. Describe how this may be beneficial in terms of energy within an ecosystem. Could there also be any concerns associated with this shift?

## Lesson 4 *VARIATION IN POPULATIONS*

NOTES

Populations are basic components of an ecosystem's structure.
- Great variation exists within populations.
- The nature of variation within populations can be described by inherited characteristics versus acquired characteristics and continuous variation versus discontinuous variation.
- Populations are adapted to their environment (e.g., drug resistance, cold tolerance).
- There is evidence to support the evolution of modern species from ancestral forms.
- Natural selection influences future populations and leads to evolutionary change.

### VARIATION IN POPULATIONS

Variation within a species is a central concept in biology. The biosphere manifests phenotypic and genotypic variation in both plants and animals. The term *variation* refers to the differences between individuals of a given species. Variation is important because it gives a species a wider range of traits to deal with environmental stress or competition for limited resources. The biodiversity of an ecosystem is largely dependent on genetic variation in order to provide added stability.

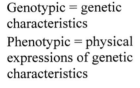

Genotypic = genetic characteristics

Phenotypic = physical expressions of genetic characteristics

Every seed of every fruit is a little different than other seeds, even within a particular species. Variation exists in humans as well. Every human is unique. Differences can be found in facial features, fingerprints, or the patterns of blood vessels in the back of the eye called the retina. These variations help identify individual humans and animals. For example, retinal scans that take a picture of the blood vessels in the back of the eye are now used for security checks. Iris scans are routinely used in many airports to positively identify international travelers. These and many more differences are evidence of variation within a species.

The variation found in a species demonstrates a typical pattern. The amount of variation of a particular trait is only slight for most individuals in a population. Extreme variation is usually found in only a small percentage of individuals within a particular species. For example, in a given species of particular plant, you find few individual plants to be very short but the majority to be of an average height typical of that species. At the other end of the scale, you will find a few individual plants will be very tall for the species. This is a typical pattern observed in all species and is referred to as the **bell curve**.

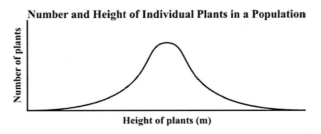

**Number and Height of Individual Plants in a Population**

Number of plants

Height of plants (m)

## SEXUAL RECOMBINATION PROMOTES GENETIC VARIATION

Asexual reproduction (also called agamogenesis) is a form of reproduction that does not involve gametes, such as an egg cell or a sperm cell. An understanding of asexual reproduction helps us better understand the importance of sexual reproduction and its relationship to variation and the survival of a species. Asexual reproduction is a very efficient and rapid form of reproduction; there is no need to search for a partner or for a sperm cell to find an egg cell. The problem with asexual reproduction is that the daughter cell or the offspring is identical to the parent cell.

Asexual reproduction in animal cells such as bacteria and yeast includes the reproductive strategies of binary fission and budding. In plant cells, asexual reproduction includes regeneration, vegetative reproduction, and spore formation. Asexual reproduction is not common among most plants and animals because it does not allow for variation. The artificial cloning of animals or plants has an identical drawback. Cloning reduces variation within a species; it is not part of a species's natural survival or development.

Sexual reproduction—that is, reproduction involving the union of male and female gametes such as sperm and eggs—is a more common and a more successful form of reproduction. Sexual reproduction assures variation, which in turn helps assure the survival of the species. Gamete formation is called **gametogenesis**. A special process known as **meiosis** produces male and female gametes (sperm cells and egg cells, respectively). Meiosis results in sex cells that have half of the genetic material, or only one of each pair of chromosomes normally found in a cell. Meiosis and random fertilization greatly increase the amount of variation within a species.

The following three sexual reproduction processes effectively ensures variation within a population.
1. Independent orientation (assortment) of chromosomes in meiosis
2. Crossing-over in meiosis (resulting in recombinant DNA)
3. Random fertilization

## VARIATION BY INDEPENDENT ORIENTATION OF CHROMOSOMES

During meiosis, homologous chromosomes (similar chromosomes) from the father and mother line up at the center of the nucleus.

Before the cell divides, the chromosomes line up on an imaginary line called the **equatorial plate**. After organizing themselves in this fashion, they then proceed to line up in a somewhat random manner.

In other words, the maternal and paternal chromosomes are not all lined up on either side of the plate unless this happens by chance. Some maternal chromosomes can line up on one side together with other paternal chromosomes. The following diagram helps explain this process. In a human being that has 46 chromosomes, there are more than eight million combinations possible as a result of the independent orientation of chromosomes.

# Independent Orientation

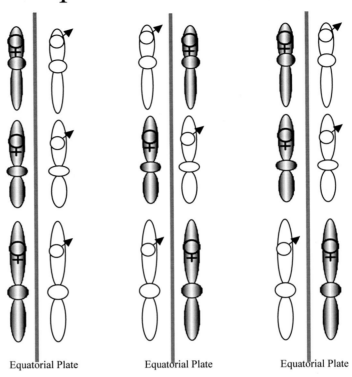

Equatorial Plate          Equatorial Plate          Equatorial Plate

Three possible ways that homologous chromosomes can line up on the equatorial plate during metaphase of Meiosis I. These different alignments of the same chromosomes result in difererent gametes because each gamete will have a different combination of maternal and paternal chromosomes.

## VARIATION BY DNA CROSSING-OVER

During the the first phase of meiosis (prophase I), chunks of genetic material from the maternal and paternal chromosome and can be exchanged.

In human chromosomes, this can often happen in more than two or three places along the chromosome. A new combination of DNA results in a chromosome that is not like the mother or father's original chromosome. What this means is that the offspring of sexual reproduction have recombined DNA (recombinant DNA) that is unique and separate from the parents (a result of the crossing-over of genetic information).

This assures even more variation in a sexually-reproducing population. The following diagram illustrates the concept of genetic recombination.

Crossing-over results in two types of gametes. One type of gamete results from crossover and is referred to as a **recombinant gamete**, while the other is identical to the parent and is called a **parental gamete**.

# Crossing-Over

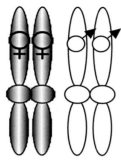

**Lining-up**
Replicated Homologous chromosomes from the father and the mother line-up beside each other forming a tetrad

— DNA found in a parental gamete

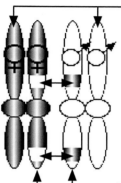

**Crossing-Over**
While the chromosomes are close to each other chunks of DNA from the maternal DNA swap with chunks of Paternal DNA.

— DNA found in a recombinant gamete

Each of chromosome in this tetrad is now different. Each chromosome is destined for a different gamete (sex cell).

## VARIATION BY RANDOM FERTILIZATION

Each parent of a sexually-reproducing species is capable of producing many gametes that are biologically different. This is the result of independent orientation and the crossing-over of genetic material.
The process by which a male gamete combines with a particular female gamete to form a zygote is completely random. With random fertilization, crossing-over, and independent orientation, a human couple is theoretically able to produce billions of genetically-different offspring.
Variation is assured in organisms that reproduce sexually.

## VARIATION IS ACQUIRED AND/OR INHERITED

We observe variation in nature when we see tall trees and short trees or fast horses and slow horses. We can see different colours of eyes, hair, and fur. When studying variations, it is important to determine if the variations are acquired or inherited. Acquired characteristics occur with an individual as a result of the environment and cannot be passed on to future generations.

The skin's response to the sun is an example of an acquired characteristic. If you are exposed to too much sunlight, your skin will respond by becoming darker or by turning red. The change in your skin colour is acquired because of environmental exposure. You are not able to pass that tanned or red colour on to your offspring. However, if you are born with dark skin, your children will likely have dark skin, regardless of the amount of time you or your children spend in the sun. In this case, the skin colour is an inherited characteristic.

The physique of an athlete is acquired and cannot be passed on to the children of that athlete. Certain environmental diseases are acquired and are not passed on unless the children are exposed to the disease. Emphysema from smoking is not likely to be passed on to the offspring of the smoker unless children are exposed to the hazard. Some diseases, such as sickle-cell anemia, are inherited. Others are a mixture of an inherited and an acquired characteristic, as in the case of heart disease.

An organism or a human being is born with inherited characteristics such as eye colour. The environment will have little or no effect on eye colour. Inherited characteristics may or may not be passed on to offspring. This depends on the dominance of the characteristic or the number of genes involved in expressing a particular characteristic. Male pattern baldness is an inherited characteristic. Those who acquire baldness through exposure to radiation are unable to pass the characteristic on to their children. Some traits can demonstrate a mixture of acquired and inherited characteristics. In the case of skin colour, some people have not inherited the pigment to tan and will only burn in the sun.

Other people with fair skin will tan when exposed to the sun because they have inherited pigments. In this case, they will tan because of inherited and acquired characteristics.

102

**Discontinuous Variation (sometimes called qualitative variation)**

Discontinuous variation is a clearly defined variation, where the varying characteristic is controlled by only one gene, a single pair of alleles (such as *RR* or *Rr* for smooth (round) peas or *rr* for wrinkled peas). There are distinct categories in this type of variation (such as round or wrinkled), but there are no categories in between. Discontinuous variation has distinct characteristics without intermediates. The sex (male or female) of most species is normally discontinuous. There are not intermediates because sex determination is controlled by one gene. Blood groups are also discontinuous variations. Discontinuous variations are always expressed in the organism; environmental conditions are not able to change or affect the characteristic.

**Continuous Variation (sometimes called quantitative variation)**

Continuous variation is a type of variation that involves a range of differences, such as foot size or plant height. A bell curve distribution is often observed in this type of variation. Continuous variation is controlled by more than one gene (polygenic). A number of genes control characteristics such as height, weight, pulse rate, intelligence, and skin colour. The exact number of genes for some of these polygenic traits is not yet known. Continuous variation is greatly influenced by the environment. Environmental conditions can turn on certain genes and turn off others. In the case of height and weight, nutrition would have an effect on the expression of specific genes.

## PRACTICE EXERCISE

1.  Variation can be best described as differences between _____ that _____ biodiversity.
    a) populations, increase
    b) populations, decrease
    c) individuals, increase
    d) individuals, decrease

2.  Which of the following statements is **true**?
    a) There is no variation between most members of a population.
    b) The frequency of extreme variation within a population is high.
    c) A bell-shaped curve illustrates the variation of a particular trait within a population.
    d) Variation produces a narrow range of traits to deal with environmental stress or competition.

3.  Which of the following events produces the **least** variation?
    a) Random fertilization
    b) Asexual reproduction
    c) Crossing-over in meiosis
    d) Independent assortment of chromosomes in meiosis

4.  _____ assures variation because of fertilization and _____
    a) gametogenesis; the random assortment of chromosome pairs
    b) agametogenesis; random assortment of chromosome pairs
    c) agametogenesis; asexual reproduction
    d) gametogenesis; asexual reproduction

5.  Which of the following organisms is associated with asexual reproduction?
    a) Birds
    b) Humans
    c) Flowering plants
    d) Bacteria and yeast

6.  An example of an acquired characteristic is
    a) eye colour
    b) emphysema
    c) skin pigment
    d) sickle-cell anemia

7.  An example of an inherited trait is
    a) eye colour
    b) tennis skills
    c) emphysema
    d) a spoken language

8.  Which of the following traits demonstrates discontinuous variation?
    a) Height
    b) Weight
    c) Foot size
    d) Human blood type

# Lesson 5  TAXONOMY AND BINOMIAL NOMENCLATURE

Ecology is considered a relatively new scientific discipline when compared with some of the other fields of biology. The concept of studying the relationship between organisms and their environment has been around since the days of Aristotle in the 4th century BC. It was not until the 18th century that scientists began to catalogue the different types of plants and animals. It was also during this time that they began to consider how groups of organisms reacted to biotic and abiotic stimuli.

According to Danish botanist Eugen Warming, the goal of an ecologist should be to use the scientific observations of an organism's morphology and anatomy to determine why species exist under certain conditions and why species in similar habitats adapt to conditions in a similar fashion.

In order to 'map' various organisms and to determine their genetic and environmental relationships, it is necessary to have a universal system of naming and organizing each organism. The naming system (or **taxonomy**) that has been accepted by the scientific community is called **binomial nomenclature**. In other words, the two most specific groupings that describe an organism are used to name that organism.

A Swedish botanist by the name of Carolus Linnaeus was the first to successfully promote the system of categorizing living things by their forms and functions. Conventional Linnaean taxonomy has seven ranks of classification. Each level below the first is a sub-group of the level above it. As one descends through the hierarchy, organisms are grouped by increasingly specific characteristics. The following are the seven ranks when grouped in order of increasing specificity: kingdom, phylum, class, order, family, genus, and species. A newer system of categorization based on phylogenetic systematics includes another hierarchical level: domain.

NOTES

Morphology = study of structure and form
Anatomy = study of the component parts of a plant or animal and how those parts interact

Phylogenetic comes from the Greek words *phyle*, which means *tribe* and *genesis*, which means *birth*.

| | | |
|---|---|---|
| Domain | Eukaryota | complex cells with nuclei |
| Kingdom | Animalia | heterotrophic |
| Phylum | Chordata | has backbone/notochord |
| Class | Aves | bipedal, egg-laying, winged |
| Order | Anseriformes | web-footed waterfowl |
| Family | Anatidae | flat-billed, copulate on water |
| Genus | Branta | migratory, black plumage |
| Species | Canadensis | found in North America/Canada |

Canada Goose
(*Branta canadensis*)

**Phylogenetics, or** cladistics, is the study of biological relatedness based on evolutionary connections and genetic structure. Phylogenetics looks at the lineage of each organism in terms of evolutionary development. According to this system, the three most fundamental branches of the "tree of life" are divided according to the genetic development of cellular structure.

NOTES

Prokaryotic: without a cell nucleus or any membrane-bound organelles

Eukaryotic: having a nucleus and complete organelles in each cell

**DOMAIN**

The broadest category for dividing organisms into distinct groups is the domain. Domains are a relatively new rank in the taxonomic system. It was introduced in 1990 by Carl Woese. All living things can be classified as belonging to one of three domains: archaea, bacteria, or eukaryota. The primary difference between the domains is the structure of the organisms at a cellular level.

Archaea (from the Greek word meaning "ancient ones") is a domain comprised of single-celled, prokaryotic organisms. They are like bacteria in that their cells do not have nuclei, but they are more closely genetically linked to the eukaryotes. Originally thought to be a small and rare group of organisms that lived in extreme conditions (like hot springs and salt lakes), it was later discovered that they are found in almost all habitats. It is now estimated that archaea could represent as much as 20% of the biomass on Earth.

Like archaea, bacteria are also prokaryotic, single-celled organisms. It was originally thought that all such prokaryotes could be classified as bacteria until it was discovered that there are two genetically distinct groups that evolved independently of one another. Bacterial life can be found in every type of habitat on Earth. They perform a number of critically important tasks in terms of maintaining the biogeochemical equilibrium. The total number of bacteria in the biosphere is approximately $5 \times 10^{30}$. These organisms make up the majority of the biomass on Earth.

One of the most critical differences between archaea and bacteria is that the cell walls of bacteria are constructed using a polymer called peptidoglycan. With the exception of one group of methane-producing archaea, organisms classified in domain Archaea have a cell wall formed from surface-level proteins that are known as S-layer proteins. This suggests that a completely different evolutionary path was taken in order to develop the individual species within those two domains.

All of the world's complex organisms fall into the domain Eukaryota, which includes all the eukaryotic, multi-cellular forms of life. Specialized membranous organelles and a nucleus in each cell allow many members of this domain to develop groups of cells to perform macrobiotic functions. Cells of the members of this domain also have cytoskeletons that are formed from microtubules and microfilaments. Animals, plants, protists, and fungi are all eukaryotic life forms.

The following diagram shows how individual species can be traced back through the model of an evolutionary tree. The length of each line translates into an estimated timeline for each branch of speciation. Because this approach uses genetic evidence to construct relationships between organisms and because those organisms branch off from central stems, it is known as a **phylogenetic tree**

## A Phylogenetic Tree of Life on Earth

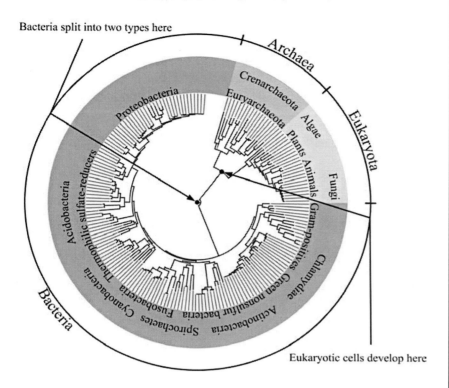

Bacteria split into two types here

Eukaryotic cells develop here

Not all scientists agree on the three-domain system of biological taxonomy. Some still adhere to the five-kingdom system, which was formalized in 1969, and a very small number accept the Archaea domain as a sixth kingdom, but not as a domain. No matter which system is applied, the remaining seven taxonomic levels are used in the same hierarchical order. The diagram below shows the top level of categorization in the different systems of biological classification.

| Two Kingdoms (1735) | Two Empires (1937) | Five Kingdoms (1969) | Six Kingdoms (1977) | Three Domains (1990) |
|---|---|---|---|---|
| | Prokaryota | Monera | Eubacteria | Bacteria |
| | | | Archaebacteria | Archaea |
| | Eukaryota | Protista | Protista | Eukaryota |
| | | Fungi | Fungi | |
| Vegetabilia | | Plantae | Plantae | |
| Animalia | | Animalia | Animalia | |

NOTES

## KINGDOM

When Carolus Linnaeus first introduced his taxonomic system in 1735, he divided living things into two kingdoms: Vegetabilia and Animalia. In other words, every organism was considered to be either a plant or an animal, respectively. Considering that Antonie van Leeuwenhoek had only published his discovery of single-celled organisms in 1676, and the Royal Society only fully accepted those findings in 1680, microbiology had not yet matured into a scientific branch that merited inclusion in Linnaeus' system. As far as he could tell, these single-celled organisms were just very small plants and animals and not different forms of life altogether.

The primary means of differentiating kingdoms has been based on modes of nutrition. As more DNA evidence becomes available for analysis, the focus has been shifting toward a greater emphasis on genetic structure. Animalia is composed of multi-cellular heterotrophs, Plantae defines multi-cellular autotrophs, and Fungi includes multi-cellular saprotrophs. Protists can be either photosynthetic or heterotrophic but are always found in single cells or in colonies of single cells. The kingdom Monera acts as a representation of all prokaryotic, single-celled life forms. It is represented by two kingdoms (Eubacteria and Archaebacteria) in a six-kingdom model.

## PHYLUM

Phyla generally define groupings of organisms within a kingdom that share certain morphological characteristics. Technically, all the members of a specific phylum should express the same evolutionary traits, but it may be more expedient to consider that a phylum defines the general body plan of an organism.

Morphology deals with the outward appearance of an organism. Physiology deals with the internal functioning of an organism.

The kingdom Animalia contains approximately 36 phyla. In terms of the number of individuals and species, phylum Arthropoda, which contains all insects and crustaceans, is clearly the dominant phylum. Arthropoda continues to grow as more species are discovered in remote areas. In terms of *megafauna*, or large-sized animals, the phylum Chordata is pre-eminent. Organisms that have evolved a backbone that contain nerve fibres are morphologically well-equipped to develop into blue whales, elephants, polar bears, and komodo dragons.

In comparison with the animal kingdom, kingdom Plantae only has approximately 11 phyla, despite the fact that most botanists refer to plant groupings at this level as *divisions*. Most plant divisions are grouped according to the types of leaves, systems of water and nutrient circulation, and means of reproduction.

Fungi have even fewer phyla. Roughly six of the phyla are primarily distinguished by their means of reproduction. The remaining kingdoms are basically the domain of microbiologists because they all include unicellular organisms. At this level, they are classified according to cellular structure and the means of metabolism and reproduction.

## CLASS

The next rank of classification in the taxonomic hierarchy is the category of class. The phylum Chordata has ten classes. Each one defines a specific group of animals that have a backbone or notochord (a sheath that covers a bundle of nerve fibres). These animals are distinguished from one another according to morphological characteristics.

For example, class Mammalia is further sub-divided into 19 orders. All of the animals classified under these orders are vertebrates that have hair, produce milk, can hear sounds, and have a four-chambered heart. Humans, platypuses, kangaroos, fruit bats, dolphins, and weasels all fit this description.

The Red-eyed Tree Frog
(*Agalychnis callidryas*)

Red Kangaroo
(*Macropus rufus*)

The production of milk in mammals is known as lactation.

In comparison to mammals, class Amphibia includes cold-blooded animals that begin life with gills for breathing underwater. As these organisms mature, they transform into air-breathing creatures. Frogs, newts, and salamanders all share these characteristics. Global amphibian populations are in decline. If one considers that there are only three orders in class Amphibia, it is easy to see that this is a serious issue. Scientists are still debating the reasons why amphibians are so easily endangered. According to the International Union for the Conservation of Nature, 29% of all known amphibian species were classified as "threatened" in 2007.

## ORDER

The next rank of increasingly specific biological classification is order. For example, the comma butterfly is part of the order Lepidoptera. It is distinguished from other insects by a four-stage life cycle and the metamorphoses that characterize each stage. Lepidopterans, which include moths and butterflies, transform from an egg to a larva (better known as a caterpillar). From caterpillar, lepidopterans cocoon

Comma Butterfly
(*Polygonia c-album*)

themselves during the pupal phase and form a chrysalis. From the chrysalis phase, they transform into an imago (an adult), complete with two pairs of wings that are covered in powdery scales. Every organism that follows this life pattern in the class Insecta is a member of the order Lepidoptera. There are 80 families that further subdivide the individual species of this order.

Metamorphosis: a change in shape.

## FAMILY

Every order is divided into different families. With only 13 or so exceptions, every family name is formed by adding a Latin suffix to the genus that most commonly expresses the form of the group. In the case of plants, the suffix –aceae is added to the genus name of the organism that best exemplifies the group. In the case of animals, the suffix–idea is added.

Venus Flytrap
(*Dionaea muscipula*)

For example, the Venus flytrap is a member of the family Droseraceae, which is named for the genus of the sundew plant, Drosera. Every member of the family is like the sundew plant because they are carnivorous, flowering plants. Family Drosera actually only has three genera: the sundews, the flytraps, and a type of aquatic carnivorous plant.

The plural of *genus* is *genera*.

## GENUS

Genus is the first term used to name each species of organism in the binomial nomenclature system. It is a taxonomic rank that acts like a family in that it is generally named for a type specimen. In other words, the Latin term for the species that best exemplifies a genus is generally used to name the genus.

Gray Wolf
(*Canis lupus*)

For example, the Latin word for dog is *canis*. Consequently, all dog-like organisms—such as wolves, jackals, and coyotes—are members of the genus *Canis*. Collectively, this family of animals are known as canines.

Whereas a species can be named arbitrarily, a genus regularly adheres to strict naming conventions. In some cases, the species name may not provide any clues as to the nature or structure of the organism at all, which demonstrates why the system of binomial nomenclature requires that both the genus and species name be used to designate a living thing.

## SPECIES

Most people have a first name and a last name. The latter is derived from a person's family, and the first name designates which member of the family that person is. In the same way, the genus name of an organism indicates who the closest relatives are. It also gives a better idea of the organism's form and shape.

As long as the species name given to a particular group of organisms is unique to those individuals and cannot be confused with another species of the same genus, the name is considered scientifically acceptable.

The scientist who discovers and publishes a genetic or morphological description of a new species has the right to name it. A new species must be clearly unique in terms of its evolutionary traits or structure.
Some scientists have been criticized for being frivolous in their assignment of species names. For example, Greg Edgecombe is a paleontologist who has discovered a number of new species of trilobite in fossil beds around the world. He has a habit of naming species after his favourite musicians. For example, the species *Avalanchurus lennoni*, *Avalanchurus starri*, *Struszia mccartneyi*, and *Struszia harrisoni* were named after the four members of The Beatles.

A species is most commonly defined as a group of organisms that can interbreed and produce viable offspring. What this means is that while two different species might be able to interbreed, the next generation of individuals will be sterile and incapable of further reproduction.
A product of this type of interbreeding is a mule. When a donkey and a horse interbreed, the offspring are called mules. Mules can neither mate nor produce offspring of their own. For this reason, they are not considered to be a distinct species.

In the past 480 years, there have been approximately 60 cases of fertile mule mares, but no fertile mule stallions.

## BINOMIAL NOMENCLATURE

The use of the genus and species names for organisms has its origins with Carolus Linnaeus. He was the first to use Latin as the foundation language for the entire taxonomial system. He chose Latin primarily because it was the language used by universities and other centres of learning.
Today, the advantage of having a system rooted in Latin and Ancient Greek is that it allows the scientific community to have a universal system for naming that does not favour one living language over another.

The entire system of biological classification can be of enormous benefit when reading scientific texts that are not illustrated.

For example, the state insect of New Mexico is the tarantula hawk. It is not apparent that this organism is an insect until the entire scientific classification is examined. Given that the tarantula hawk belongs to the kingdom Animalia and the phylum Arthropoda, it can already be determined that it is not a bird, as the word *hawk* suggests. It is a member of class Insecta and order Hymenoptera, which specifies that it is a *winged* insect.
The family Pompilidae and genus *Pepsis* are enough information to determine that it is a spider-hunting wasp.

Tarantula Hawk
(*Pepsis formosa*)

Hymenoptera derives from the Greek word *humen*, which means *membrane* and *pteron*, which means *wing*.

NOTES

### Example 1

Use a taxonomic system to determine how to store a specific item purchased on a grocery trip.

*Solution*

The easiest way to construct a taxonomic system is to remember that it is based on similarities and differences. The best way to explore those differences is to ask very broad questions at first. Next, proceed by asking more specific questions until you have identified a single, individual item.

According to the following 'decision tree', one can see that if the item is food, perishable, and a vegetable, it should be stored within the refrigerator, specifically, in the crisper drawer. Likewise, if something is food, perishable, and not to be eaten within a week, it should go into the freezer.

**Taxonomy of Groceries**

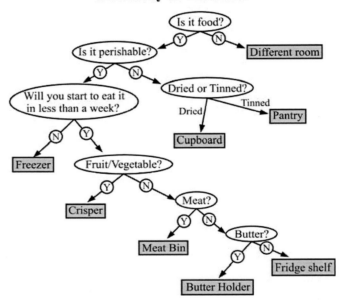

A series of questions that divide a group into two sub-groups creates a **dichotomous key**.

### Example 2

Given the following nomenclature, determine an approximate description of the organism.
- Domain:   Eukaryota
- Kingdom:   Plantae
- Phylum:   Magnoliophyta
- Class:   Magnoliopsida
- Order:   Caryophyllalles
- Family:   Cactaceae
- Genus:   *Carnegiea*
- Species:   *gigantea*

*Solution*

Even without a background in ancient languages, an English-speaking person should be able to draw some deductions about this organism. As a member of the kingdom Plantae, the organism will have chlorophyll and be able to photosynthesize. Phylum Magnoliophyta are seed-bearing, flowering plants. The next big clue is the family name. *Cactaceae* most likely refers to a cactus, and the species name of *gigantea* would logically suggest that this is a large plant.

Saguaro Cactus
(*Carnegiea gigantea*)

*Gigantea* is closely related to the word *gigantic*.

Even without the benefit of a physical description, a person should be able to imagine the characteristics of an organism using the biological classification system. The degree of specific information that could be communicated may vary, but if one knows that there are only three domains and only five or six kingdoms, then it does not require a large amount of memorization to understand approximately what an organism is and how it functions.

**Example 3**

A single-celled organism has a nucleus and chloroplasts within its cell wall. How specifically can the organism be classified according to the three-domain system?

*Solution*

Using a dichotomous key, the first question that should be asked is whether or not the cell has a nucleus. If it does, then it is eukaryotic and therefore a member of the domain Eukaryota. Within that domain, the fact that the organism is single-celled should indicate that it is a member of kingdom Protista. Because it has chloroplasts, it is very likely to be a member of phylum Chlorophyta.

Therefore, from those three characteristics, it is possible to narrow down the identity of the organism from an estimated 1.6 million species to one of only 7 000 species. The organism is a type of green algae.

Some classification systems place phylum Chlorophyta in kingdom Plantae for phylogenetic reasons.

## PRACTICE EXERCISE

1. According to the five-kingdom system, which kingdom contains the **most** individual organisms?
   - **a)** Protista
   - **b)** Monera
   - **c)** Plantae
   - **d)** Animalia

2. According to the six-kingdom system, which kingdom comprises the **majority** of the biomass in the biosphere?
   - **a)**
   - **b)** Protista
   - **c)** Eubacteria
   - **d)** Archaebacteria

3. In which domain would you find the edible golden chanterelle mushroom (*Cantharellus cibarius*)?
   - **a)** Protista
   - **b)** Archaea
   - **c)** Bacteria
   - **d)** Eukaryota

4. Which phylum represents the **greatest** number of individual species within kingdom Animalia?
   - **a)** Mollusca
   - **b)** Chordata
   - **d)** Arthropoda
   - **d)** Echinodermata

5. Which of the following statements **best** demonstrates the relationship of phylogeny to taxonomy?
   - **a)** All species within domain Eukaryota have a cell nucleus.
   - **b)** All species within kingdom Fungi are saprophytic.
   - **c)** All species within phylum Chordata lay eggs.
   - **d)** All species within class Aves have feathers.

6. What is the **main** physiological difference between archaea and bacteria?
   - **a)** Bacteria have flagella, whereas archaea have pseudopodia.
   - **b)** Archaea have cell nuclei, whereas bacteria have free nucleic acids.
   - **c)** Archaea have complete organelles, whereas bacteria have mitochondrial cell walls.
   - **d)** Bacteria have peptidoglycan-bonded cell walls, whereas archaea have surface-layer proteins.

7. Which of the following statements about kingdom Plantae is **true**?
   - **a)** No species within the kingdom is carnivorous.
   - **b)** No phylum within the kingdom reproduces using spores.
   - **c)** All phyla within the kingdom have more than one species.
   - **d)** All species within the kingdom have chloroplast organelles.

8. What rank does the taxon Mammalia have?
   - **a)** Kingdom
   - **b)** Phylum
   - **c)** Species
   - **d)** Class

## Lesson 6  *EVOLUTION AND NATURAL SELECTION*

The theory of evolution refers to the gradual process of change and adaptation that causes a species to develop new traits and characteristics. This theory can be divided into two categories: *microevolution* and *macroevolution*. *Microevolution* refers to the changes that occur within a species as they respond to their environment over time (often a short period of time). Microevolution is easy to observe in nature, and those observations can be used as empirical evidence. Macroevolution suggests that a species changes over millions of years in such a way that new species developed from ancestral species. This theory suggests that life on earth began as a simple organic form and then developed into simple plant cells (prokaryotic cells), which developed into eukaryotic cells that became increasingly complex multi-cellular organisms: invertebrates, vertebrates, and finally hominids (primates) and humans. The change in the species arises first from a change in the variation, diversity, and adaptation of a population. There is less empirical evidence for this theory, but there are documented natural observations that may support some aspects of macroevolution.

Microevolution involves studying the relationships between populations of plants and animals that are found on Earth today. Macroevolution involves studying and comparing the interactions in the biosphere with earlier forms of plants and animals, as preserved in rocks, ice, and amber. The evolution of the horse is a good example of a species that has an excellent fossil record. Island biogeography also helps supports the theory of macroevolution. A basic premise of evolution is that it takes a very long time for an organism to change. In other words, the life that exists on Earth today may have taken hundreds of millions of years to develop. This theory of macroevolution was first proposed and published by Charles Darwin in 1859, which was based on his studies of life on the Galápagos Islands.

Aspects of microevolution contribute to the understanding of macroevolution.

### MICROEVOLUTION

Microevolution involves changes that occur within species during short periods of time (as populations go through natural selection). Much of Darwin's theories and observations are centered around the empirical evidence of microevolution.

The idea is simple: individuals with a useful trait survive; those without that trait die off.
This distinctive trait is then passed on to the next generation. It is important to understand that individuals themselves do not 'evolve'. Individuals can change or adapt to their environment. It takes many individuals of a species for evolution to occur.

# MICROEVOLUTION IS A RESULT OF NATURAL FORCES THAT CHANGE POPULATIONS OVER TIME

1. Natural selection
2. Gene flow
3. Genetic drift
4. Mutations

## NATURAL SELECTION

Natural selection is perhaps one of the most important factors in determining changes within plants and animals. These changes allow well-adapted plants and animals to survive stressful environmental changes. In other words, nature 'selects' them for survival.

Because of variation and environmental stresses, not all zygotes or offspring have the same chances of survival. For example, if a baby duck lags behind all its siblings, its chances for survival are greatly reduced (it becomes more susceptible to predation). If the reasons the chick falls behind are genetic, then those genes are less likely to show up in the next generation. This is natural selection.

In the absence of natural selection, all zygotes have the same chance of survival. The absence of natural selection is a rare occurrence in nature.

## KEY CONCEPTS OF NATURAL SELECTION

- Resources are limited.
- Species must struggle (compete) for limited resources.
- Variation exists within each species.
- Some individuals of a species are better adapted than others.
- The fit, or the better-adapted, survive.
- The fit reproduce.
- Some parents leave more offspring than others.
- Surviving offspring have a new variation of their parents' fitness.

### Resources are limited

The available food, minerals, oxygen, water, and sunlight are limited.

### Competition

A struggle exists among species and among individuals in a population for limited resources. Environmental stress can also increase competition, as it often results in changes or limitations in food supply or living conditions.

### Variation

The biosphere is biologically diverse. Each population has great variety. Mutations, recombinant DNA, independent orientation, crossing-over, and random fertilization are natural processes that assure genetic variation. There are significant differences among members of the same species. For example, some humans are short, some are tall, some are thin, and others are heavy. Some have good vision, while others have poor vision.

Some can distinguish colour and others cannot. These are all variations within a species.

### Fitness Varies

Some individuals in a population are more fit or have a greater advantage than others to succeed in obtaining the limited resources and to succeed in having offspring that survive.

### Survival of the Fittest

There is a higher frequency of survival among individuals that are the fittest. The fit are those individuals that have the characteristics that make them well adapted to the environment. Fitness and survival depend on two characteristics. First, fit organisms inherit certain traits that allow them to successfully compete in their environment. Second, fit organisms produce more surviving offspring.

### The Fit Reproduce

The successful individual is selected to breed and is able to contribute offspring to the next generation. The characteristics that allowed the parents to survive are inherited by the offspring. Favourable variations are passed on to offspring, and their genetic make-up becomes more common within the population, or gene pool.

## THREE TYPES OF NATURAL SELECTION

1. Directional Selection
2. Stabilizing Selection
3. Disruptive Selection

### Directional Selection

Variation exists in all populations. That variation can often be expressed in terms of a bell curve. The most common characteristic is represented by the height, or amplitude, of the curve; the least common characteristics are found on either end of the curve.

In directional selection, one end of the bell curve is favoured. One of the less common characteristics is favoured because of some change in the ecological niche. This type of selection leads to the propagation of individuals that at one time were considered uncommon.

An example of this type of selection can be observed in nature and in the lab. The average fruit fly will fly directly into a light source. A laboratory experiment selected fruit flies that did not readily fly toward a light. The flies that were not attracted to the light were used as parents. This was repeated generation after generation until a fly population developed that had a low attraction to light. The genes controlling this behaviour would thus be less frequent in the population.

**Stabilizing Selection**

A well-adapted population in an environment that is reasonably constant will demonstrate stabilizing selection. In this type of selection, the average is favoured over the ends of the bell curve. This type of selection ensures optimum performance until environmental changes occur.

A good example of stabilizing selection is found in data collected from obstetric wards (delivery wards) of hospitals. It has been found that babies of average weight demonstrate a better chance of survival than either underweight or overweight babies.

**Disruptive Selection**

This type of natural selection lacks the direction or stabilization of the other forms of selection. There is a back-and-forth cycle of selection and change in the population. This is normally found in unstable environments.

The finches studied on the Galapagos are a good example of this type of selection. Due to a climatic condition called *El Nino*," these islands experience dramatic cycles of very wet and dry years. During the drought years, fewer leaves, grasses, small seeds, and insects were found on the island. This change in food supply dramatically affected the bird populations.

Studies indicated that many smaller finches with small beaks disappeared. These birds were affected by a drastic decrease in the supply of small seeds. Larger birds, however, were able to crack the big seeds in order to get at the kernels inside. Their larger and deeper beaks ensured their survival. As the droughts come and go on the island, the finch populations adjust.

**Gene flow**

Gene flow is the result of migration (leaving a habitat) or immigration (moving into a habitat). As new members move into a habitat, cross-fertilization can change the gene pool of a given population. Gene flow often increases the genetic variation of a population.

## Genetic Drift

Genetic drift refers to random fluctuations in the gene frequencies of a population. This drift is not related to natural selection, as it is completely random. Genetic drift could occur if a natural disaster such as a forest fire were to wipe out all but a handful of the deer population in that area.

The genetic pool of this deer population drifts toward the type of phenotypic characteristics—good or bad—that those five or so deer happen to have. The common genetic disorders of the entire population that is killed are lost, and the disorders of the surviving deer become more prominent in subsequent generations. This new emphasis on less-common genetic disorders is an example of what is referred to as the **founder effect**.

Genetic drift can occur in all populations; however, small populations more rapidly demonstrate genetic drift. The rate of population growth also affects genetic drift. Populations that grow slowly drift less than rapidly growing populations.

## Mutations

Genetic mutations are commonly found in any population, including humans. They are common enough to be considered a natural part of the gene pool of a species. It is speculated that humans carry no less than seven recessive alleles for mutations in their genetic make-up (genome). It is also estimated that $\frac{1}{3}$ to $\frac{1}{2}$ of all human fertilized eggs (zygotes) die due to fatal mutation. As this happens in the first days after fertilization, most females would be unaware of the occurrence.

Some mutations lead to the death of the individual. Others prevent the individual from reaching reproduction age, or they can even leave the individual sterile. These types of mutations have no effect on the gene pool of the population and eventually disappear.

Many mutations lead to genetic disorders or inconveniences. Inconveniences could include extra fingers or toes, missing teeth, nearsightedness, or a deformed nasal septum. Serious genetic disorders or genetic diseases may include albinism, cystic fibrosis, hemophilia, sickle-cell anemia, and Tay-Sachs disease.

Some mutations are beneficial. Beneficial mutations can also be found among plants. High-yielding crops have arisen by mutations. In some cases, whole chromosome sets have doubled in these plants as a result of mutation. Mutations allow for unpredicted variation that may flourish in the event of an unpredicted environmental change. A mutation could change a single cell into a multi-celled organism. A mutation could change the shape of a beak or foot without causing any noticeable inconvenience to the individual. In a changing environment, those mutations that seem aberrant could be naturally selected.

NOTES

The founder effect refers to the prominence of genetic expressions of recessive or uncommon traits.

## PUNCTUATED EQUILIBRIUM

Punctuated equilibrium refers to a theory that contends that evolution did not occur slowly over time, but instead happened in rapid spurts. Fossil records partly support this theory.

Natural selection is an observable event. Many scientists proposed that natural selection occurred very slowly over many generations, perhaps over millions of years. This theory is known as **phyletic gradualism**. However, scientists are currently observing natural selection in action in more than 100 different populations. Rapid changes have been observed in peppered moths of England adapting to blackened trees, finches adapting to the droughts on the Galapagos, grasses becoming tolerant to the lead in mine tailings, and bacteria becoming resistant to antibiotics.

Punctuated equilibrium suggests that populations do not change gradually, but instead demonstrate rapid change when they need to survive an environmental change.

## PHYLETIC GRADUALISM

The proposition that species change slowly through time because of the accumulation of many small changes is called **phyletic gradualism**. This macroevolutionary term suggests that natural selection operates on a constant basis within the broader context of the theory of evolution.

## GENETIC EQUILIBRIUM

A population that demonstrates stability and has no need to change is said to be in **genetic equilibrium**. The frequency of alleles in its genetic composition remains the same for generations. Genetic equilibrium is generally found in large populations.

## GENETIC NON-EQUILIBRIUM

A population that demonstrates genetic drift and undergoes many changes in the frequency of its alleles is said to be in **genetic non-equilibrium**. Genetic non-equilibrium occurs in dynamic populations that experience environmental stresses, which forces members to move in or move out of the population area. Non-equilibrium populations are subject to predators and parasites. They may also have non-random mating strategies.

## EXAMPLES OF NATURAL SELECTION

The selective forces of natural selection, genetic flow, gene flow, and mutations can happen rapidly and may be noticed over a period of years or even months. The faster an organism reproduces, the faster natural selection occurs. This has been observed among insects and bacteria. Insect populations can become resistant to pesticides, and bacteria can become resistant to antibiotics.

Phyletic gradualism describes a slow and steady development in genetic lineages in a process known as **anagenesis**.

In the case of insects, a good example was the use of DDT (Dichloro-Diphenyl-Trichloroethane) to kill mosquitoes. Initially, very low concentrations of DDT were used effectively in killing mosquitoes. Because of variation, a small group of aberrant mosquitoes survived, and they produced young that also had the ability to resist the DDT. Increased concentrations are then needed to kill the mosquito. Again, because of the variation in subsequent generations of the resistant mosquitoes, some could survive the increased concentrations. Eventually, most of the population of mosquitoes becomes resistant to DDT. Unfortunately, DDT worked its way through the food chain and threatened the extinction of certain predatory birds. The use of this chemical was banned in the 1970s.

As a consequence of natural selection, certain pathogenic (disease causing) bacteria have become resistant to antibiotics. The over-use of broad-spectrum antibiotics causes increased drug resistance. In a given population of bacteria, some of its members may be genetically resistant to a certain drug. If an antibiotic dosage is not correct or the patient does not take the full dose prescribed by a doctor, the bacteria are more likely to have more members of its population survive the medication.
The few bacteria that survive are able to produce many offspring that are fully resistant to the antibiotic. These bacteria are able to pass the resistance on to other bacteria by a process of DNA (plasmid) exchange between bacteria of the same species. Some bacteria can develop *multiresistance*, which means they become resistant to several antibiotics. These antibiotic-resistant bacteria are often called *super bugs* and can be difficult to combat. A bacterium called *Stephlococus aureus* is one such super bug and is commonly found in hospitals. This bacterium is known to cause blood poisoning. Alternative drugs, vaccinations, and attention to cleanliness are required in places where super bugs exist.

A classical example that has been used to support natural selection is the story of the white peppered moth of England. The peppered moth had the alleles for a whitish colour or a dark black colour in its gene pool. Initially, the white peppered moth flourished because their colouring helped camouflage them against the white bark of certain trees in the English forests. During the industrial revolution, many of the forest trees became dark with soot. The white peppered moth became an obvious prey and was singled out. Moths that had a greater amount of black-pepper colouration were now better camouflaged. The black peppered moth soon flourished because it was better equipped to survive in the changed environment.

## MACROEVOLUTION

Macroevolution refers to the overall theory that complex life forms gradually developed from simple life forms over four billion years. Macroevolution includes changes as one species develops into another (speciation); new species form as less-fit species become extinct. Macroevolution is evolutionary change on a grand scale. It encompasses the origin of new taxonomic groups, evolutionary trends, adaptive radiation, and mass extinction.

Macroevolution suggests that the organic chemicals of the environment somehow organized into simple, single cells that progressed and developed into complex organisms. During this process, many species became extinct. It also suggests that many new species developed as a result of environmental pressure and genetic variability. The processes by which new species are formed are called **speciation**.

## HUMAN EVOLUTION

Comparative anatomical and physiological studies of humans and other animals indicate similarities in design. These similarities may suggest a biological relationship between the animal kingdom and humankind. A theory suggests that humans are part of macroevolution, and their developmental roots can be found in the records of animal evolution. As evidence, one could consider that most species within class Mammalia—including whales, giraffes, weasels, and humans—have seven cervical (neck) vertebrae.

This is not to say that humans came from chimpanzees. Chimpanzees evolved through a distinctly different path than modern humans. Biochemical similarities provide indirect evidence for biochemists to suggest that the divergent paths between the evolution of the chimpanzee and *Homo sapiens* (humans) occurred only three million years ago. Paleontologists that study the fossil records suggest the divergence was fifteen million years ago. It is generally agreed that eight million years of divergent paths is a reasonable compromise. Several branches of development occurred during the eight million years of human evolution. Only in the last 2.5 million years have the Homo sapiens existed on the earth.

Biochemical and paleontological evidence suggest that modern humans may have first appeared between 150 000 and 200 000 years ago. The informal name for this distinctive human form is Neanderthal. The name Neanderthal comes from the site in Germany where the fossils were first discovered. Neanderthals weighed about 68 kg (150 lb) and were about 168 cm (5 feet-6 inches) tall. They had very similar body structure and had a brain size of about 1 500 millilitres, which is slightly larger than the brain of an average human. In the scheme of macroevolution, modern humans are the most recent development of primate evolution.

Distinctive characteristics of modern humansinclude the following four characteristics:
- brain capacity and brain size
- hand and thumb development
- speech development
- production and use of tools

The following is the general Order of Progressive Evolutionary Change. It is arranged according to increasing complexity.

- Organic molecules
- Macromolecules
- Simple, single cells
- Single-celled plants
- Multicellular plants and animals
- Water vertebrates and land plants
- Amphibians
- Reptiles (and birds)
- Dinosaurs
- Mammals
- Primates
- *Homo erectus*
- Modern humans

## CO-EVOLUTION

Co-evolution is the process that is driven by the interactions of one species with another species. A species will adapt to ecological pressures imposed by the other. One adaptation leads to a counter-adaptation and so on.

Prey-predator relations demonstrate the strongest example of co-evolution. Co-evolution is much like an arms race between two warring nations. As one country introduces more advanced weapons, the other country responds by acquiring more advanced detection equipment and perhaps stronger offensive weapons. The first country will then need to upgrade its weapons to outsmart the new equipment of the rival nation.

The bat and moth predator-prey relation is a good example. The bat has a special way of locating moths at night by emitting a high-pitched sound that echoes off the moth. The moth, on the other hand, has developed specialized hearing that can distinguish the sound of the bat before the bat arrives. The moth also has a second hearing device that is in tune to the lower pitches of the bat's movement. This allows the moth to predict the path of the approaching bat, which gives it time to take evasive manoeuvres that will ultimately confuse the bat's detection system (echolocation).

Another common type of co-evolution is the relationship between a passion flower and a butterfly (heliconius). The caterpillars of this butterfly prey on passionflower leaves. The passionflower has developed a poison that prevents most insects from eating its leaves. The caterpillar, on the other hand, has developed a detoxifying chemical that resists the poison.

Furthermore, the butterfly lays bright yellow eggs to ward off other butterflies from laying their eggs on the same passionflower leaf. This protects the food supply for the larvae. The plant has co-evolved by mimicking this behaviour. It randomly spots its own leaves with bright yellow bumps to ward off butterflies. Butterflies are fooled by the plant into the assumption that the leaves are littered with eggs. Therefore, the butterfly looks for another plant.

## ADAPTIVE RADIATION (DIVERGENT EVOLUTION OR BRANCHING EVOLUTION)

A population changes after moving from one habitat to another. Through the process of adaptive radiation, several species can develop from the ancestral species from the original location. On the Galapagos Islands, Darwin observed many examples of adaptive radiation. Darwin speculated that one particular finch species migrated to the Galapagos. As the original finches moved to different islands, they needed to adapt (mostly through natural selection) to the new conditions of those islands. After some years, over 13 different species of finches appeared in the Galapagos, all fit for the environment of the island they settled. A more extreme example of adaptive radiations would be the movement of fish from aquatic environments to land, perhaps to avoid predators. This movement from the aquatic environment led to the development of amphibians. The movement of amphibians to dry locations led to the further development of land vertebrates.

In general, adaptive radiation (divergent evolution) refers to newly developed species (speciation) over time. The greater the competition for limited resources or the greater the environmental change, the faster a species modifies its structures and changes its appearance.

## CONVERGENT EVOLUTION (PARALLEL EVOLUTION)

Convergent evolution is opposite to divergent evolution. Sometimes there is a tendency for completely different species to become more alike because they are living in similar environments. If differing species are found in similar ecological niches, but in different areas of the world, the environments will encourage the selection of similar traits. Species living today may develop similar characteristics of species living in the past because of strong selection pressures of similar environments.

Convergent evolution has been noted in Australia where similar ecological niches have allowed marsupial (pouched) mammals to develop similar sizes, structures, and functions as placental mammals on other continents. Examples would include the similarities of the flying squirrel and Australia's flying phalanger or the wolf and the Tasmanian wolf.

## SPECIES

The term species comes from a Latin word meaning *kind* or *appearance*. In order to understand macroevolution, it is important to understand the definition of a species. A species includes organism that are similar to each other in very specific ways. Species are characterized by their uniqueness when compared to other species. Central to the definition of a species is the ability of its members to interbreed so as to produce fertile offspring. The biochemistry of a species can also be taken into account. Members of a species have the same number of chromosomes and similar arrangements of the genes. They also look similar to each other at corresponding stages of their life cycle. Males and females of a species may look different; however, the males within the species look similar, and females of the same species look similar to each other.

## ADAPTATION

Adaptation refers to changes in an individual's characteristics or traits that help it meet stressful demands or changing environments. All organisms have the ability to make minor adaptations to their environment. Major adaptations are less common. Tanning of the skin is a physiological adaptation to increased levels of sunlight. Adaptation may also occur in the genetic makeup of a population. Over time, certain genes become lost from the gene pool or are simply not expressed, while other genes are expressed more frequently in a population.

## CREATION AND EVOLUTION

There are many different accounts to explain the existence of life on earth. Various Aboriginal and religious groups have spiritual accounts of the origin of life on Earth. These accounts are based on important cultural and spiritual beliefs and are best understood within the context of the respective cultures.

Holy Scriptures (Genesis 1 and 2) offer an explanation of creation that is also best understood within the context of spirituality and culture. Using scriptures to develop a doctrine for the origin of all matter and living forms is referred to as **creationism**. The explanation offered by scripture is not based on empirical evidence or scientific theory. Scripture deals with the spiritual aspects of creation that are based on faith and that are beyond the boundaries of scientific facts and theory. It is important to understand that the theory of evolution is a scientific theory and is completely different from creation as it is recorded in scripture or other spiritual accounts. They can be compared and contrasted, but they are not the same type of explanation nor are they used for the same purpose.

Scripture describes a relationship between God and his creation, which is based on spiritual values and faith. On the other hand, the theory of evolution describes the relationship between species and their environment, which is based on hypotheses and observations of the natural world.

# DIRECT EVIDENCE FOR MACROEVOLUTION

## Fossils

Fossils offer the most direct form of evidence for macroevolution. Fossils have been recovered from Antarctica to the Arctic Circle. A high concentration of fossils are found throughout southern Alberta, Saskatchewan, Montana, Utah, Colorado, New Mexico, and south-east Australia.

In the spring of 1994, 350 km southwest of Regina, an intact skeleton of one of the largest Tyrannosaurus Rex dinosaurs was discovered. These fossils offer direct evidence about the earth's prehistoric past.

Fossils are usually the result of a plant or animal being buried in sediment. The calcium in the bones of animals tends to solidify or mineralize. Sedimentary fossils are preserved well because of the dark, cool, and oxygen-free conditions of the sea bottom. The preserved sediments of mineralized bones go through various changes to become metamorphic or igneous rock. This forms a solid and permanent record of the past.

Fossils are usually arranged in order of age (older fossils are in deeper strata). Carbon-dating and the careful study of rocks give scientists a reasonably accurate age of the rock and the fossils they contain. Fossil arrangements and carbon-dating support the theory of a progressive development of plants and animals. The progressive development indicates greater complexity over time.

Fossils trapped in other materials preserve other aspects of the plant or animal. Ice (glaciers), tar pits (asphalt), and permafrost are found to preserve soft tissue of plants and animals. Volcanic ash and lava also serve as good materials to preserve fossil records. Paleontologists discovered bone beds containing more than 10 000 duckbill dinosaur fossils in prehistoric volcanic areas in Montana and Alberta in 1982.

Fossils include more than plant or animal body parts; they can also include animal tracks, burrows, or other signs of a species' activity in its prehistoric ecosystem.

Chemical fossils of amino acids, proteins, or nucleic acids that are trapped in amber or ice also have been used to determine the age of a species. Amber—a hardened tree resin (sap)—has been found to preserve microorganisms and genetic material that is over 220 million years old.

Amber is good for preserving three-dimensional detail and cellular structure. DNA has been recovered from an amber insect fossil. In 1992, scientists recovered bits of DNA from insects that had been encased in amber for nearly 40 million years. DNA has also been extracted from Egyptian mummies and frozen mammoths.

These DNA fossils were the basis of the Steven Spielberg movie *Jurassic Park*. As suggested in this movie, scientists have been able to isolate bits of DNA from fossils.

Scientists are able to separate the proteins and nucleic acid to isolate portions of ancient DNA. They then replicate the DNA with the polymerase enzyme. The replication of the ancient DNA allows scientists to conduct repeated studies on the DNA. Some scientists imagine the possibility of obtaining ancient DNA and cloning it to produce prehistoric animals. However, unlike the movie *Jurassic Park*, scientists are unable to recreate a species because the recovered DNA often is damaged and largely degraded. Most, if not all, of the genes are needed to replicate complete species. Even with all the genes, other limitations such as gene imprinting and the lack of embryological support would hinder the success of cloning prehistoric animals.

Radioactive isotope dating can be discussed in terms of carbon-dating, half-life, and the determination of the age of a sample by using a simple half-life decay of parent material into daughter material.

## INDIRECT EVIDENCE FOR MACROEVOLUTION

### Homologous Structures/Comparative Anatomy

Vertebrates contain similar organs and structures for similar functions. These similar structures are called **homologous structures** and suggest common ancestry. The pattern of bones in the limbs of mammals is very similar. Blood circulation and other systems demonstrate a similar pattern. These systems only differ in terms of complexity. Structures that are dissimilar for similar functions are referred to as **analogous structures** and suggest no common ancestry. The eyes of an octopus and a dog have the same function; however, they are very different structurally, which indicates they have no common ancestry.

### Vestigial Structures

Vertebrates, including humans, have structures that are not used. These unused structures are called **vestigial structures**. They often resemble functional structures in other animals. The human appendix is a vestigial organ that seems related to the digestive structures of ruminant mammals. Humans also have the muscles required to wiggle their ears, but these muscles generally do not function. The coccyx is a small bone at the end of the human spine that resembles the tailbone of other vertebrates. This bone serves no purpose in humans.

Other animals also have vestigial organs. Whales and dolphins have the bone structures that resemble the appendages of land mammals. For example, they have hipbones, which are not required for animals of the sea. Snakes also have hipbones and vestigial leg bones.

## COMPARATIVE EMBRYOLOGICAL DEVELOPMENT

Comparative embryology is the study of structures that appear during the development of different organisms. Early research in this area has been discredited as fraudulent. However, the hypothesis is that most vertebrates demonstrate similarity in the appearance of their embryos as they develop. During their development, human embryos will temporarily display gill-like structures and structures that look like tails. This may suggests common ancestry with other species. The more closely related an organism is to another organism, the greater the similarity between their shapes and patterns (morphologies) during embryological development.

## BIOCHEMICAL (DNA SEQUENCING) EVIDENCE

A careful study of the chemistry of different species reveals some suggestions of common ancestry. For example, if the amino acids in the blood (hemoglobin) of different species are studied, similarities and differences can be observed. Similarities in the chemical composition of blood are used to suggest common ancestry.

| Species | Approximate time (in million years) where ancestors of the species are first noted in fossil records | Number of amino acid differences compared to human hemoglobin |
|---|---|---|
| Gorilla | 7 | 1 |
| Rhesus monkey | 40 | 8 |
| Mouse | 150 | 27 |
| Chicken | 190 | 45 |
| Frog | 360 | 67 |
| Lamprey (jawless fish) | 500 | 125 |

Because amino acids are coded according to nucleotides, this study also suggests that the DNA of gorillas is more similar to human DNA than the DNA of a frog or lamprey. Scientists use DNA sequencing to produce a phylogenetic tree (family tree) that shows how organisms may be related through evolution. Each branch in a family tree gives the path of common ancestry. Other biochemical studies include antibody/antigens as well as hormone similarities between different species.

# PRACTICE EXERCISE

1.  Which of the following terms refers to the gradual process that causes a species to develop new characteristics that are unlike its ancestors?

    **a)** Evolution

    **b)** Adaptation

    **c)** Natural selection

    **d)** Survival of the fittest

2.  Which of the following terms refers to changes that allow well-adapted plants and animals to survive stressful environmental changes?

    **a)** Evolution

    **b)** Adaptation

    **c)** Natural selection

    **d)** Survival of the fittest

3.  Fitness describes an organism's ability to

    **a)** breed over many years and have surviving offspring

    **b)** live longer than others of its species obtain food

    **c)** be stronger than others of its species

    **d)** obtain food and have surviving offspring

4.  Which of the following statements with regards to mutations is **true**?

    **a)** They are often advantageous.

    **b)** Most result in stronger organisms.

    **c)** They can help or harm an organism.

    **d)** A true mutation must be passed on to the next generation.

5.  Darwin proposed the theory of

    **a)** creationism

    **b)** natural selection

    **b)** convergent evolution

    **d)** punctuated equilibrium

6.  Fossils would be described as _____ evidence for evolution. The oldest are usually found _____.

    **a)** direct, in deeper strata

    **b)** direct, near the surface

    **c)** indirect, in deeper strata

    **d)** indirect, near the surface

7.  Which of the following structures would be considered biochemical evidence for evolution?

    **a)** DNA

    **b)** Fossils

    **c)** Vestigal structures

    **d)** Homologous structures

8.  Analogous structures suggest that the two organisms

    **a)** are of the same species

    **b)** structures have different uses

    **c)** have a recent common ancestor

    **d)** have no recent common ancestor

# *REVIEW SUMMARY*

- An ecosystem is the combination of all the biotic (living) and abiotic (non-living) components of an area of any size.
- Abiotic components of the biosphere are the nonliving chemical and physical factors of the biosphere. They include terrestrial (physiographic, climatic, and edaphic) and aquatic (physical and chemical) components. Biotic factors are the living interactions and components of the biosphere.
- Ecology is organized according to levels of organization, which are arranged from most inclusive to least inclusive.
- Biomes are large areas with many landscapes or seascapes. A biome has a distinct climate. There are six major terrestrial biomes: rainforest, deciduous forest, coniferous forest, desert, grassland, and tundra.
- Geographic range refers to the activities and living interactions across several biomes.
- The biosphere is the broadest geophysical area of study in ecology: it includes the water (hydrosphere), air (atmosphere), and the ground (lithosphere) where life exists.
- Succession, or community changes, leads to a stable biological environment.
- Secondary succession includes the gradual changes that reclaim land or water that once supported life.
- Primary succession is when life forms move into an area that previously had not supported life.
- Food chains chart a direct flow of creatures that are consumed by other creatures.
- Creatures are classified according to their position in the flow of energy on a food chain; these classifications are called trophic levels.
- Environmental matter, including natural elements and man-made chemicals, can accumulate in higher levels of the food chain, which cause harm to higher-level predators.
- Food webs show more complex interactions between organisms in an ecosystem. This demonstrates the multiple food sources of a portion of consumers in an ecosystem.
- Energy and number pyramids can be used to demonstrate the loss of energy or numbers of organisms in an ecosystem.
- Variation refers to the differences between individuals of a species and is important because it gives species a wider range of traits to deal with environmental stress or competition for limited resources.
- Asexual reproduction is a form of reproduction that does not involve gametes such as an egg cell or sperm cell; it is an efficient and rapid form of reproduction, but it does not allow for variation.
- Sexual reproduction is more common and successful; it ensures variation and thus the survival of the species.
- Variation occurs during meiosis through independent orientation or DNA crossing-over.
- Taxonomy is the naming system employed to map various organisms. It is also used to determine their environmental and genetic relationships.
- The taxonomic hierarchy has the following ranks: kingdom, phylum, class, order, family, genus, and species.
- The theory of evolution refers to the gradual and slow process of change and adaptation that causes a species to develop new characteristics that are unlike its ancestors. This theory can be divided into two categories: microevolution and macroevolution.

# *PRACTICE TEST*

1.  Variation is important because it give a species a _____ range of traits to deal with environmental stress or competition for limited resources. Variation _____ the stability of an ecosystem.
    a) wider, increases
    b) wider, decreases
    c) narrower, increases
    d) narrower, decrease

2.  The type of variation of a particular trait within a species is most often _____. A bell curve would place organisms with extreme variation _____.
    a) extreme, towards the middle
    b) extreme, towards the ends
    c) slight, towards the middle
    d) slight, towards the ends

3.  Which of the following statements is true?
    a) Asexual reproduction is a very inefficient and slow form of reproduction.
    b) Asexual reproduction is a very efficient and fast form of reproduction.
    c) Sexual reproduction uses strategies such as fission and budding.
    d) Sexual reproduction produces identical daughter cells.

4.  What is the final product of gametogenesis?
    a) Clones
    b) Daughter cells
    c) Sperm and egg cells
    d) Exact copies of the parent

5.  Which of the following organisms uses only sexual reproduction?
    a) Fungi
    b) Yeast
    c) Flower plants
    d) Trembling Aspen

6.  The skills demonstrated by a professional hockey player are _____ characteristics. These _____ be passed on to offspring.
    a) acquired, cannot
    b) inherited, cannot
    c) acquired, can
    d) inherited, can

7.  Hair color is an _____ characteristic. These _____ be passed on to offspring.
    a) acquired, can
    b) inherited, can
    c) acquired, cannot
    d) inherited, cannot

8.  Exposure to light can darken skin pigment. The formation of a tan is an _____ characteristic. These _____ be passed onto offspring.
    a) inherited, cannot
    b) acquired, cannot
    c) inherited, can
    d) acquired, can

9.  Which of the following traits demonstrates continuous variation?
    a) The sex of an organism
    b) Human blood type
    c) Plant height
    d) A pea being smooth or wrinkled

10. The form of evolution most observable within a species is _____. This is because it has _____ empirical evidence.

   **a)** microevolution; little
   **b)** microevolution; more
   **c)** macroevolution; little
   **d)** macroevolution; more

11. Charles Darwin proposed that the driving force for the evolution of a species is natural selection. Which of the following statements is **least likely** to represent an aspect of this theory?

   **a)** There must be variation within a population.
   **b)** There must be competition.
   **c)** The strongest will survive.
   **d)** The fittest will survive.

12. The development of a bat's echolocation and a moth's adaptive evasion strategies is an example of

   **a)** co-evolution
   **b)** divergent evolution
   **c)** convergent evolution
   **d)** punctuated equilibrium

13. The height of a population of plants is measured. Plants shorter and taller than the population average are chosen. What type of selection process has occurred?

   **a)** Directional Selection
   **b)** Stabilizing Selection
   **c)** Disruptive Selection
   **d)** Natural Selection

14. A colony of Richardson's ground squirrels experiences a flood. Most members are eliminated; however, six breeding pairs are left. If these pairs produce offspring, what has occurred?

   **a)** Genetic Equilibrium
   **b)** Genetic Mutations
   **c)** Genetic Flow
   **d)** Genetic Drift

15. The structural similarity of a large number of different species in the early stages of their development is considered _____ evidence in support of evolution. This commonality is seen with humans having structures such as _____.

   **a)** direct, webbed hands and fins
   **b)** indirect, webbed hands and fins
   **c)** direct, gill-like structures and tails
   **d)** indirect, gill-like structures and tails

16. Explain why sexual reproduction produces greater variation than asexual reproduction.

17. Describe the key factors necessary for natural selection.

18. What is difference between homologous and analogous structures? When species are compared, what do these structures suggest about how these species are related? ?

# PHOTOSYNTHESIS AND CELLULAR RESPIRATION

When you are finished this unit, you will be able to…

- understand the nature of light energy and the mechanics by which plants use it
- describe the processes of photosynthesis and cellular respiration and the flow of electrons through each process
- compare and contrast chloroplasts and mitochondria
- compare and contrast the two different systems of capturing sunlight in the light-dependent process of photosynthesis
- understand the process and importance of the Calvin-Benson cycle
- demonstrate how and why water breaks apart during photolysis
- understand the importance of membranes in the chemiosmotic production of ATP
- understand the structure, uses, and importance of ATP
- demonstrate how glycolysis, the Krebs cycle, and chemiosmosis act in unison to make ATP
- tell the difference between fermentation, and anaerobic and aerobic respiration
- understand the impact of pollutants on cellular respiration
- compare and contrast photosynthesis with cellular respiration
- interpret photosynthetic and respiratory activities as being thermodynamic processes
- summarize and explain the role of ATP in cellular metabolism (including active transport, cytoplasmic streaming, phagocytosis, biochemical synthesis, muscle contraction, and heat production)

## PREREQUISITE SKILLS AND KNOWLEDGE

Prior to starting this unit, you should be able to...

- outline the atomic model and understand the difference between ionic and covalent bonding
- understand the role of electrons in transferring energy from one atom or molecule to another
- describe the structure and organisation of plant and animal cells
- describe diffusion and osmosis in relation to a semi-permeable membrane
- compare passive transport of matter by diffusion and osmosis with active transport

## Lesson 1  PHOTOSYNTHESIS

Photosynthesis = light + combine or assemble

Photosynthesis is the process that acts as the foundation for all life on Earth. It is the critical process that transforms solar energy into chemical energy and then stores it in biologically usable forms. The word itself comes from the Greek words "*phos*" (light) and "*synthese*" (to combine). The process of photosynthesis transforms the elements from the four matter cycles of the biosphere into organic compounds. These compounds form the constituent parts of all living things. It is estimated that plants are responsible for creating 160 billion metric tons of biomass each year. There are two basic reactions involved in photosynthesis: the light-dependent reaction and the light-independent reaction. These are often called the "light" and "dark" reactions because the first requires sunlight, whereas the second one does not. It is, however, misleading to call the light-independent reaction 'dark' because it operates both in sunlight and in darkness.

The energy used by plants comes from the visible parts of the electromagnetic spectrum. Electromagnetic waves have three main aspects: frequency, wavelength, and amplitude. Frequency indicates the number of waves over time, wavelength is the distance between waves, and amplitude indicates the height of the waves.

Wavelength is a measure of the distance between one wave and the next.

**Green Light**

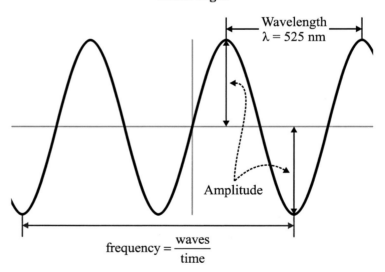

$$\text{frequency} = \frac{\text{waves}}{\text{time}}$$

A nanometre is one-billionth of a metre.

Visible light has wavelengths between 380 and 750 nm.

The portions of solar radiation that are in the visible spectrum have wavelengths that range from 380 to 750 nanometres. Aerial water vapour and crystal prisms can split white visible light into the seven distinct colours of the rainbow, each colour corresponding to a specific wavelength. Longer wavelengths produce a reddish colour and have less energy than the shorter wavelengths of bluish or violet colour. The colour green is almost directly in the middle of the range of wavelengths in visible light.

Plant cells are able to use solar radiation by absorbing all of the wavelengths of visible light except green (500 to 550 nm), which is reflected. The reflection of green light means that when examined by human eyes, plants appear green.

There are a number of coloured pigments within plant cells, the most notable being the magnesium-based **chlorophyll *a***. It is found within all organisms that photosynthesize. Other pigments are known as **accessory pigments** because they transmit energy to chlorophyll *a*. They include chlorophyll *b*, chlorophyll *c*, chlorophyll *d*, chlorophyll *e*, carotenoids, phycoerythrin, and phycocyanin. Chlorophyll *b* is mainly found in terrestrial plants, whereas chlorophylls *c*, *d*, and *e* are generally found in marine algae.

The other accessory pigments are named for the colours that they reflect rather than the colours they absorb. Carotenoids tend to reflect yellow-orange light and are responsible for the colouration of carrots, tomatoes, and autumn leaves. Phycoerythrin reflects reddish light, whereas phycocyanin reflects bluish light.

Accessory pigments have other properties. For example, carotenoids can shield chlorophyll *a* from harmful radiation, thus performing what is known as **photoprotection**.

Generally, chlorophyll is only found in an organelle called a **chloroplast**. With the exception of some prokaryotic producers, all photosynthetic processes are performed in chloroplasts.

Chloroplasts contain pigments, proteins, enzymes, and three different membranes. All of these operating together use radiant energy to fix the carbon from carbon dioxide into useful hydrocarbons such as glucose. A diagram of a chloroplast can be seen below.

NOTES

Chlorophyll *a* is a magnesium-based pigment found in all plants.

Accessory pigments absorb light at different wavelengths than chlorophyll and transfer the energy from those wavelengths to chlorophyll *a*. Phycocyanin reflects blue-green light, whereas phycoerythrin reflects red light. In bacteria, phycoerythrin can be the primary light-processing pigment.
http://www.iscid.org/ encyclopedia/ Phycoerythrin

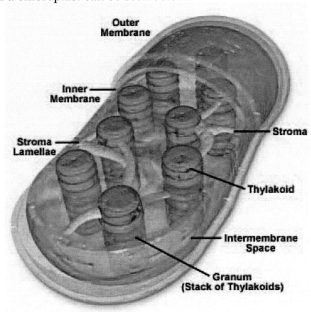

Outer Membrane

Inner Membrane

Stroma Lamellae

Stroma

Thylakoid

Intermembrane Space

Granum (Stack of Thylakoids)

Thylakoids are fluid-filled sacs that contain chlorophyll.
A granum is a stack of thylakoids.
Stroma lamellae connect grana.

RuBisCO is an important enzyme in carbon fixation.

Pyrenoids are grains of starch or sugar within chloroplasts.

The three membranes of a chloroplast are the smooth outer membrane, the thin inner membrane, and the membrane that surrounds a tiny structure called a **thylakoid**. Thylakoids are named from the Greek word meaning *sac-like*. They are fluid-filled compartments that are formed in stacks of one to two hundred called **grana** (or singular, granum). Each chloroplast can house between 40 to 60 grana, and they are interconnected by bridges called stroma lamellae. It is possible to have over 6 000 thylakoids within a single chloroplast. A square millimetre of healthy, young leaf surface can have upwards of a half million chloroplasts.

The outer membrane is six to eight nm thick and is permeable to ions as well as the ingredients of the products of the reactions that take place within the chloroplast.

The inner membrane is also six to eight nanometres thick and encloses a viscous fluid called **stroma**. Stroma contains an important enzyme called **RuBP carboxylase**, which is often referred to by its shortened name, **RuBisCO**. RuBisCO is the most abundant protein on Earth, and acts as an important enzyme in the carbon fixation part of photosynthesis. There are also special pores and active transport proteins that regulate the passage of sugars and proteins.

Thylakoids are the site of the light-dependent reactions of photosynthesis and contain important enzymes such as ATP synthase and $NADP^+$ reductase. These enzymes facilitate and accelerate the production of high-energy molecules that can then be used to fuel the light-independent reactions of photosynthesis. The flattened forms of the thylakoids help increase the surface area relative to volume.

In vascular plants, chloroplasts are found in an area of leaves or needles called the **mesophyll**. The mesophyll is generally protected from wind and radiation by a waxy covering atop the leaves or needles called the **cuticle**. It helps ventilate oxygen and water through pores called stomata on the undersides of leaves or needles.

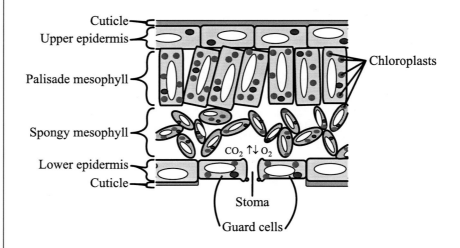

Under a microscope, most chloroplasts will appear green and look like tiny watermelons. Some chloroplasts may appear to have dark spots or stains. Grains of starch or sugar stored in the chloroplasts generally cause this type of discolouration. These grains are called **pyrenoids**.

Chemical substances that are used to suppress or arrest plant growth are called herbicides. Herbicides are often pigment inhibitors and are generally used to kill weeds or other plants that would compete with crops, lawns, or other 'desirable' plants for nutrients.

One particular herbicide called clomaxone blocks the formation of new carotenoids. Without the photoprotection afforded by the carotenoids, chlorophyll *a* is easily damaged by ultraviolet radiation. Clomaxone is considered a bleaching herbicide because leaves with damaged and destroyed chlorophyll turn white, cease to photosynthesize, and die of starvation.

NOTES

Some herbicides operate by inhibiting the photoprotection of chlorophyll *a*.

The phenomenon of leaf colour change is associated with the onset of the fall season. The deep greens of summer gradually transform into brilliant shades of yellow, orange, and red. These changes are the result of decreased daylight and a drop in the daily average temperature. These two factors combine to slow down and eventually stop the production of chlorophyll, which, as with all pigments, is normally produced and broken down on a regular basis. The lack of chlorophyll greatly reduces the reflection of green wavelengths and also allows remaining pigments and tannins to stand out. Carotinoids reflect yellow, orange, and shades of brown. In certain plants, anthocyanins pigment production increases during the fall. These purple and pink pigments produce the characteristic reds seen in red maple, sumac, and white and scarlet oak trees. Brown colouration is due to the presence of tannins. These form as a result of the accumulation of waste materials within leaves.

### Example 1
Why are plants green?

*Solution*
Plant chlorophyll pigments reflect light with a wavelength range of approximately 500 to 550 nm. All other wavelengths of light are absorbed. The naked eye only sees the reflected light, so the apparent colour of photosynthetic tissue is green. The green colouration comes from the trace amounts of magnesium that are found in chlorophyll.

**Example 2**

Explain how photosynthesis is critically important to life on Earth.

*Solution*

Photosynthesis is the primary process in carbon fixation, in which either aerial or aqueous carbon dioxide is transformed into organic material. Photosynthesizers are responsible for building biomass and organic molecules that later form the basis of all life forms in the biosphere. In addition, the gas exchange element of photosynthesis removes carbon dioxide from either the atmosphere or the hydrosphere and produces oxygen, which is necessary for cellular respiration in both plants and animals.

**Example 3**

What is photoprotection, and why is it important?

*Solution*

Photoprotection is the process that involves different pigments and plant components that helps shield chlorophyll *a* from harmful exposure to sunlight. Ultraviolet rays are one type of harmful radiation that can damage chloroplasts and impede a plant's ability to photosynthesize. The cuticle of a leaf surface, some carotenoids, and the cell walls of the epidermal cells all act to protect chloroplasts that contain chlorophyll *a*.

## PRACTICE EXERCISE

1. Where are chlorophyll *a* and *b* located?

    **a)** Xylem             **b)** Cuticle

    **c)** Thylakoids       **d)** Mitochondria

2. What are carotenoids?

    **a)** Enzymes         **b)** Pigments

    **c)** Herbicides        **d)** Membranes

3. Which of the following components is necessary for plants to produce oxygen?

    **a)** Water             **b)** Biomass

    **c)** Pyrenoids         **d)** Herbicides

4. Which of the following membranes is **not** a membrane that belongs to a chloroplast?

    **a)** Transpiration membrane       **b)** Thylakoid membrane

    **c)** Inner membrane              **d)** Outer membrane

5. What is RuBisCO?

    **a)** Starch           **b)** Glucose

    **c)** Enzyme         **d)** Pyrenoid

6. Which metal gives chlorophyll its green colour?

    **a)** Iron               **b)** Nickel

    **c)** Copper          **d)** Magnesium

7. Phycoerythrin and phycocyanin are

    **a)** stroma lamellae        **b)** oxidized cyanides

    **c)** accessory pigments      **d)** photosynthetic inhibitors

8. A microscope can reveal dark spots within a chloroplast. These are called pyrenoids. Pyrenoids are made of

    **a)** grains of sand             **b)** grains of starch

    **c)** granules of chlorophyll     **d)** oxygen-rich membranes

## *Lesson 2* **LIGHT-DEPENDENT PHOTOSYNTHESIS**

Light-dependent photosynthesis has two processes: photosystem I and photosystem II.

There are two processes within the light-dependent phase of photosynthesis: photosystem I and photosystem II. However, the numbering does not describe the flow of electrons. The cycles were named in the order that they were discovered, not because of the way they operate. Each of the two processes has what is called a **light-harvesting complex (LHC)** that is composed of 250 to 400 antenna pigments. These pigments collect energy and transfer it to a key chlorophyll *a* pigment called a **reaction centre**.

Photosystem II can operate as an independent system of **cyclic photophosphorylation**. This means that solar radiation excites the atoms in chlorophyll *a* and the accessory pigments. The energized electrons form an energy gradient between the thylakoids and the surrounding material in the stroma.

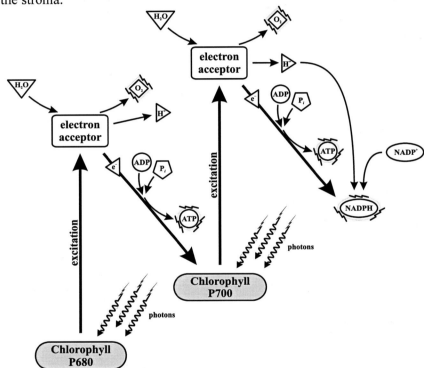

Photosystem II relies upon P680 chlorophyll to receive activation energy from sunlight and antenna pigments.

P in P680 stands for pigment.

ATP molecules are formed by chemiosmotic energy through the processes of dehydration synthesis and phosphorylation.

Photosystem II splits water to produce oxygen, ATP, and electrons.

Basically, photosystem II collects all of the energy from antenna pigments in LHC II and transfers that energy to a reaction centre that contains a type of chlorophyll called P680 chlorophyll. P680 chlorophyll absorbs light of wavelength 680 nanometres. When P680 chlorophyll is excited by radiant energy, it emits two high-energy electrons into what is known as an **electron transport chain**. In a process called **photolysis,** one of the electrons is donated by a water molecule when it is split. The oxygen that is released by photolysis becomes $O_2$. The chloroplast then actively transports the free oxygen from a plant cell as a gas.

The net effect of this production of electrons is to create an ionic imbalance between the interior of the thylakoid and the fluid in the stroma. Essentially, the fluids within a thylakoid will begin to act as though they were acidic. In order to restore balance, protons will migrate from the thylakoid into the stroma. When migrating protons interact with an enzyme called ATP synthase, they perform dehydration synthesis on adenosine diphosphate molecules (ADP) and phosphate units in the stroma ($P_i$) to form adenosine triphosphate. The migration of protons builds potential energy that becomes chemiosmotic energy, since it requires a semi-permeable membrane.

The two electrons that have been produced are then moved through an electron transport chain. Carrier molecules absorb extra energy from the electrons, and at the end of the chain of reactions, the electrons can do one of two things:
1. They can return to the reaction centres of P680 chlorophyll and power another cycle of photosystem II, thus performing cyclic photophosphorylation.
2. Alternatively, the electrons can excite pigments of chlorophyll *a* called P700 chlorophyll.

P700 chlorophyll reaction centres are the foundation of photosystem I and are supplied directly with light energy and pigments in LHC II. Now that there are high-energy molecules of ATP and electrons created by photosystem II within the chloroplast (added to light energy with a wavelength of 700 nm), P700 chlorophyll can jump to a higher state of excitation. Photosystem I is non-cyclic because the electrons and hydrogen ions are used in conjunction with $NADP^+$ reductase to form nicotinamide adenine dinucleotide (NADPH). NADPH is used in the light-independent reaction to produce glucose.

The primary difference between photosystem I and photosystem II is found in the pigment that forms the basis of the reaction to light. Discrete units of light—known as photons—charge different arrangements of pigment depending on the wavelength. Photosystem II uses photons that have a wavelength of 680 nm. These photons are of a higher energy than the 700 nm light used by photosystem I.

The two systems interrelate because photosystem I requires an extra boost of energy from photosystem II in order to compensate for the fact that the light being used by P700 has less energy. Primitive bacteria use only a simple system of cyclic photophosphorylation photosynthesis because the food energy requirements for a single-celled organism are relatively low. Only more advanced forms of algae and plants use both photosystems I and II.

The suffix–*ase* usually denotes an enzyme. Enzymes accelerate biological reactions without being consumed by them.

Light that has a wavelength of 680 nm has more energy than light with a wavelength of 700 nm.

NOTES

**Example 1**

What makes up the complexes of LHC II and LHC I?

*Solution*

The light-harvesting complexes associated with photosystems II and I are composed of antenna pigments, including chlorophylls *a*, *b*, *c*, *d*, and *e*; carotinoids; phycoerythrin; and phycocyanin. The 250 to 400 pigments in each complex absorb a range of light wavelengths and transfer the energy to reaction centre chlorophyll molecules.

**Example 2**

Describe the process used to create ATP from ADP.

*Solution*

The energy used by photosystem II is stored by the process of photophosphorylation. During this process, electrons are freed from splitting water molecules and from forming proton pumps.
These pumps are basically just a discrepancy in the concentration of protons on either side of a semi-permeable membrane.
As protons leave the thylakoids and migrate into the stroma, they interact with adenosine diphosphate and, using ATP synthase, bond a $P_i$ group with ADP through the process of dehydration synthesis.

The production of ATP occurs via ATP synthase and the creation of a proton gradient within the thylakoid space.

**Example 3**

How is the production of NADPH different from the production of ATP?

*Solution*

The ATP produced as a result of photosystem II has stored chemical energy because the process of chemiosmosis powers the enzymatic action of ATP synthase and synthesizes a phosphate group with ADP, thus phosphorylating it. NADPH stores energy by assimilating electrons and hydrogen ions by using the enzyme $NADP^+$ reductase in a process known as reduction.

The generation of ATP does not occur during the transfer of electrons by either of the electron transport chains.

The following diagram shows the absorption of sunlight according to the wavelength of the light. Given that the wavelength of green or greenish light is from approximately 495–570 nm, the importance of accessory pigments becomes apparent.

Both chlorophyll *a* and chlorophyll *b* show very low energy absorption in the range of wavelengths that corresponds to the colour green.
The green light reflects from the surface of plants and thus appears to have a greenish colour in the visible spectrum of light. Plants draw very little light energy from that part of the spectrum. They do, however, absorb energy from other wavelengths of light that are not green.

Accessory pigments such as phycoerythrin and phycocyanin, on the other hand, absorb a great deal of energy from the green end of the spectrum and reflect more bluish and reddish light waves.

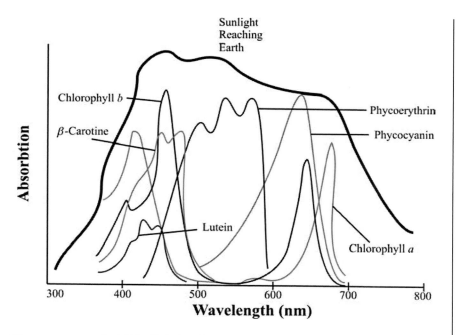

The spectrum of visible light begins around 380 nm at the colour violet and ends around 750 nm at the colour red. Wavelengths shorter than 380 nm are considered ultraviolet, and wavelengths longer than 750 nm are considered infrared.

Beta-carotene pigments absorb light almost exclusively from the violet and blue ends of the spectrum and reflect green, yellow, orange, and red light. Chlorophyll *b* has a very high absorption of light energy at the blue end of the spectrum, which corresponds to the majority of energy carried by sunlight to Earth. Unlike beta-carotene, the chlorophyll *b* pigments can also absorb sunlight near the 650 nm wavelength range, which corresponds to reddish light.

As you can see from the above diagram, the only two pigments that absorb light at both ends of the spectrum are chlorophyll a and b. Both pigments are unable to absorb wavelengths at the centre of the visible spectrum, but that energy can be absorbed by phycoerythrin and phycocyanin. Therefore, a large amount of the total energy input of solar radiation is transformed into biologically usable chemical energy.

## PRACTICE EXERCISE

1. Which of the following process donates electrons to Photosystem II?

   **a)** Photolysis                          **b)** Chemiosmosis

   **c)** Reduction of NADPH       **d)** Electron Transport Chain

2. Which of the following statements regarding the function of a thylakoid membrane is **true**?

   **a)** It actively transports $O_2$.

   **b)** It forms a single disc called a grana.

   **c)** It creates a proton concentration gradient.

   **d)** It allows photolysis to occur within its membrane.

3. Which of the following compounds is **not** a product of photosystem II?

   **a)** ATP                               **b)** $CO_2$

   **c)** Oxygen                        **d)** NADPH

4. How many antenna pigments can be found in each light-harvesting complex?

   **a)** 1–4

   **b)** 20–40

   **c)** 50–100

   **d)** 250–400

5. What does the P stand for in P700 chlorophyll *a*?

   **a)** Proton                         **b)** Pigment

   **c)** Pyrenoid                     **d)** Photosystem

6. Which of the following compounds acts as an antenna pigment?

   **a)** ADP                           **b)** Phycocyanin

   **c)** $NADP^+$ synthase        **d)** Phosphate group ($P_i$)

7. Where does the energy to phosphorylate ADP come from?

   **a)** ATP synthase            **b)** Chemiosmosis

   **c)** Stroma lamellae         **d)** Electron transport chain

8. Which of the following ions is **not** a principle product of photolysis?

   **a)** $O_2$                             **b)** $H^+$

   **c)** $N_2$                             **d)** $H_2$

# Lesson 3   LIGHT-INDEPENDENT PHOTOSYNTHESIS

The entire process of light-dependent photosynthesis is to harness light energy and transform it into usable chemical energy. Photon energy through the two photosystems is trapped in molecules of ATP and NADPH. Thus far, nothing has really been formed, assembled, or anabolically produced. The processes of chemical reduction in photosystem I and chemiosmosis in photosystem II only serve to 'charge' the molecular batteries within a plant's cells.

The extra chemical energy latent in the bonds of ATP and NADPH is needed to power the processes of carbon-fixation in something called the **Calvin-Benson cycle**. The Calvin-Benson cycle does not require light and so is often referred to as 'dark' photosynthesis. This, however, is somewhat misleading because the cycle operates perfectly well in both light and darkness.

The Calvin-Benson cycle is also referred to as light-independent photosynthesis. Light-independent photosynthesis is the process that constructs glucose and other hydrocarbons and stores the energy provided by light-dependent photosynthesis within carbon molecules.

The Calvin-Benson cycle was discovered by and named for Melvin Calvin and Andrew Benson from the University of California, Berkeley in 1961. They were able to describe the operation of carbon fixation in the stroma of chloroplasts.

In this operation, ATP, $CO_2$, water, and hydrogen carriers like NADPH interact to produce glucose. The chemiosmotic energy absorbed by ATP during photosystem II and the hydrogen ions from photolysis in photosystem I act in concert to power the reactions that transform carbon dioxide into usable starches and sugars.

The full net chemical equation of the Calvin-Benson cycle can be seen below.

$$6CO_2 + 12NADPH + 12H^+ + 18ATP$$
$$\rightarrow C_6H_{12}O_6 + 6H_2O + 12NADP^+ + 18ADP + 18P_i$$

Because the process is cyclical, an examination of the Calvin-Benson cycle can begin at any point. It may be advantageous to begin with ribulose 5-phosphate, which is a string of carbon atoms that have a phosphate group attached to the fifth carbon. Ribulose 5-phosphate is found floating freely in the stroma of chloroplasts. When it interacts with a specific enzyme and a molecule of ATP, the ATP will phosphorylate the ribulose molecule. A phosphate group is also donated along with some energy.

The phosphorylated molecule now has two phosphorus (Pi) groups, one attached to the fifth carbon in the molecule and a second attached to the first carbon in the chain. The new, energetically charged molecule is called **ribulose 1,5-bisphosphate**. Notice that the numbers in the molecule indicate which carbons have phosphate groups attached to them. Ribulose 1, 5-bisphosphate is also known by the abbreviation **RuBP**.

Light-independent photosynthesis is synonymous with the Calvin-Benson cycle.

The Calvin-Benson cycle takes place in the stroma of chloroplasts.

The Calvin-Benson cycle is dependent upon the NADPH and ATP produced by the light-dependent reactions of photosynthesis.

RuBisCO forces carbon dioxide to bond with RuBP.

When RuBP encounters an enzyme called ribulose 1, 5-bisphosphate carboxylase (also known as RuBisCO), it becomes involved in carbon fixation. RuBisCO forces a free carbon dioxide molecule to bond with RuBP, which then yields in a total of six carbon atoms within the molecule. This reduces the overall chemical stability of the compound.

In fact, the new six-carbon molecules are so unstable that they spontaneously split up to form two individual three-carbon molecules called 3-phosphoglycerate (or 3PGA).
At this point, the energy in the cycle is beginning to run down, so another set of ATP molecules donate more high-energy phosphate groups to the 3PGA.
The addition of another phosphate group to the 3PGA transforms it into 1,3-bisphosphoglycerate (1,3BPGA).

Finally, NADPH donates an extra hydrogen ion per molecule and returns to photosystem I as $NADP^+$. The molecule 1,3BPGA becomes glyceraldehyde
3-phosphate, or G3P.

One molecule of G3P spins off the cycle at this point. When two molecules of G3P encounter one another, they can form into glucose.
For every one molecule of G3P that is ejected from the cycle, five more are recycled and transformed through a series of enzymatic reactions into RuBP, which is where this discussion of the cycle began.

The entire Calvin-Benson cycle does not appear very efficient. It takes six repetitions of the whole cycle just to make a single molecule of glucose. Over the course of the repetitions, 18 molecules of ATP are dephosphorylated, and 12 molecules of NADPH are transformed into $NADP^+$. The light-dependent reactions of photosystems II and I need to absorb a lot of photons to continue fueling the light-independent reactions.

The actual efficiency of the system lies in the storage capacity of the sugar molecule produced by the cycle. The glucose that is produced stores 90% of the chemical energy used to create it within its bonds. The remaining 10% of the energy is released as exothermic heat from the reactions.
The Calvin-Benson cycle can be simplified into three stages.

**Phase 1–Carbon Fixation**

Carbon dioxide is added to a five-carbon molecule (RuBP) in an enzymatic reaction with RuBisCO.

**Phase 2–Reduction**

Captured energy (in the form of ATP and NADPH) from photosystems II and I in the light-dependent reaction, is used to make the sugar G3P (glyceraldehyde-3-phosphate). Two molecules of G3P can form one molecule of glucose.

Six rotations of the Calvin-Benson cycle produce two glyceraldehyde-3-phosphate molecules (G3P) that combine to form glucose.

**Phase 3–Regeneration**

The five-carbon molecule (RuBP) that began the cycle is rebuilt using energy from ATP. RuBisCO enzymes prepare the RuBP to accept another incoming carbon dioxide molecule, and the cycle then returns to phase 1.

The type of photosynthesis described is typical of plants found in temperate zones (like oak trees). The plants that use this system are classified as $C_3$ plants because they use carbon dioxide directly from the air to make a three-carbon molecule called 3PGA, which is converted to glucose in the mesophyll cells of leaves.

$C_3$ plants are generally found in temperate climates.

Plants that are commonly found in tropical or desert regions often need to conserve water. Therefore, they restrict their interactions with the environment. When they close the stomata of their leaves, this not only helps conserve water from evaporation and transpiration but also reduces the amount of carbon dioxide that can be imported and used to feed the Calvin-Benson cycle.

Plants such as cactus are classified as CAM plants because they use a different biochemical pathway to fix carbon dioxide. CAM plants draw in carbon dioxide during the night and fix it into a four-carbon molecule that can be re-fixed by the Calvin cycle during the day.

CAM plants are generally found in desert regions.

Another group of plants, known as $C_4$ plants, include tropical species such as sugar cane. $C_4$ plants have a specialized enzyme that fixes carbon dioxide into four-carbon molecules within mesophyll cells. They then pump these molecules directly into another group of cells called **bundle-sheath cells**, where the Calvin cycle transforms them into sugars. This system makes $C_4$ plants more efficient in terms of sugar production in hot regions with intense sunlight.

$C_4$ plants are found in hot, tropical conditions with intense sunlight.

**Example 1**

Discuss the inter-relation of photosystems II and I in light-dependent photosynthesis with the Calvin-Benson cycle in light-independent photosynthesis.

*Solution*

Light-dependent photosynthesis traps radiant light energy in high-energy organic molecular bonds. Photosystem II uses chemiosmotic energy, photolysis, and an important enzyme called ATP synthase to phosphorylate ADP and create ATP. Photosystem I produces another high-energy molecule known as NADPH.
ATP and NADPH act as the energy sources that drive the Calvin-Benson cycle. To produce a single molecule of glucose, light-independent photosynthesis requires 18 ATP molecules and 12 NADPH molecules.

NOTES

**Example 2**

What are the characteristics of RuBisCO?

*Solution*

Ribulose 1,5-bisphosphate carboxylase, also known as RuBisCO, is an enzyme that facilitates carbon fixation. As an enzyme, RuBisCO accelerates and activates the bonding of a carbon dioxide molecule to a five-carbon structure called ribulose bisphosphate (RuBP).
The unstable six-carbon molecule that results from this reaction splits into two molecules of 3-phosphoglycerate (3PGA). The molecules of RuBisCO do not actively react, bond, or decompose with the other molecules involved in carbon fixation. RuBisCO is most commonly found in the stroma of chloroplasts and is considered the most abundant protein in the biosphere.

**Example 3**

Describe the role of phosphorus in the Calvin-Benson cycle.

*Solution*

Phosphorus, in the form of phosphate groups, forms the basis of chemical energy storage throughout all of the photosynthetic processes. The Calvin-Benson cycle requires the energy released from the dephosphorylation of ATP and the splitting of NADPH in order to drive the reactions that are involved in carbon fixation.
Looking at the Calvin-Benson cycle, all of the major molecules that form the spine of the reaction contain phosphorus. Only the final glucose molecule lacks a phosphate group after two glyceraldehyde 3-phosphate (G3P) molecules dephosphorylate and bond with one another. The $P_i$ phosphate groups that separate from G3P can then travel back to the light-dependent processes, where chemiosmotic energy can be used to reattach them to ADP molecules to form ATP.

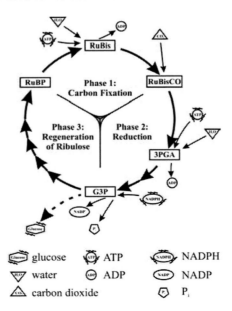

glucose    ATP    NADPH

water    ADP    NADP

carbon dioxide    $P_i$

## PRACTICE EXERCISE

1. Where does the Calvin-Benson cycle occur?

   **a)** Stroma
   **c)** Outside chloroplast
   **b)** Thylakoid space
   **d)** Thylakoid membrane

2. Which of the following events **best** describes the function of the light-independent reactions?

   **a)** Fixation of $CO_2$
   **c)** Production of $CO_2$
   **b)** Production of $O_2$
   **d)** Production of ATP and NADPH

3. Why is it misleading to call light-independent reactions *dark photosynthesis*?

   **a)** RuBisCO requires light.
   **b)** They occur in both light and darkness.
   **c)** They are not performed in chloroplasts.
   **d)** Carbon dioxide only enters the stomata at night.

4. Which molecule fixes carbon dioxide in a $C_3$ plant?

   **a)** G3P
   **c)** 3PGA
   **b)** RuBP
   **d)** NADPH

5. How many molecules of carbon dioxide are fixed to produce one molecule of glucose?

   **a)** 3
   **c)** 9
   **b)** 6
   **d)** 12

6. In what type of climate would one expect to find $C_4$ photosynthesis?

   **a)** Cold and dry
   **c)** Hot and sunny
   **b)** Wet and cloudy
   **d)** Completely aquatic

7. Which of the following compounds helps 'drive' the Calvin-Benson cycle?

   **a)** $O_2$
   **c)** ADP and $NADP^+$
   **b)** Glucose
   **d)** ATP and NADPH

8. How many molecules of G3P are required to form one molecule of glucose?

   **a)** 1
   **c)** 3
   **b)** 2
   **d)** 6

# *PRACTICE QUIZ*

1. Photosynthesis converts

   a) glucose into oxygen
   b) oxygen into carbon dioxide
   c) chemical energy into light energy
   d) light energy into chemical energy

2. Which process generates oxygen, protons, and electrons from water?

   a) Photolysis
   b) PS II and PS I
   c) Calvin-Benson cycle
   d) Light-dependent reactions

3. Which colour is absorbed the least by chlorophyll *a* or *b*?

   a) Red
   b) Blue
   c) Green
   d) Orange

4. A stack of discs located within a chloroplast is called

   a) a stroma
   b) a granum
   c) an antenna
   d) a thylakoid

5. Which of the following statements **best** describes the immediate effect of a plant being placed in the dark?

   a) The Calvin-Benson cycle will stop.
   b) The excitation of electrons will stop.
   c) The fixing of carbon dioxide will stop.
   d) Photosystems will compensate by using antennae pigments.

6. What is the correct location and order of the photosystems?

   a) Thylakoid membrane, PS II - PS I
   b) Thylakoid membrane, PS I – PS II
   c) Thylakoid space, PS II – PS I
   d) Stroma, PS I – PS II

7. Where is the enzyme RuBisCO normally found?

   a) Stroma
   b) Thylakoid space
   c) Thylakoid membrane
   d) Outside of chloroplast

8. How does a plant maximize its ability to absorb light energy within the range of visible light (approximately 380–750 nm)?

   a) Production of extra ATP
   b) Increased production of chlorophyll
   c) Through the use of antennae pigments
   d) Calvin-Benson cycle provides energy-rich glucose.

9. A product from photolysis is $H^+$. An increase in concentration of $H^+$ ions helps generate a proton gradient that forces these protons through a protein imbedded in the thylakoid membrane. What is this protein?

   a) RuBP
   b) NADPH
   c) Chlorophyll
   d) ATP synthase

10. During the creation of a proton gradient, where is the greatest concentration of $H^+$ found?

   a) Stroma
   b) Thylakoid space
   c) Thylakoid membrane
   d) Outside of choloroplast

11. Which of the following compounds is the final acceptor after electrons pass through PS II and PS I?

   a) ADP
   b) Water
   c) Oxygen
   d) $NADP^+$

12. The Calvin-Benson cycle is also described as

   a) Photosystems II and I
   b) the light-dependent reaction
   c) the light-independent reaction
   d) the electron transport chain

13. Carbon fixation is used to describe

   a) the addition of $CO_2$ to RuBP
   b) the production of $O_2$ from water
   c) the production of ATP and NADPH
   d) the excitation of electrons by light energy

14. Which process can continue to occur without the input of light energy?

   a) PS II and I
   b) Photolysis
   c) Electron transport chain
   d) Calvin-Benson cycle

15. Which of the following molecules acts as a catalyst for carbon fixation?

   a) ADP
   b) $NADP^+$
   c) Glucose
   d) RuBisCO

16. A CAM plant would **most likely** be found in a environment that is

   a) cool and has low light levels
   b) humid and has low light levels
   c) humid and has high light levels
   d) arid (dry) and has high light levels

**17.** Describe the location and primary function for each of the following:

    **a.** PS II and PS I

    **b.** Photolysis

    **c.** ATP synthase

    **d.** The Calvin-Benson cycle

**18.** The generation of a proton concentration gradient is essential for the production of ATP. Identify the source of the protons and the process that generates ATP.

**19.** The Calvin-Benson cycle for $C_3$ plants cannot fix $CO_2$ under dark conditions. Explain why this occurs.

## Lesson 4  CELLULAR RESPIRATION

**Respiration releases potential energy from organic compounds.**

- Cellular respiration involves the release of stored energy from carbohydrates, as well as other organic molecules.  Carbon dioxide and water are by-products of cellular respiration.

- Carbohydrates are oxidized by glycolysis and the Krebs cycle to produce molecules of reducing power:  nicotinamide adenine dinucleotide (NADH), flavin adenine dinucleotide ($FADH_2$), and chemical potential in ATP.  Glycolysis occurs freely in the cytoplasm of the cell and the Krebs cycle occurs inside the cristae of the mitochondria.

- Chemiosmosis converts the reducing power of NADH and $FADH_2$ to the chemical potential of ATP.  Chemiosmosis occurs on the inner membrane of the mitochondria of the cell.

- Oxygen increases the energy produced in cellular respiration (aerobic).  In the absence of oxygen, the energy produced by cellular respiration (anaerobic) is less.

- ATP participates in metabolism (e.g., synthesis, movement, active transport).

- Environmental pollutants, like cyanide or hydrogen sulfide, inhibit cellular respiration.

### Energy and Cellular Respiration

Living organisms require energy in order to operate, much like a car needs fuel to work.  Most of this energy comes from the sun.  Plants convert the sun's energy into a type of sweet fuel or a hydrocarbon sugar called **glucose**.   All living organisms (plants and animals) are able to use glucose and water to produce useful chemical energy.  That chemical energy in living cells is called **adenosine triphosphate (ATP)**.

In cellular respiration, the glucose produced by plants is broken down atom –by atom.  As it is broken down, cell structures carefully capture electrons and protons and pass them on to oxygen, which is also provided by plants.  As electrons are transferred to oxygen, chemiosmotic energy is produced and used to make ATP.  The broken pieces of glucose are returned to the atmosphere as carbon dioxide.  The waste products of cellular respiration ($CO_2$ and water) are a plant's delight.  In the end, the resulting energy is used for most of the cellular processes for both plants and animals. In short, the energy that was locked up in the glucose molecule by photosynthesis is released into a kind of chemical energy that the cell is able to use.

If glucose is not available, other monosaccharides produced by plants—such as fruit sugars (fructose) and galactose—can be used, as they easily convert into glucose. The double sugars (disaccharides), including table sugar (sucrose), cereal sugar (maltose), and milk sugar (lactose) are also easily converted to glucose and therefore can be used to produce ATP. If there is low sugar concentration in your blood, then fats or lipids can be broken into sugars. If there are no fats (as would be the case during starvation), then proteins can be converted into sugar and oxidized (burned) to make energy in the form of ATP.

The production of this chemical energy (ATP) from sugar occurs in an organelle called the **mitochondria** (plural form of mitochondrion). Surprisingly, many of the processes, enzymes, and proteins are similar to what we have already studied in photosynthesis (the first part of this unit). Again, you will see chemiosmosis; oxidation and reduction; ATP synthase; nicotinamide adenine dinucleotide; $NAD^+$ less its phosphate; glyeraldehyde-3-phosphate (G3P); and ATP and ADP. Watch for the reappearance of these important processes and molecules as we discuss cellular respiration. Interestingly, the organelles of the mitochondria and the chloroplast work together and seem to exhibit a tight inter-relationship. This relationship between the chloroplasts and mitochondria are summarized at the end of this unit.

Cellular respiration involves the release of stored energy from carbohydrates that are mainly produced by plants. Why do plants go through the trouble of making glucose when animals turn around and consume that glucose? Would it not be simpler if plants made ATP instead of glucose? Animals use ATP for all their energy requirements and so do plants. Why bother with glucose? Besides, the primitive light reaction known as Photosystem I by itself makes ATP with a simple cyclic electron flow.

There are several reasons why solar energy is stored in glucose. The first and most obvious reason is the size of ATP. By studying the following diagrams, you can see the difference in 'size' between these two molecules. ATP is larger and has heavy phosphates. Glucose is lighter and is a smaller molecule. Additionally, ATP is not very stable, whereas glucose is a very stable molecule. Look at the diagrams again. Notice the negative charges on ATP. These negative charges make it hard for ATP to move though the hydrophobic lipid interior of cellular membranes. Glucose can move with relative ease. Finally, although ATP is an important energy carrier, it only holds a small amount of usable energy, which ranges between 7.3 and 11.7 Kcal/mol. Glucose potentially holds 686 Kcal/mol when it is fully broken down. It also stores energy more efficiently.

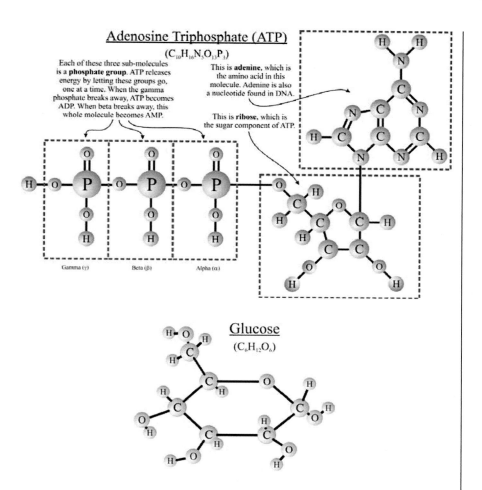

### Adenosine Triphosphate (ATP)
($C_{10}H_{16}N_5O_{13}P_3$)

Each of these three sub-molecules is a **phosphate group**. ATP releases energy by letting these groups go, one at a time. When the gamma phosphate breaks away, ATP becomes ADP. When beta breaks away, this whole molecule becomes AMP.

This is **adenine**, which is the amino acid in this molecule. Adenine is also a nucleotide found in DNA.

This is **ribose**, which is the sugar component of ATP.

Gamma (γ)      Beta (β)      Alpha (α)

### Glucose
($C_6H_{12}O_6$)

A good analogy is that of energy currency. ATP is the pocket money you take to the mall or the market to buy the things you need, whereas glucose is the debit card that gets you more money when you need it, the moment you need it. Bank machines make it easy to take currency from your account. Starch and glycogen are like a savings account that you can dip into when your debit account is low. Also, if it is payday, you can put extra money into the account. Fats are the term deposits, which are harder to liquidate, and proteins are the fixed assets, like the house and the car, which are sold only if all other resources are used up.

Another important concept to remember is that glucose is not just used for energy. It is also a precursor for very strong building materials such as **cellulose**. Cellulose gives strength to plant cellwalls and serves as the backbone for most plants. Glucose can also be used as a building block to make other storage carbohydrates such as starch (in plants) and glycogen (in animal cells). Additionally, glucose can be used as the basic building block in the synthesis of protein, lipids, and nucleic acids. Glucose is an important and very flexible molecule that stores a lot of energy. Nature knows its importance.

NOTES

Most living creatures use glucose to produce energy. Living cells, with the aid of many enzymes, co-enzymes, vitamins, special carrier molecules, and oxygen systematically break down glucose. As the glucose $(C_6H_{12}O_6)$ is broken down, carbon dioxide $(CO_2)$, and water $(H_2O)$ are released, provided that oxygen $(O_2)$ is available to fuel the reaction. This process of energy production is called cellular respiration because it occurs in the cells and because oxygen and carbon dioxide are greatly involved in the process.

The general formula for cellular respiration is:
$$C_6H_{12}O_6 + 6O_2 \rightarrow 6CO_2 + 6H_2O \text{ (plus 36 ATP and heat)}$$

Cellular respiration is a series of chemical reactions involving oxygen, glucose, and water that lead to the production of carbon dioxide, water, and chemical energy. Cellular respiration that involves oxygen occurs in a tiny organelle found in most plant and animal cells. This organelle is called mitochondria.

**Mitochondria** are special rod-shaped and double-membrane organelles that are found within the cytoplasm of eukaryotic cells. Mitochondria are found in the clear fluid portion of the cytoplasm. This clear fluid is called **hyaloplasm**. Prokaryotic cells such as bacteria do not have mitochondria. Mitochondria produce large amounts of chemical energy for cellular use in the form of **ATP** (adenosine triphosphate) and are therefore often called the "**powerhouse**" of the cell. A cell may contain hundreds to thousands of mitochondria.

In the human body, the cells of tissues that require more energy (such as muscle tissue) have more mitochondria than skin cells or connective tissue cells. An egg cell can have over 100 000 mitochondria, whereas sperm cells may have only 100 mitochondria. An egg cell needs the mitochondrial energy to build new cells and materials; a sperm cell simply needs the mitochondrial energy for locomotion.

Mitochondria serve as the exact location of oxygen-driven cellular respiration. Chemical energy (ATP) production occurs mostly inside the inner membrane, which is called the **cristae**. Oxidative phosphorylation (by chemiosmosis) and the Krebs cycle occur in the fluid found in this inner region of the mitochondria. This thick fluid is similar to the stroma of the chloroplast and is called the **matrix**. The matrix is full of hundreds of enzymes and proteins needed to carry out the chemistry of ATP production. The matrix also has ribosomes, RNA, and DNA.

If a cell has no mitochondria, it is still able to make a little ATP, as all cells initially split the sugar molecule (glucose) in half and capture some of the energy. This sugar-splitting process is called **glycolysis** and occurs in the cytoplasm of the cell. **Glycolysis does not require the mitochondria.**

The mitochondria take broken pieces of sugar from glycolysis and digest them to produce large amounts of energy from what would otherwise go to waste. As a result, the mitochondria produce 95% of the cell's chemical energy (ATP). The remaining 5% of the cell's energy is produced in the cytoplasm without the use of mitochondria.

Mitochondria have a double membrane. The outer membrane is smooth like that of chloroplasts. However, the inner membrane is folded, which provides a greater surface area for enzyme and chemical reactions to occur. This inner membrane is called the **cristae**.

| Mitochondrial Membranes | Composition | Physical Characteristic |
|---|---|---|
| Outer membrane | Has more phospholipids by weight and sizable protein pores | Smooth |
| Inner membrane (cristae) | Has more protein by weight than most membranes (with many imbedded proteins, including ATP Synthase)<br><br>Highly regulatory (restricts most molecules from moving across the membrane) | Folded and rough to increase surface-to-area ratio |

Mitochondria contain their own private DNA and their own ribosomes. DNA contains the genetic code for the mitochondria, and the ribosomes are able to build proteins. Therefore, if there is a need for extra energy, the mitochondria have what they need to grow and to reproduce inside the cell.

# Mitochondrion

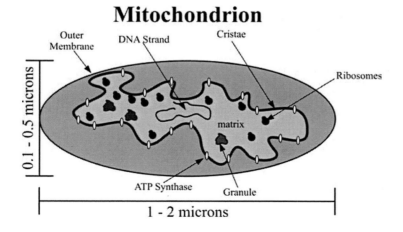

It is believed that the mitochondrion was once a single cell that was engulfed by a larger cell. This theory is suggested because the mitochondrion has its own DNA, its own ribosomes, and it has a double membrane, which is unlike other organelles of the eukaryotes.

The larger cell had a biological advantage because it did not digest this foreign body (the mitochondria) as most cells would. The cooperative arrangement between the host cell and the mitochondria afforded the larger host cell a greater amount of energy for cellular functions. This theory is called **endosymbiosis** and has also been suggested as the origin of the chloroplasts as well.

**Adenosine Triphosphate (ATP)**

Adenosine triphosphate is vital for almost all biological processes that occur in plant and animal life forms. It is an interesting molecule.

At any given moment, an animal or plant cell may have 10 billion ATP molecules floating around the cell. The cell uses energy in the form of ATP for heat production, growth, cellular repair, cellular movement, and chemical transport. More specifically, ATP is used by cells to help engulf food particles through the process of phagocytosis; muscle contraction and relaxation; sperm motility; hormone, pigment, and neurotransmitter production; and the active transport of salts for the transmission of nerve impulses.

ATP is a special molecule that contains the nitrogenous base called adenine that is combined with a small sugar molecule called ribose and a chain of three bonded phosphate molecules. One of the phosphate groups is joined with a high-energy bond. In particular, the last phosphate group of the ATP molecule is linked by a chemical bond that, when broken, releases in the order of 8–12 kilocalories of energy per mole of ATP. This is about 33–50 kilojoules. For daily living requirements, the human body needs about 10 000 kJ or 2 400 kilocalories of energy. The energy released from ATP is in a form that the cell can use to perform work.

Note that one calorie, or 4.187 Joules, is equal to the amount of heat needed to raise one cubic centimetre of water by one degree Celsius.

The cell uses ATP for many different functions. The human body breaks down 1–2 billion ATP molecules per minute, per cell. With 20 to 30 trillion cells in the human body, a lot of ATP is broken down in a given minute. In fact, it is calculated that 40 kg (90 pounds) of ATP would be needed each day to meet the body's demands. You would have to eat a lot of food to meet such a demand. Fortunately, the cell does not completely destroy or use up each ATP molecule every time it needs energy. When the cell requires energy, ATP releases it by only breaking off the last phosphate of the phosphate trio. This is accomplished with the help of an enzyme. The rest of the molecule is recycled. The remaining portion of the ATP molecule, now called adenosine diphosphate (ADP), is released into the cytoplasm. The broken-off phosphate molecule, called **inorganic phosphate ($P_i$)**, is also released into the cytoplasm. More energy must be collected from the energy-rich glucose molecule to reunite the ADP molecule with the phosphate group in order to restore it back to ATP.

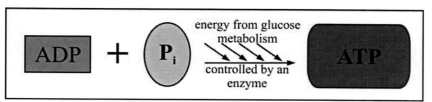

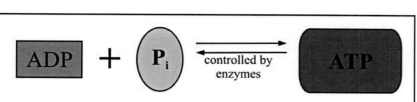

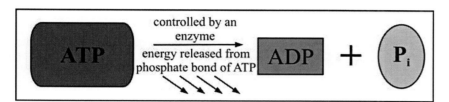

The $P_i$ unit that breaks away from ATP to form ADP is the gamma phosphate unit.

## PRACTICE EXERCISE

1.  What is the original energy source that is stored in organic compounds such as glucose?

    **a)** Oxygen          **b)** Water
    **c)** ATP             **d)** Light

2.  Glucose allows for the storage of large quantities of chemical energy. However, organisms cannot use this energy until it is converted into a usable product. What is this usable form of energy?

    **a)** Oxygen          **b)** Water
    **c)** ATP             **d)** Light

3.  If glucose is not available as an energy source, which of the following compounds acts as a cell's next source of energy?

    **a)** Fat             **b)** $O_2$
    **c)** Water           **d)** Protein

4.  Which of the following structures oxidizes glucose to form ATP during aerobic cellular respiration?

    **a)** Mitochondria    **b)** Chloroplast
    **c)** Thylakoids      **d)** Nucleus

5.  The following formula is missing two variables.

    $$\text{_____} + 6O_2 \rightarrow 6CO_2 + 6H_2O \text{ (plus _____ and heat)}$$

    Which of the following completes the equation?
    **a)** $C_6H_{12}O_6$, 2ATP          **b)** 2ATP, $C_6H_{12}O_6$
    **c)** $C_6H_{12}O_6$, 36ATP         **d)** 36ATP, $C_6H_{12}O_6$

6.  Cristae describes a mitochondria's

    **a)** outer membrane                        **b)** double membrane
    **c)** fluid within the inner membrane space **d)** folds produced by the inner membrane

7.  The theory of endosymbiosis has been proposed as a cooperative arrangement between

    **a)** host cells, mitochondria, and chloroplasts  **b)** mitochondria, chloroplasts, and ATP
    **c)** glucose and mitochondria                    **d)** host cells and ATP

8.  The breakdown and use of ATP per cell is estimated to be

    **a)** 1–2 per minute          **b)** 100–200 per minute
    **c)** 1–2 million per minute  **d)** 1–2 billion per minute

# Lesson 5  ANAEROBIC RESPIRATION

**Anaerobic respiration**

Sometimes oxygen is not available for a cell's use.  When this occurs, the mitochondria will shut down.  The cell must then turn to an alternative method of producing the energy it requires.  Fortunately, the cell is able to produce small amounts of energy in the absence of oxygen.

The production of a small amount of chemical energy in the absence of oxygen is called **anaerobic respiration** (from the Greek, *–an*, meaning *without*; *–aer*, meaning *air*; and *–bios*, meaning *life*), or **fermentation**.  Anaerobic respiration in muscle cells results in the build-up of lactic acid, which produces the feeling of fatigue.  This can occur during and after vigorous exercising, for example.  Too much lactic acid can cause the painful cramping of striated muscle.  Lactic acid build-up in the heart can lead to severe pain or a heart attack.  Anaerobic respiration involving yeast converts sugar (glucose) to alcohol and is used in the beer and wine industries.  This is referred to as **fermentation**.   Fermentation can also be used to make lactic acid that is used to preserve foods. The science of fermentation is called **zymology**.

**The Process of Fermentation**

Lactate Fermentation

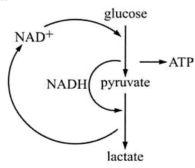

Ethanol Fermentation

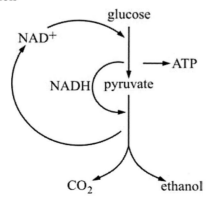

Anaerobic respiration provides energy for a very short period of time. It often is an emergency measure to provide small amounts of energy until oxygen becomes available again. Brain and heart cells are not able to survive long on the amount of energy produced by anaerobic respiration. Red blood cells, however, function routinely with anaerobic respiration. This may seem odd considering that red blood cells carry oxygen; however, they cannot use this oxygen themselves. As a result, red blood cells are not big producers or consumers of energy.

In the case of yeast, the alcohol by-product also limits the process of anaerobic respiration. As the alcohol levels build up, the yeast die, and the process stops.

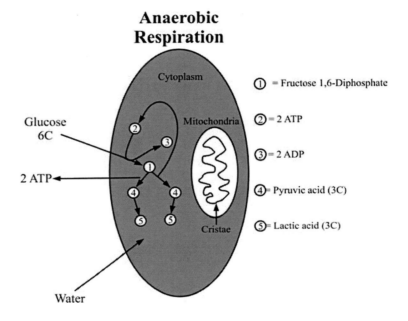

**RESPIRATION SUMMARY**

| Respiration | Conditions | Formula | Energy (kJ mol$^{-1}$) Released | ATP Produced | By-products |
|---|---|---|---|---|---|
| Anaerobic respiration | No oxygen, with yeast and some bacteria | $C_6H_{12}O_6 \rightarrow C_2H_5OH + CO_2$ | 118 | 2 ATP | Ethanol and carbon dioxide |
| Anaerobic respiration | No oxygen (in muscle cells) | $C_6H_{12}O_6 \rightarrow 2C_3H_6O_3$ | 120 | 2 ATP | Lactate |
| Aerobic respiration | With oxygen (in most living cells) | $C_6H_{12}O_6 + 6O_2 \rightarrow 6CO_2 + 6H_2O$ | 2 830 | 36 ATP | Carbon dioxide and water |

## PRACTICE EXERCISE

1. Anaerobic respiration occurs in _____ oxygen concentrations and produces _____ ATP than aerobic respiration.

   **a)** high, more
   **c)** high, less

   **b)** low, more
   **d)** low, less

2. Where does fermentation occur?

   **a)** Outer mitochondrial membrane
   **c)** Cytoplasm

   **b)** Inner mitochondrial membrane
   **d)** Matrix

3. Which molecule must be oxidized prior to fermentation?

   **a)** ATP
   **c)** Ethanol

   **b)** Glucose
   **d)** Lactic acid

4. Which of the following arrangements is in the correct order?

   **a)** ethanol → pyruvic acid → glucose
   **c)** glucose → pyruvic acid → ethanol

   **b)** pyruvic acid → lactic acid → glucose
   **d)** glucose → lactic acid → pyruvic acid

5. In the absence of oxygen, what is the final product of cellular respiration in muscle cells?

   **a)** 36 ATP
   **c)** Pyruvic acid

   **b)** Lactic acid
   **d)** Ethanol and $CO_2$

6. Which of the following is the only common product from fermentation in yeast and muscle cells?

   **a)** $CO_2$
   **c)** 2 ATP

   **b)** $H_2O$
   **d)** NADH

7. Which process must occur prior to fermentation?

   **a)** Krebs cycle
   **c)** Oxidative phosphorylation

   **b)** Glycolysis
   **d)** Creation of a proton gradient

8. Which molecule donates a proton to pyruvate during anaerobic conditions?

   **a)** ATP
   **c)** Glucose

   **b)** NADH
   **d)** NADPH

## *Lesson 6   AEROBIC RESPIRATION AND GLYCOLYSIS*

### Aerobic Respiration

Cellular aerobic respiration refers to the cell's ability to produce chemical energy (ATP) by using oxygen, water, and glucose.  If the cell uses oxygen in its production of energy, it is called aerobic cellular respiration.  Aerobic respiration occurs within the mitochondria and results in large amounts of energy (ATP) being made from the glucose molecule.  The waste products released from this energy factory are carbon dioxide and water.

Aerobic respiration involves many chemical reactions.  However, the following are the four major chemical steps of aerobic respiration:

1. Glycolysis (in the cell cytoplasm)
2. Oxidative decarboxylation (transition into mitochondria)
3. Krebs cycle, or Citric acid cycle (in the matrix of the mitochondria)
4. Oxidative phosphorylation, or chemiosmosis (on the membrane of the cristae)

### Glycolysis

Glycolysis  is the first step in preparing glucose to release the energy it carries.  Glycolysis is the splitting of the glucose molecule in half, which results in two molecules of **pyruvic acid** and some **ATP** production.

Glycolysis begins as the glucose molecule passes through the plasma membrane and enters the cytoplasm of the cell.  Two phosphate molecules are added to each end of the glucose molecule, which effectively lock the glucose in the cytoplasm of cells so that it cannot escape.  This also makes the glucose a little more chemically reactive.  The steps that lead to this phosphorylation (addition of phosphate) of glucose have cost the cell two ATP molecules in order to provide the phosphate and the energy.  Glycolysis up to this point has spent two ATP and produced none.

This phosphate-coated glucose molecule is unstable and energetically splits into two molecules.  We saw this occur in the Calvin cycle when $CO_2$ was added to RuBP.  After phosphorylation, the six-carbon molecule also was unstable and split.  The result in glycolysis is a molecule called **dihydroxyacetone phosphate** that rapidly converts to a familiar molecule called glyceraldehyde-3-phosphate (G3P).  G3P is the all-important product of the Calvin cycle that is used to make glucose, and now we see its return.  However, it does not stick around for long.

Two hydrogen atoms break off from each newly formed G3P molecule, and phosphate is added.  Each group of hydrogen atoms is picked up by a separate hydrogen-carrier molecule (like a little hydrogen truck).  This hydrogen carrier is called **nicotinamide adenine dinucleotide ($NAD^+$)**.  $NAD^+$ is made from vitamin B3.  The carrier is closely related to the $NADP^+$ we saw in photosynthesis.  At the same time, another phosphate molecule is added to G3P.  This particular phosphate molecule comes from the cell's cytoplasm and not from ATP.

Our new G3P molecules are now highly reactive because they have been 'upgraded'. They begin to chemically twist and turn. As they wrench themselves into a new shape, they release their phosphate groups one at a time to any nearby ADP, which produces ATP. Each molecule releases two phosphates and results in the total production of four ATP. After the phosphates are released, two molecules that have three carbons each are the final result of this reaction. These three carbon molecules (3C) are called pyruvic acid.

The overall results of glycolysis include the production of two molecules of pyruvic acid, the donation of four hydrogen atoms to two $NAD^+$ hydrogen carriers, the production of four molecules of ATP, and the expenditure of two molecules of ATP. It is important to note that glycolysis has only a net production of two ATP molecules (if you take into account its expenditure of ATP).

## Formula for Glycolysis

$$\text{Glucose} + 2ADP + PO_4 \rightarrow 2ATP + 4H + 2 \text{ Pyruvic Acid}$$

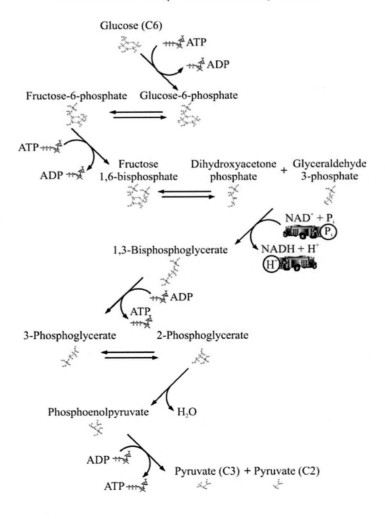

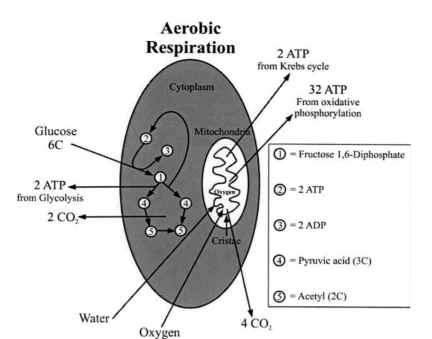

**Aerobic Respiration**

2 ATP
from Krebs cycle

32 ATP
From oxidative
phosphorylation

Cytoplasm

Glucose
6C

Mitochondria

① = Fructose 1,6-Diphosphate

② = 2 ATP

③ = 2 ADP

④ = Pyruvic acid (3C)

⑤ = Acetyl (2C)

2 ATP
from Glycolysis

2 $CO_2$

Oxygen

Cristae

Water

Oxygen

4 $CO_2$

If oxygen is not present, for example, in the mitochondria of a muscle cell, pyruvic acid collects back hydrogen and is converted into a toxic chemical called lactic acid. Lactic acid builds up in the cytoplasm and eventually will stop any further chemical reactions from occurring.

**Oxidative Decarboxylation**

If oxygen is present, the pyruvic acid that is produced in the cytoplasm of the cell begins to break down even further. A transport protein located in the outer membrane of the mitochondria allows pyruvate through. This process is followed by the breaking off of a carbon dioxide molecule ($CO_2$) from the pyruvic acid molecule and the $NAD^+$ hydrogen carrier (that little hydrogen truck again) 'snatching up' two hydrogen atoms that twist off the molecule. Once this occurs, pyruvic acid, which is now called **acetyl**, is small enough to be picked up by a co-enzyme located in the inner membrane of the mitochondrion. It now enters the world of the mitochondrion in the form of a molecule called **acetyl-Coenzyme A**.

**Formula for Oxidative Decarboxylation**
**2 Pyruvic Acid + 2 Coenzyme A → 2 Acetyl-CoA + 4H + 2CO$_2$**

**Krebs Cycle (Citric Acid Cycle)**
Once acetyl-CoA is in the mitochondria, a rather strange turn of events occurs. This small two-carbon molecule combines with a four-carbon molecule called oxaloacetate and water to form citric acid. However, acetyl-CoA has joined only to find itself ripped off the citric acid molecule.

It is ripped off in bits: carbon dioxide by carbon dioxide, and hydrogen pair by hydrogen pair. Within seconds, the original four-carbon molecule has returned and is ready to pick up another acetyl molecule after guiding the previous one through its demise.

For each acetyl group in this cycle, two molecules of carbon dioxide are released, six hydrogen atoms are picked up by three $NAD^+$ hydrogen carriers, and one weaker hydrogen carrier picks up two hydrogen atoms. This hydrogen carrier molecule is called **flavin adenine dinucleotide** (FAD) and is derived from riboflavin, which is a type of vitamin $B_2$.

Even after all this chemical activity, only one ATP molecule was formed. Two acetyl molecules will spin through this cycle for each molecule of glucose. Consequently, for each glucose molecule that is broken down in the Krebs cycle, only two ATP molecules are produced.

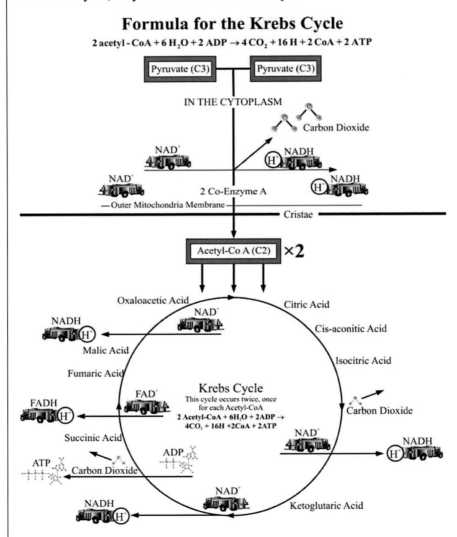

**Formula for the Krebs Cycle**

$$2\,acetyl\text{-}CoA + 6\,H_2O + 2\,ADP \rightarrow 4\,CO_2 + 16\,H + 2\,CoA + 2\,ATP$$

**Oxidative Phosphorylation and the Oxidation of NADH and FADH$_2$**

Up to this point, the process of producing ATP from glycolysis would seem to be largely unsuccessful.  A net of only two ATP has been produced from glycolysis, and only two ATP have been produced from the Krebs cycle.  At most, this will only render 240 kJ/mole of glucose, when the molecule has the potential of yielding 2 800 kJ/mole.  That would be the end of the story if was not for those little hydrogen carriers.

These carriers (NADH and FADH$_2$) are able to carry a great deal of energy.  The hydrogen carriers (this little trucking system) are beginning to collect inside the mitochondria.  Two NADH molecules (trucks) had picked up the hydrogen atoms in glycolysis.  The trucks have had a long journey from the cytoplasm, passing several membranes to get into the matrix of the mitochondria.  As a result, they have spent some of the fuel energy (reducing power) they are carrying.

Two NADH molecules (trucks) picked up hydrogen before the Krebs cycle.  Their journey was not that long as this occurs in the matrix.

Six NADH molecules picked up hydrogen by the Krebs cycle in the matrix.  Two additional, weaker hydrogen carriers called FADH$_2$ were also produced in the Krebs cycle.  They get on the road at a different entry point.

In total, ten NADH and two FADH$_2$ carriers have been collected.  Each NADH carrier splits and releases its hydrogen as protons and electrons.  These electrons and protons are then passed down a system of proteins to the final electron acceptor (oxygen) as a variety of reactions take place.

**Oxidative Phosphorylation**

**Oxidation of NADH and FADH$_2$**

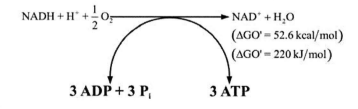

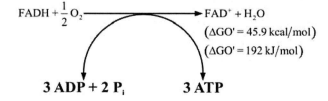

$$NADH + H^+ \rightarrow NAD^+ + 2H^+ + 2e^-$$

$$\frac{1}{2}O_2 + 2H^+ + 2e^- \rightarrow H_2O$$

$$NADH + H^+ + \frac{1}{2}O_2 \rightarrow H_2O + NAD^+$$

Produces 3 ATP, except for the carriers from glycolysis.

The making of water and the breaking of NADH act in unison. These reactions have a total electric potential of 1.14 V and may produce 222 kJ/mol (53 kcal/mol). As electrons are transferred to oxygen, water is also produced. $FADH_2$ goes through a similar process as NADH, but it produces less energy because the electrons are passed to the cytochrome–electron transport chain at lower level. It is like getting onto the highway at different point that is a little closer to the factory. Less energy results from the transport of FAD electrons.

$$FADH_2 + \frac{1}{2}O_2 \rightarrow H_2O + FAD$$

This reaction may only produce 192 kJ/mol (45.9 kcal/mol) and 2 ATP.

The electrons pass from the carriers and are picked up by progressively stronger electron acceptors that are found in the inner membrane of the mitochondria (cristae). The electron acceptors that are embedded in this membrane are called the **cytochrome carrier system**. Cytochrome carriers specialize in passing electrons from weak to progressively stronger carriers.

Meanwhile, the protons from hydrogen collect in the spaces between the cristae and the outer membrane of the mitochondrion. The electrons are eventually transported to the strongest and final electron acceptor in the mitochondria, which is oxygen. As this happens, the now negatively charged oxygen molecule attracts the hydrogen ions back through the cristae and forms a molecule of water. The energy released in the process is enough to produce three molecules of ATP for each hydrogen pair released by the NADH carriers. The hydrogen in the weaker $FADH_2$ carrier provides enough energy to produce two molecules of ATP.

Altogether, 32 ATP are produced by oxidative phosphorylation, two ATP by Glycolysis, and two ATP by the Krebs cycle. The complete breakdown of glucose by the mitochondria of the cell during aerobic respiration leads to the production of 36 ATP. (Refer to the following chart.)

In anaerobic respiration, oxidative phosphorylation and the Krebs cycle do not take place. Glycolysis is the only metabolic pathway that occurs in anaerobic respiration. This means that anaerobic respiration can only produce two ATP from each molecule of glucose.

# Oxydative Phosphorylation by Chemiosmosis

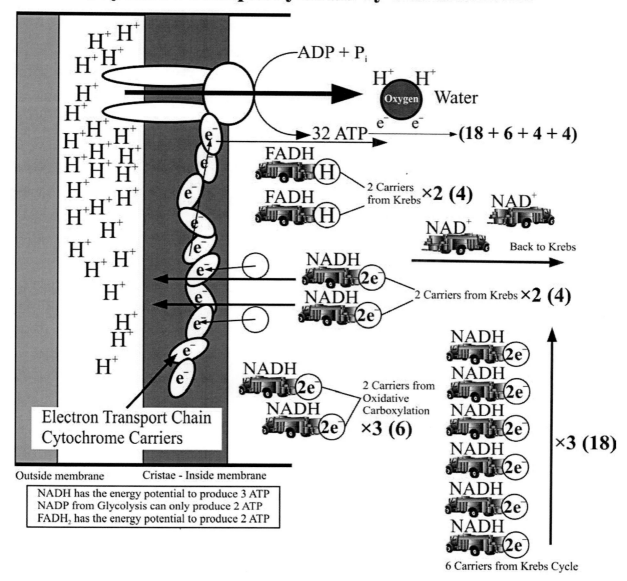

Electron Transport Chain
Cytochrome Carriers

Outside membrane        Cristae - Inside membrane

NADH has the energy potential to produce 3 ATP
NADP from Glycolysis can only produce 2 ATP
FADH$_2$ has the energy potential to produce 2 ATP

2 Carriers from Krebs ×2 (4)

2 Carriers from Krebs ×2 (4)

Back to Krebs

2 Carriers from Oxidative Carboxylation ×3 (6)

×3 (18)

6 Carriers from Krebs Cycle

ADP + P$_i$

Water

32 ATP → (18 + 6 + 4 + 4)

## PRACTICE EXERCISE

1.  Which is the first process required to begin aerobic respiration?

    **a)** Glycolysis        **b)** Krebs cycle

    **c)** Oxidative phosphorylation        **d)** Oxidative decarboxylation

2.  Which of the following processes occurs outside of the mitochondria?

    **a)** Glycolysis        **b)** Krebs cycle

    **c)** Oxidative decarboxylation        **d)** Oxidative phosphorylation

3.  Which of the following process does not require oxygen?

    **a)** Oxidative phosphorylation        **b)** Oxidative decarboxylation

    **c)** Krebs cycle        **d)** Glycolysis

4.  What is added to the glucose to 'lock' the molecule within the cytoplasm of a cell?

    **a)** 2 phosphates from 2 ATP        **b)** 2 carbons from 2 $CO_2$

    **c)** 2 $H^+$ from 2 NADH        **d)** 2 $H^+$ from $FADH_2$

5.  What is the net amount of ATP produced by glycolysis?

    **a)** 0        **b)** 2

    **c)** 4        **d)** 36

6.  Oxidative decarboxylation occurs between

    **a)** glycolysis and fermentation

    **b)** glycolysis and the Krebs cycle

    **c)** oxidative phosphorylation and fermentation

    **d)** oxidative phosphorylation and the Krebs cycle

7.  What is the primary function of the Krebs Cycle?

    **a)** Release oxygen        **b)** Produce 36 ATP

    **c)** Fix carbon dioxide        **d)** Produce NADH and $FADH_2$

8.  Which process produces the **greatest** amount of ATP?

    **a)** Glycolysis        **b)** Krebs cycle

    **c)** Fermentation        **d)** Oxidative phosphorylation by chemiosmosis

# *REVIEW SUMMARY*

## **ANAEROBIC RESPIRATION**

| Process | Hydrogen Released | Hydrogen Picked up | ATP Produced | End Products |
|---------|-------------------|--------------------|--------------|--------------|
| Glycolysis (fermentation) | 2 hydrogen used to convert pyruvic acid to lactic acid | 0 NADH | 4 ATP – 2 ATP<br>**= 2 ATP** | 2 lactic acid |

## **AEROBIC RESPIRATION**

| Process | Hydrogen Released | Hydrogen Picked up | ATP Produced | | End Products |
|---------|-------------------|--------------------|--------------|---|--------------|
| Glycolysis | 4 hydrogen | 2 NADH | 4 ATP – 2 ATP<br>**= 2 ATP** | | 2 pyruvic acid |
| Oxidative decarboxylation transition from glycolysis to the Krebs | 4 hydrogen | 2 NADH | **0 ATP** | | 2 acetyl<br>2 carbon dioxide |
| Krebs cycle | 16 hydrogen | 6 NADH<br>2 FADH$_2$ | **2ATP** | | 4 carbon dioxide<br>2 CoA |
| Oxidative phosphorylation | Hydrogen ions and electrons combine with oxygen to form water | From glycolysis:<br>$2 \text{ NAD}^+ \times 2 \text{ ATP}$ | | **4 ATP** | Water |
| | | From oxidative decarboxylation:<br>$2 \text{ NAD}^+ \times 3 \text{ ATP}$ | | **6ATP** | |
| | | From Krebs cycle:<br>$6 \text{ NAD}^+ \times 3 \text{ ATP}$ | | **18 ATP** | |
| | | From Krebs cycle:<br>$2 \text{ FAD} \times 2 \text{ ATP}$ | | **4 ATP** | |
| | | | **Total = 32 ATP** | | |

# *PRACTICE TEST*

1.  Which of the following sugars is an isomer of the monosaccharide glucose (same chemical formula but different arrangement)?

    **a)**  Lactose
    **b)**  Sucrose
    **c)**  Maltose
    **d)**  Fructose

2.  In which organelle would you expect to find the proton carrier NADH?

    **a)**  In chloroplasts only
    **b)**  In mitochondria only
    **c)**  In both chloroplasts and mitochondria
    **d)**  In neither chloroplasts nor mitochondria

3.  Where is the location of the bond with the **greatest** potential energy in a molecule of ATP?

    **a)**  Inside ribose
    **b)**  Inside adenine
    **c)**  First phosphate (closest to ribose)
    **d)**  Third phosphate (furthest from ribose)

4.  Glucose can be stored as long chains (or polysaccharides). What is the storage form of glucose found in animal cells?

    **a)**  Starch
    **b)**  Ethanol
    **c)**  Cellulose
    **d)**  Glycogen

5.  The following formula for cellular respiration is missing two portions.

    $C_6H_{12}O_6$ + _____ $\rightarrow$ $6CO_2$ + $6H_2O$ (+ 36 ATP and _____)

    Which of the following completes the equation?

    **a)**  $6O_2$, heat
    **b)**  heat, $6O_2$
    **c)**  $C_6H_{12}O_6$, 36ATP
    **d)**  36ATP, $C_6H_{12}O_6$

6.  The matrix describes a mitochondrion's

    **a)**  outer membrane
    **b)**  inner membrane
    **c)**  double membrane
    **d)**  fluid-filled area enclosed by the inner membrane

7.  In which cell would the **greatest** number of mitochondria be found?

    **a)**  Skin cells
    **b)**  Muscle cells
    **c)**  Prokaryotic bacteria
    **d)**  Connective tissue (tendons)

8.  Which structure contains the protein that produces the **greatest** amount of ATP in aerobic conditions?

    **a)**  Matrix
    **b)**  Cytoplasm
    **c)**  Outer mitochondrial membrane
    **d)**  Inner mitochondrial membrane

9.  What is the common pathway for both aerobic and anaerobic respiration?

    **a)**  Oxidative phophorylation
    **b)**  Fermentation
    **c)**  Glycolysis
    **d)**  Krebs cycle

**10.** Which of the following formulas for fermentation in yeast is correct?

   **a)** Glucose → 2 ethanol
   **b)** Glucose → 2 lactic acid
   **c)** Glucose → 2 ethanol + $2CO_2$
   **d)** Glucose → 2 lactic acid + $2CO_2$

**11.** What is the final product of cellular respiration in muscle cells (in the presence of oxygen)?

   **a)** 36 ATP
   **b)** Lactic acid
   **c)** Pyruvic acid
   **d)** Ethanol and $CO_2$

**12.** Which of the following statement regarding glycolysis is **true**?

   **a)** Two NADH donate two $H^+$. .
   **b)** The pathway requires oxygen.
   **c)** The net production is four ATP.
   **d)** One glucose produces two pyruvate.

**13.** The reaction that occurs in the intermembrane space is

   **a)** two carbons donated by acetyl-CoA to the Krebs cycle
   **b)** the oxidation of glucose into two pyruvate
   **c)** the conversion of pyruvate to acetyl-CoA
   **d)** the oxidation of glucose into lactic acid

**14.** What is the number of ATP produced by the Krebs cycle?

   **a)** 0
   **b)** 2
   **c)** 4
   **d)** 34

**15.** What are the differences between mitochondrial oxidative phosphorylation and substrate-level phosphorylation?

**16.** Describe the role oxygen gas has in cellular respiration.

**17.** Provide two similarities and two differences between chloroplast and mitochondrial oxidative phosphorylation.

# HUMAN SYSTEMS

When you are finished this unit, you will be able to…

- identify the principal structures of the digestive and respiratory systems
- describe the chemical nature of carbohydrates, lipids, and proteins (and their enzymes)
- explain enzyme action and factors influencing their action
- describe the chemical and physical processing of matter through the digestive system into the circulatory system
- explain the exchange of matter and the transfer of thermal energy between the body and the environment though the mechanisms of breathing, gas exchange, removal of foreign material, and heat loss
- identify the principal structures of the heart and its associated blood vessels
- describe the action of the heart, blood pressure, and the general circulation of blood through the coronary, pulmonary, and systemic pathways
- describe the structure and function of blood vessels
- describe the main components of blood and their role in transport, clotting, and resisting the influence of pathogens
- explain the role of the circulatory system at the capillary level and how it aids the digestive, respiratory, and motor systems' exchange of energy and matter with the environment
- explain the role of blood in regulating body temperature
- describe and explain, in general terms, the function of the lymphatic system
- list the main cellular and non-cellular components of the human defense system, and describe their roles
- describe the ABO and Rh blood groups on the basis of antigens and antibodies
- identify the principle structures in the excretory system
- identify the major and associated structures of the nephron
- describe the function of the kidney in excreting and expelling metabolic wastes
- identify the role of antidiuretic hormone (ADH) and aldosterone in water and sodium-ion reasbsorption, excretion, and blood pressure regulation
- explain how the motor system supports body functions
- describe, in general terms, the action of actin and myosin in muscle contraction and heat production.

177

# PREREQUISITE SKILLS AND KNOWLEDGE

Prior to starting this unit, you should be able to...
- define the characteristics of a living cell
- describe the similarity and differences between cells, organs, tissues, and systems
- compare and contrast anabolic, metabolic, and catabolic processes
- define a concentration gradient
- list the characteristics of passive and active transport through membranes
- describe patterns of specific variables given a body of data

## *Lesson 1* **THE DIGESTIVE SYSTEM**

The human organism's digestive and respiratory systems exchange energy and matter with the environment.

Human beings, like other organisms, must exchange energy and matter by extending concepts of surface area to volume ratio and membrane transport.

### DIGESTIVE SYSTEM

The alimentary canal is a tube—or pathway, rather—that runs through the body from the mouth to the anus. This tube contains twists, turns, bulges, and clamps to prevent any chunk of food from falling through too fast. The digestive tract, from mouth to anus, can stretch about 9 to 12 metres.

There are three primary processes that occur in the digestive system.

1. **Ingestion** is the process of taking in food.

2. **Digestion** is the process of breaking down complex food particles into small molecules that can be transported via the blood plasma. The two types of digestion are chemical digestion and mechanical digestion.

3. **Absorption** is the process of passing nutrients, such as sugars and vitamins, from the digestive tract into the blood stream.
   The absorption process is facilitated by **villi** (plural form of villus) in the digestive tract.

The movement of food in the digestive system is achieved through two processes.

1. Stomach contractions: mixing movements powered by stomach muscles

2. **Peristalsis:** a wave-like constriction of tubular muscles that moves materials along the GI tract (gastrointestinal tract)

### DIGESTIVE ANATOMY

#### MOUTH

The mouth is an important part of the digestive system and performs several functions. It moistens food with secretions of saliva from the salivary glands.

It grinds the food to increase its surface area, which creates more edges for chemical digestion. Chewing helps in the formation of a manageable ball of food called a **bolus**. The digestion of starches also begins in the mouth (as a result of the action of an enzyme called **salivary amylase, which** is released by the salivary glands). Finally, the mouth directs the food down the appropriate tubes. The flap of skin at the back of the throat, called the **uvula**, prevents food from going up the nasal passage.

The trachea must also be closed by another flap of skin called the **epiglottis** (or simply the **glottis**). As you swallow, you can feel your larynx moving up, which closes off the trachea.

NOTES

The esophagus transports food to the stomach using peristaltic movement.

## ESOPHAGUS

The esophagus is the tube that carries food into the stomach. It is a smooth, muscular tube that contracts in peristaltic wave motion, pushing the bolus of food along. Peristaltic motion is so effective that a person can drink a glass of water while hanging upside-down. The esophagus does not have protection against strong acids and digestive enzymes. As a result, the release of gases from the stomach or pressure on the stomach can result in acids from the stomach getting into the esophagus. This can be painful and can cause ulcer formation and is discussed later in the chapter.

## STOMACH

The stomach is a muscular, J-shaped sac that has three main functions.

1. It provides storage for one to two litres of material for about three to five hours.

2. It mixes gastric juices through a muscular wave-like movement from the top to the bottom of the stomach.

3. It sets the rate of digestion. The speed of digestion ranges from four hours (bread) to 24 hours (spinach). Fats and cold food slow down digestion and the rate of muscular contractions in the stomach. Alcohol speeds up digestion by encouraging enzymes and stomach acids.

The entrance to the stomach is controlled by the cardiac, or gastroesophagel, sphincter.

The entrance to the stomach is controlled by the **cardiac sphincter** (**gastroesophageal sphincter**). The stomach wall is made up of three smooth, involuntary muscular layers. The inside of the stomach has a network of strong, muscular, and wrinkled folds called **rugae**. Rugae increase the surface area inside the stomach and aid in mixing and grinding of the food. This mixing action is a form of mechanical digestion that results in long-chain molecules breaking into smaller components.

Folds called rugae increase the surface area of the inner stomach and help grind food down to simpler substances.

The pyloric sphincter controls the exit from the stomach.

The stomach contracts approximately once every 20 seconds to mix and churn the food into an acidic, soupy mixture called **chyme**. Once chyme is at the right consistency and acidic level, it is released from lower stomach and enters the small intestine. The exit door (an important one-way valve) that releases chyme out of the stomach is called the **pyloric sphincter**.

The unique characteristics of the stomach are listed below.

| Stomach Trivia | |
|---|---|
| 1. | The outer skin of the stomach blushes when your face blushes. |
| 2. | The stomach also turns 'pale from fear' the way your face turns pale when you are frightened or startled. |
| 3. | Excitement or stress can cause the digestive processes to decrease. |
| 4. | The action of the stomach slows down if it is cold, such as after an ice-cream cone. |

| 5. | The stomach 'sleeps' during the night. |
|----|----------------------------------------|
| 6. | The stomach repairs itself quickly: a wound that can take several days to heal outside the body will repair in several hours in the stomach. Cells in the stomach lining are replaced every three days. |
| 7. | The stomach is very neat and orderly, carefully layering food as it enters. |
| 8. | The stomach is very fussy and will not allow any materials to be absorbed, other than water and alcohols. |

## Stomach lining

*Digestive secretions*
The epithelial lining of the stomach contains over 35 million glands that release about 2–3 litres of gastric juices each day. Each of the gastric glands is made up of several different types of special cells.

One type of cell that makes up the gastric gland is called **a chief cell, which** produces an inactive enzyme called **pepsinogen**. Pepsinogen converts into an active, protein-slicing enzyme called **pepsin** in the presence of acid. This conversion only occurs when the acidity of the stomach is high (pH of 2).

Pepsinogen becomes the active enzyme pepsin in low-pH conditions.

The stomach lining also releases an enzyme called **rennin** that aids in the coagulation and digestion of milk proteins.

The production of acid is also an important function of the gastric glands. This task is accomplished by special cells called **parietal cells**. The parietal cells secrete hydrochloric acid, which aids in the rapid denaturation of protein and kills the numerous bacteria that are ingested each day.

*Protective Secretions*
The high acidity (low pH) and the pepsin are a very powerful protein-digesting combination. This deadly combination could easily digest the proteins that hold your body together. Your stomach is protected from being "ripped apart" by having a rapid rate of repair and, more importantly, the special protective stomach lining.

The epithelial lining of the stomach has special cells called **clear columnar cells** or **mucus neck cells** that secrete a substance called **mucin**. Mucin—a thick, sticky, alkaline mixture—keeps acid off the walls of the stomach and thus prevents holes from forming along the stomach walls. The mucin covering can be 1 to 1.5 mm thick. Pepsin only functions in the presence of mucin, which is an additional safe measure against the powerful acids and enzymes of the stomach. This special lining, which is covered with mucin, is called the **mucosa**.

Pepsin can only break down proteins in the presence of **mucin**.

## Hormonal Regulation of the Stomach

Cells in the lower lining of the stomach walls also produce a hormone called **gastrin**. , Gastrin is a short protein chain **(polypeptide)** that is released into the blood only to return to the gastric glands to stimulate them into producing increased amounts of gastric juices such as HCl and pepsinogen. Gastrin also stimulates the movement of the stomach walls. This hormone is activated by the presence of undigested food that moves into the stomach as well as by a special system of nerves called the **parasympathetic nervous system**.

Gastrin and other digestive hormones have a psychological effect on humans. They tend to cause one to feel a sleepy a sense of well-being, like after a big meal. This relaxing effect of gastrin is useful as it encourages an individual to rest after eating. This reduces the blood supply to muscles and other organs in order to increase the supply to the digestive organs that require more blood to actively function in the presence of food.

It has been recently discovered that gastrin plays a role in the release of insulin from the pancreas and acts to stimulate the growth and repair of the mucus lining in the stomach (the mucosa). Gastrin acts as a "gut-growth hormone." (Scientific American, July 1989)

Other cells in the lining of the stomach and small intestine produce a hormone called **somatostatin**. Somatostatin inhibits or blocks the effect of other hormones. It is a 'work-stopping' hormone. Somatostatin decreases intestinal movement, stops the release of acids and enzymes, and prevents the growth of the digestive organs.

## LIVER

The liver acts as an auxiliary digestive organ
The liver is the chemistry lab of the body. It is a bright red and spongy organ. It is the largest organ (gland) in the body and can perform over 500 tasks. The liver produces over 1 000 different enzymes and many other important proteins. Every day, 0.5–1 litre of an acid-neutralizing and fat-dissolving agent called **bile** is produced and released into the small intestine.
Bile breaks down (emulsifies) fats and neutralizes the strong acids that the stomach releases into the **duodenum**, which is the first section of the small intestine. Under normal conditions, the liver only uses 15% of its capacity. 85% of the liver is excess capacity, reserved for emergency situations.

*Hepatic* refers to the liver.

The liver, unlike most organs, has a dual blood supply: blood rich in food material from the intestinal walls comes in from the hepatic portal vein, and freshly oxygenated blood enters from the hepatic artery. As a result, over a litre of blood passes through its spongy tissue each minute.
This aspect of the liver allows it to make up for any sudden losses of blood and also allows it to absorb any blood surges passing through the cardiovascular system.

Other functions of the liver include the following.

*Chemical Producer*

The liver produces, or manufactures, antibodies. Antibodies are special proteins that work against infections and foreign protein bodies. The liver also manufactures the proteins **prothrombin** and **fibrinogen** that aid in blood clotting. In addition, the liver takes old red blood cells, rips them apart, and converts them into bile or other needed materials.

*Sugar Manager*

The liver converts excess glucose into the polysaccharide **glycogen, which** can be converted back into sugar and released gradually as the body needs it.

The liver also converts fructose and galactose into glucose.

The liver converts extra sugar into fat, and if the body is short of sugar, it will aid in converting body fats into sugar.

*Storage Broker*

The liver stores important dietary components such as glycogen; fats; and vitamins A, B12, and D. It also stores metals (iron and copper). Proteins and amino acids, however, cannot be stored in the liver.

*Protein Recycling*

The liver takes excessive amino acids from the excess protein in the blood and removes the amino groups in order to convert the rest of the molecule into a useful form for energy.

The resulting amino groups become ammonia, which is toxic.

The liver then must convert the ammonia into urea and export it back into the blood so that it can be filtered out of the body by the kidneys.

*Enzymes*

The liver also breaks down poisonous materials that enter the blood stream. The process of breaking down poisons or toxins is called **detoxification**. The liver must detoxify many common items that are ingested on a daily basis so that other organs are not damaged. The liver will use enzymes to detoxify materials such as alcohol, nicotine, caffeine, barbiturates, poisons, and excess hormones. Alcohol dehydrogenase enzymes in the liver are responsible for the breakdown of alcohol.

An American and Italian research team has recently discovered the same enzymes are found in the stomach lining of males. Females lack this enzyme, which puts them at a biological disadvantage in terms of metabolizing (hydrolyzing) alcohol. As a result, the livers of females must work harder to metabolize alcohol.

(Science News, January 20, 1990, page 39)

## PANCREAS

### Pancreatic Hormones

The pancreas is a large, greyish, tongue-shaped organ that is located on top of the small intestine, below the stomach and liver. It is considered an endocrine gland because it releases hormones into the blood, and an exocrine gland because it releases chemicals into the small intestine.

Its duties as an endocrine gland include producing the hormones that are released into the blood stream. These hormones include the following.

- Insulin: Produced in pancreatic cells called the **islets of Langerhans**, insulin controls the removal of glucose from the blood stream.
- Glucagon: This hormone stimulates the release of glucose into the blood stream.
- Somatostatin: This hormone inhibits the action of insulin and other hormones.

### Pancreatic Enzymes

The pancreas is considered to be an auxiliary digestive organ because it produces enzymes that aid in digestion. The pancreas manufactures and exports these enzymes into the small intestine, via the **pancreatic duct**. However, the pancreas never comes in direct contact with the materials that need to be digested.

This particular work of the pancreas is considered an exocrine activity because digestive enzymes are released or excreted directly into the digestive tract that eventually leads out of the body.

The enzymes that the pancreas manufactures and then excretes include amylase, lipase, trypsin, nucleases, and peptidase. The pancreas also produces a neutralizing chemical called sodium bicarbonate, which reduces the acidity of material released from the stomach to a pH of approximately 8.

Trypsinogen is an inactive form of trypsin that is produced by the pancreas. Trypsinogen will convert into trypsin when acted upon by a certain enzyme called enterokinase or by other active molecules of trypsin. It is important that the proteolytic enzymes (enzymes that digest protein) are in an inactive form so that pancreatic tissue is not digested.

Trypsinogen and pepsinogen are inactive enzymes. They become active, respectively, in the presence of acids and when in contact with active trypsin or enterokinase.

**Pancreatic Secretions**

| Pancreatic Secretion | Chemical Action Against the Reactant | Product That Results |
|---|---|---|
| Sodium Bicarbonate | Reduces the acidity in the duodenum (no digestion) | (No Digestion) |
| Peptidase (Carboxypeptidase) | Hydrolysis of peptide bonds at the carboxyl group of amino acids | Amino Acids |
| Lipase | Hydrolysis of lipids (triglycerol) | Fatty Acids and glycerol |
| Amylase | Hydrolysis of starch | Maltoses (disaccharide) |
| Trypsin and Chymotrypsin | Hydrolysis of specific peptide bonds | Amino acids |
| Nuclease | | |

## DIGESTIVE ORGANS

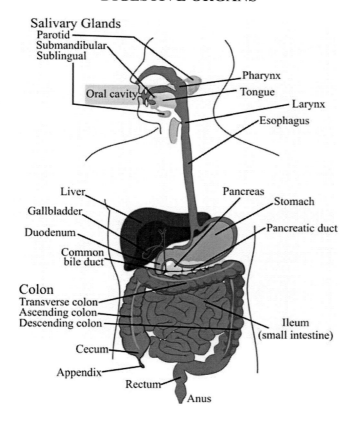

## GALL BLADDER

The gall bladder, which is lodged in one of the lobes of the liver, is a light muscular bag that stores and releases a concentrated form of bile.
Bile is produced in the liver for the emulsification of fat and the reduction of acidity in the small intestine. The gall bladder does not manufacture bile; it only stores bile.

A special duct that carries bile out of the gall bladder is called the **cystic duct**. The cystic duct joins the common bile duct and then empties the bile into the duodenum of the small intestine. The bile then goes to work on those undigested lipids by emulsifying or breaking them down.
Hormones such as cholecystokinin are released from the small intestine when the lining of the intestine has come in contact with undigested lipids. These hormones excite the gall bladder, causing it to contract and squeeze bile out of its sack into the duodenum via the cystic duct.

## SMALL INTESTINE

The small intestine is an important digestive organ that measures six metres. The stomach empties into the small intestine. The acidic digestive juices released from the stomach create a bacteria-free mixture that is released into the small intestine. Unlike the large intestine, the small intestine normally remains bacteria-free.

The majority of digestion and absorption processes occur in this area of the digestive tract. There is a layer of the intestine that contains a rich supply of capillaries in order to provide the blood an opportunity to pick up the digested substances. The nutrients are mostly broken down into simple molecular structures such as amino acids, glycerol, fatty acids, glucose, and nucleic acids.

The small intestine is made up of three sections: the first region is the **duodenum** (20 to 30 cm in length), the next region is the **jejunum** (120 cm in length), and the final region of the small intestine, which is the longest, is the **ileum** (160 cm long). The small intestine releases about 8 litres of fluid a day to produce digestive juices.

Many mucus-producing glands (**Brunner's glands**) are located in the duodenum. These glands release secretions that protect the small intestine from the acidic chyme the stomach releases. These glands do not function well during high levels of stress.

The inside epithelial layer of the small intestine contains small ridges that increase the surface area by about three times. These ridges are noticeable without the aid of a microscope. Each ridge has small bumps called **villi** that increase the surface area another 10 times. Each villus is made of cells with microscopic finger-like projections called **microvilli** that increase the surface area another 20 times. All of these structures together increase the surface area of the intestine by about 600 times. The estimated interior surface is 250–700 square metres, which is more than the floor space in an average-sized house.

The small intestine has three areas. Digestion proceeds from the stomach into the duodenum, the jejunum, and finally through the ileum.

The lining of the small intestine performs many important tasks. It is involved in selective absorption of nutrients, the secretion of hormones that control the functions of distant organs, the production and secretion of enzymes, the special packaging of lipid molecules, as well as very rapid growth and repair.

Most nutrients are moved through the intestinal lining via active transport. This process requires the intestinal cells to have many specific carrier molecules for each nutrient that is absorbed by the body. This system requires the expenditure of ATP. Active transport ensures that the body will get what it needs from the food you eat.

*Intestinal Enzymes*
The intestinal epithelial lining has an important exocrine function. The cells in this lining produce many important enzymes that do the majority of the chemical digestion. The intestinal enzymes are needed to break nutrients into their smallest chemical components so that they can be absorbed into the blood stream. Large molecules—such as most proteins, polysaccharides (starch), and disaccharides (lactose, maltose, and sucrose)—are too large to move into the blood stream. They must first be broken down in the small intestine by the intestinal enzymes. Glucose, galactose, and fructose are single-unit, 6-carbon molecules called **monosaccharides**. The intestinal lining produces and excretes the enzymes listed in the following table into the lumen (centre) of the small intestine.

Proteins, starches, and disaccharides are broken down into smaller chemical compounds in the small intestine.

## INTESTINAL ENZYMES

| Enzyme | Reacts with: | Product: |
|---|---|---|
| Peptidase | Protein | Amino Acids |
| Maltase carbohydrase | Maltose - Disaccharide | Glucose (monosaccharide) |
| Lactase carbohydrase | Lactose | Glucose and galactose ( monosaccharide) |
| Sucrase carbohydrase | Sucrose | Glucose and fructose |
| Lipase | Lipids | Fatty acids and glycerol |

*Intestinal Hormones*
The lining of the duodenum produces an important digestive hormone called **secretin**. Increased acidity in the small intestine or nervous activity causes the release of secretin by the lining of the small intestine.

This hormone is released into the blood stream and causes the nearby pancreas to step-up production of alkaline digestive juices to neutralize acidic materials that the stomach is beginning to release. In this way, the lining protects itself from the 'wrath' of acidic chyme.

Secretin causes the pancreas to produce more alkaline juices in order to counteract the acidity of gastric juices from the stomach.

Secretin also carries a chemical message to halt the release of gastric juices in the stomach. Secretin quite amazingly stimulates the growth and repair of the small intestine and pancreas. (Scientific American, July 1989) Some cells in the lining of the small intestine produce a hormone called **cholecystokinin, which** stimulates the pancreas and the gall bladder to release their respective secretions.

**Villi – with Lacteals**
The villi of the small intestine are specifically designed for effective absorption of nutrients and vitamins. The villi are supplied with a rich internal supply of blood capillaries that form a network or a web-like pattern just below the surface of the villi. Nutrient-poor blood enters the villi and then leaves nutrient-rich. These blood vessels pick up most of the digested materials that diffuse or are actively transported through the lining of the intestine. Some small fatty acid chains from digested lipids are allowed to pass directly into the blood stream; however, most digested or undigested lipids are not allowed to pass through.

Lipids have a special transport mechanism. A rather peculiar vessel runs through the centre of the web of capillaries in the interior of the villi. This dead-end vessel does not circulate blood. It instead circulates a clear liquid body fluid called **lymph**. This lymph vessel that is in the villi is specifically called a **lacteal**.

Lacteals absorb digested lipids.

Lacteals are responsible for the absorption of digested lipids. Digested lipids—including long fatty acid chains and glycerol, a few cholesterol molecules and phospholipids—are first transported with the help of bile into the epithelial cells of the small intestine. The epithelial cells then reconstruct the digested lipids into triglycerol (triglyceride) molecules. They are neatly packaged (with the cholesterol and phospholipids) in tiny protein packs of fat are called **chylomicrons**. These packages are then excreted into the interior of the villi and are absorbed by the lacteal vessel through the process of **pinocytosis**. They then circulate throughout the body by the lymphatic system and eventually are released into the circulatory system.

Part of the reason for packaging the lipids in protein is to disguise them from water. Lipids are hydrophobic (they do not dissolve or react with water) and are repelled by water in body fluids. Once the lipids are packaged, there is no conflict. Eventually, the lymphatic system delivers the lipids safely to the circulatory system.

Fat-soluble vitamins are vitamins that dissolve easily in fat. The fat-soluble vitamins include vitamins A, D, E, and K. These vitamins can only move with the packaged fats into the lacteal. If one eats a fat-free diet, these important vitamins will not be absorbed into your blood.

Other vitamins, such as vitamin C and most of the B vitamins, are water-soluble vitamins and diffuse across the intestinal lining; they move directly into the capillaries.

## LARGE INTESTINE (COLON)

The large intestine is nearly three metres long, but it is shorter than the small intestine. Even though it is shorter, it is called the large intestine because it is larger in diameter than the small intestine.

The large intestine is made up of three distinct sections: the **transverse colon**, the **ascending colon**, and the **descending colon**. These colons are designed to go up, across, and then down so that materials move slowly through this area of the GI tract, which allows for sufficient time to remove excess water from feces.

There is an important one-way valve or door called the **ileocecal valve** that prevents backflow of fecal contents from the colon into the small intestine. More importantly, there are two one-way valves called **sphincters** that control the release of feces (solid waste) out of the body. The last of these two sphincters is called the **anal sphincter** and is controlled voluntarily.

The colon, like the small intestine, contains a rich supply of capillaries for the absorption of water into the blood stream. However, there is not nearly as much activity within its lining as compared to the small intestine. There are no villi or microvilli in the large intestine, and there is no enzymatic production; therefore, no digestion occurs here.

The main function of the large intestine is to absorb water and to slow the progress of material through the digestive process. The colon also secretes mucus to help solids slide through the intestinal tubing.

The large intestine absorbs some important salts, such as sodium and chloride. On the other hand, it will secrete sodium bicarbonate via active transport. The sodium bicarbonate acts to counter the acidic by-products of the bacterial activity in the large intestine.

There is a great deal of activity by the 'foreign' organisms that take up residence in the large intestine. There are over one thousand varieties of bacteria that live in the large intestine. These bacteria are normally very useful for decomposition of solid wastes and vitamin production.

The large intestine stores and eliminates solid wastes. It can slow down the movement of digested food 12–24 hours in order to allow for the gradual absorption of up to ten litres of water. The area of the large intestine that stores feces until they are ready to be released is called the **rectum**.

There are over 1 000 species of bacteria (known as **intestinal flora**), though technically, they are not plants.

## FOUR FUNCTIONS OF THE LARGE INTESTINE

| | |
|---|---|
| 1. | Absorbs water, minerals and salts |
| 2. | Decomposes left-over organic material with the help of resident bacteria |
| 3. | Produces vitamin B, vitamin K, and folic acid (needed for red blood cell production) |
| 4. | Stores and eliminates solid wastes (feces) when appropriate |

# DIGESTIVE DISORDERS

## CIRRHOSIS OF THE LIVER

Cirrhosis of the liver occurs as portions of the liver enlarge and later shrink and harden. This damaged area is replaced by a scar tissue. Cirrhosis is six times more common among alcoholics than the general population. In the early 1980s, cirrhosis was the fourth leading cause of death among people between the age of 25 and 65. Symptoms include jaundice (yellow skin), loss of appetite, and the vomiting of blood in the advanced stages of the disease.

## GALLSTONES

The gall bladder is embedded between the lobes of the liver and stores the bile that is produced in the liver. Bile is squirted out of the gall bladder and into the duodenum after eating a meal that contains fats. This bag can hold on the average of only 50 mL of bile, which is not enough when you consider that your body uses 500–1 000 mL each day. However, bile is stored in a concentrated form that is 10 to 12 times more than the amount that is normally needed.

Water is released from the liver and mixed with the concentrated bile as it is needed. Therefore, the gall bladder can actually hold nearly a day's supply of bile.

A disadvantage of this tricky space-saving mechanism is that bile is so concentrated that it can easily form into solid crystals. These crystals join and form stones that can then jam up in the cystic duct that drains from the gall bladder into the common bile duct and finally into the duodenum. This blockage will cause material to back up and be forced into the circulatory system. Jaundice (yellow skin) results as bile moves through the body and collects in body tissues.

When this occurs, a doctor may advise to have the gal bladder surgically remove. If this is done, the doctor will also recommend that the patient reduce the fat content in their diet. This has to do with the fact that bile aids in the emulsification of fats.

## PEPTIC ULCERS

An ulcer is caused by the inflammation of the membranes that cover the intestinal walls or the stomach. As the tissue dies, a hole forms in the absence of the dead cells. Ulcers can be caused by the excessive production of gastric juices (acid and pepsin) that are normally used to break down proteins in food. The gastric juices can digest the stomach lining if they are too concentrated or if there is no food in the stomach. Ulcers may also be caused by insufficient production of anti-acids that are normally produced in the liver and pancreas.

These anti-acids are released into the duodenum to counter the 'nasty' acid mixture that the stomach releases. Acid build-up in the stomach can be caused by such things as smoking, irregular meals, over-drinking, and stress. The extra acid production can leads to ulcers.

There are three main types of digestive ulcers. The **gastric ulcer** is in the stomach, the **esophageal ulcer** is in the esophagus, and the **duodenal ulcer** is in the duodenum. Recent studies have found two key causal agents of peptic ulcers. Although peptic would seem to refer to a stomach ulcer, the term in fact refers to the actions of pepsin. These ulcers can occur in the duodenum as well as in the stomach. It is believed that one of the major causes is the bacteria *Helicobacter pylori*, which in sufficient numbers can damage the cells lining the digestive tract.

This damage is caused in part by the bacteria's production of toxic amounts of ammonia and results in the loss of regulation by the hormone gastrin, which produces excessive gastric secretions. The other causal agent has been linked to the use of anti-inflammatory (heartburn) medication.

This medication relieves pain by reducing the inflammation of affected tissue; however, they have also been implicated in the reduction of mucin. This secretion is essential for the protection of epithelial tissue within the digestive tract. A lack of mucin allows for tissue to be damaged by the combined actions of pH and enzymatic degradation.

## HEPATITIS

Hepatitis is a general term for an infection or inflammation of the liver. Infectious hepatitis is caused by a virus. Some of its symptoms include tiredness, yellowing of the skin and eyes, dark-colored urine, and fever. The liver usually becomes enlarged and tender. People with hepatitis are often unable to work, as they can experience extreme fatigue and thus require bed rest. A moderate and limited protein and fat diet is recommended so the liver can rest from its normal production of bile and deamination of amino acids. A high sugar diet is usually needed in order to give the liver an opportunity to repair itself. If care is not taken, permanent liver damage is possible, which can lead to many other physiological problems because of the many important functions of the liver.

Poor sanitation tends to be a contributing factor in the spread of hepatitis, which is extremely contagious. In fact, the hepatitis virus is more contagious than the AIDS virus.

Ulcerative colitis is a digestive disease that results in lifelong problems with diarrhea, stomachaches and severe weakness. This disease causes inflammation and bleeding in the large intestine. There is no known cure for this disease other than surgically removing a portion or the entire large bowel (a procedure known as a colectomy).

NOTES

There are three types of ulcers: gastric, esophageal, and duodenal.

## PRACTICE EXERCISE

1. Explain how astronauts can properly digest food in a zero-gravity environment.

2. Describe the hormones that regulate the release of gastric, pancreatic, and intestinal enzymes. Describe the conditions necessary to trigger their release.

3. List three general functions of the digestive system.

4. List five functions of the liver.

5. List four functions of the large intestine.

**6.** What is peristalsis?

*Use the following information to answer the remaining questions*

The alimentary canal is a hole or tube that runs through the body from the mouth to the anus. This tube contains twists, turns, bulges, and clamps, which prevent food from falling through too fast.

**7.** What are the three primary processes that occur in the digestive system?

    **1.** _____

    **2.** _____

    **3.** _____

**8.** What are the two mechanical processes responsible for the movement of food through the digestive system?

    **1.** _____

    **2** _____

**9.** What are the three different types of ingested substances that can change the rate of digestion?

    **1.** _____

    **2.** _____

    **3.** _____

**10.** List two important hormones that are released by the digestive linings to control digestion:

    **1.** _____

    **2.** _____

**11.** What are three components necessary for the digestion of protein?

    **1.** _____

    **2.** _____

    **3.** _____

# Lesson 2  THE RESPIRATORY SYSTEM

## RESPIRATORY STRUCTURES

### NASAL CAVITY

The nasal cavity is the air conditioner of the respiratory system.
Air passes through and is warmed or cooled by a rich supply of blood
vessels that are found in the nasal cavity.  As well as controlling the
temperature, the cavity acts as a humidifier by supplying moisture from the
tear glands (lacrimal glands) to incoming air.  The air is filtered by hairs in
the cavity and mucus, which helps trap larger particles.

### PHARYNX

The pharynx is the passageway that extends from the nasal cavity to the
larynx and the esophagus.  It is a muscular tube that makes up the superior
section of the throat.  The pharynx is lined with a mucous membrane for
further cleansing.  It serves as a common passage for both the respiratory
and the digestive tract.

### LARYNX

The larynx is a structure made of cartilage that is located in the upper
region of the respiratory tract between the pharynx and trachea.
The larynx is commonly known as the Adam's apple and contains the
voice box.

### TRACHEA

The trachea is commonly called the windpipe.  It is easy to locate as it can
be felt in the anterior portion of the neck.  The trachea is approximately
2–3 cm in diameter and 10–12 cm long.  The inner layer of the trachea is
lined with a ciliated mucous membrane.  Its middle layer is strengthened
with cartilage.  The outer layer is made up of 10–20 C-shaped rings.
The C-rings protect the trachea and still allows food to pass through the
esophagus.  The inside of the trachea contains special cells that secrete
mucus, which helps trap harmful pollutants.  It also contains ciliated cells
(microscopic hairy cells) that move the mucus into the mouth to be
coughed up or swallowed.  These ciliated cells move back and forth about
12 times a second.

### BRONCHI (SINGULAR FORM – BRONCHUS)

Bronchi are major tubes that branch from the trachea.  One primary
bronchus goes to each lung.  Each bronchus divides into
secondary bronchi.  Airflow is rapid in the bronchi, and the air is warmed
and picks up moisture to reach a suitable temperature and humidity.
Like the trachea, the bronchi have cartilage in order to prevent them from
collapsing.  The only function of the bronchi is to conduct air.

## BRONCHIOLES

Bronchioles are smaller branches that lead from the bronchi and spread out to the alveoli. They are roughly the thickness of a human hair. This tubing does not have the cartilage rings and is made up of muscle. During spasms (sudden, rapid muscular contractions), they can block the flow of air. The bronchioles are needed to slow down the rate of air movement.

## ALVEOLAR SACS

Alveolar sacs look like a cluster of grapes (alveoli). There are 300–600 million alveoli in the lungs. The sacs increase the surface area of the lungs by 300 times. Your skin has a large surface area, but the surface area of alveoli combined is 25 times greater. The sacs are very thin (0.2 microns). Each alveolus contains cilia (microscopic hairs) that help keep the inside of the lungs clean. There is a capillary net that consists of about 1 600 km (more than double the distance between Edmonton and Calgary) of capillaries that pass over and surround the alveolar membranes. This cobweb of blood and lymphatic vessels is necessary for gas and fluid exchange. Gases that move from the lungs into the blood must dissolve in water before they are able to diffuse. Therefore, the alveoli must be kept moist in order to absorb gases.

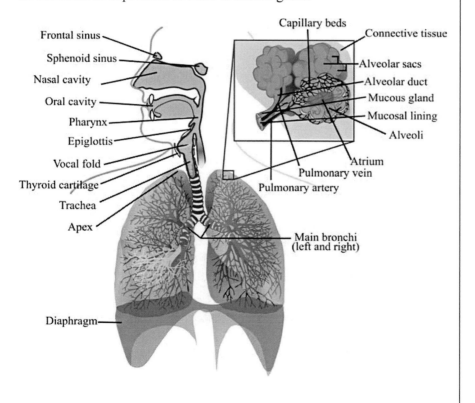

## LUNGS

The lungs are made of alveolar sacs. Therefore, they are less like a hollow bag and more like a mass of spongy material. The collection of microscopic sacs forms into lobes of lung tissue. The right lung has three lobes and is larger than the left. The left lung has two lobes, which allow space for the heart. The lungs are protected from dust and microbes by cilia and special white blood cells called monocytes that hide in lung tissue for years, waiting to feast on any foreign substances or bacteria.

The lungs are sealed within the thoracic cavity and depend on the movement of the chest. The lungs are allowed to slip on the chest wall as it moves. As the chest moves up and out, the lungs fill with air. When a baby is first born, the lungs are sealed in the chest cavity (but are not stuck to the chest wall). A doctor slaps the baby so that the baby gasps for air, which causes its chest to grab the lungs. They then inflate and remain stuck to the chest for the rest of the baby's life (lungs only collapse if there is an accident or a chest operation).

The lungs have a shiny smooth membrane that covers them. It is called the **visceral pleura**. Another membrane called the **parietal pleura** covers the chest cavity. A fluid between the chest membrane and the lung membrane is responsible for the attachment of the lungs to the inside chest wall. The lungs and chest remain paired in this way for life.

## BREATHING

### RATE OF BREATHING

The breathing rate is the number of times you need to breathe in each minute. This rate is controlled by the amount of carbon dioxide ($CO_2$) in the blood and not the amount of oxygen ($O_2$). If the $CO_2$ is high because of increased exercise, your breathing rate will speed up in order to get rid of the excess $CO_2$. It is convenient that as the body hustles to get rid of the $CO_2$, it also picks up extra oxygen.

The normal breathing rate is between 12–20 times per minute depending on the body size. Women tend to breathe more rapidly than men at about 16–20 breaths per minute. Reduced activity lowers the breathing rate. Lying down reduces the rate more than sitting does. Physical activity increases the breathing rate because of the increased buildup of $CO_2$. However, athletes at rest tend to use oxygen effectively and have more developed lung capacity, which causes their respiration rate to be lower than normal. Children breathe twice as fast as adults because the lungs of children have less surface area for gases to exchange. Babies breathe 40–60 times per minute.

## BREATHING SOUNDS – AUSCULTATION

Doctors can listen to the lungs and other internal organs with a stethoscope, which involves a branch of diagnostic medicine known as **auscultation**. Crackling sounds could indicate pneumonia. A rubbing sound could indicate a condition called pleurisy (inflammation of the pleural cavity). A continuous high or low-pitched sound could indicate asthma or mucus in the bronchi. Harsh disconnected sounds may indicate bronchitis or edema (collection of water on the lungs).

These respiratory disorders are explained at the end of this chapter.

## BREATHING VOLUMES

The amount or volume of air that moves in and out of the lungs can be measured with a **spirometer**. It is useful to measure these volumes as a way to measure your breathing fitness.

The total volume of air that normal lungs can hold is called the **total lung capacity** and can range between 4 000 and 6 000 mL. This amount would be the equivalent of 2–3 large milk cartons. The total volume depends on the size, sex, and fitness of the individual. Total lung capacity is much greater than what is used during breathing . The volume of air that moves into or out of the lungs during breathing (while at rest) is called **tidal volume** and is about 500 mL, which is a small fraction of the total capacity. If a person inhales a maximum amount of air after taking a normal breath, it is called the **inspiratory reserve volume**, which is about 2 000–3 000 mL. The inspiratory capacity is the maximum amount of air that can be taken in, including the volume of a normal breath (tidal volume). The inspiratory capacity is therefore about 1 500 mL greater than the inspiratory reserve volume. After normal exhalation, if one uses a maximum effort to force further air out of the lungs, the amount of forced air is called the **expiratory reserve volume**. This volume is about 800–1 200 mL.

**The vital lung capacity** is the volume of air that can move into and out of the lungs with the maximum effort in a single breath. This volume would equal the inspiratory reserve volume, expiratory reserve volume, and the tidal volume. The vital lung capacity is approximately 3 300–4 700 mL.

Finally, there is some air in the lungs that is needed for the lungs to remain inflated and attached to the chest wall. This reserve air is called the **residual air volume**, which is about 1 000–1 300 mL. The residual air volume never leaves the lungs, except as a result of an accident such as a breaking a rib or puncturing the lungs.

Residual volume can increase as you get older and as your lung tissue becomes less elastic and less able to squeeze the air out of its pockets. Old lung tissue would be much like a sponge that is too rigid to squeeze out the extra water it holds.

Total lung capacity: total amount of air in the lungs after the deepest possible breath

Tidal volume: normal breath

Inspiratory reserve volume: air required beyond tidal volume to totally fill the lungs

Expiratory reserve volume: extra air left over in the lungs after exhaling tidal volume.

Vital lung capacity: total lung capacity, minus the air that cannot be forced out.

# MECHANICS OF BREATHING

## EXHALATION

For air to go out of the lungs, the pressure must be higher on the inside of the lungs (or in the alveoli) than on the outside. Air moves from an area of high pressure to an area of low pressure. This high-pressure area is created by quickly changing the volume of the thoracic cavity or the chest. If the volume is decreased, the air pressure increases inside the chest and air rushes out. This is what happens when a person gets 'the wind knocked out of them'. The internal volume of the chest is abruptly reduced, the pressure very quickly goes up, and the breath is 'knocked out'.
However, most of the time this is a passive process while the muscles relax and the rib cage slowly drops.

## MUSCLES OF EXHALATION

The following muscles are responsible for breathing out.

- The **external intercostal (chest) muscles** relax, which causes the rib cage to move down and air to move out of the lungs.
  These muscles are found between the ribs on the outside of the chest cavity.
- The **diaphragm**, a muscle between the abdominal and thoracic cavities, relaxes and moves up to its normal position, which causes air to move out of the lungs.
- The **internal intercostal muscles** can also contract to increase pressure on the chest and force exhalation with a little more power. These muscles are found between the ribs on the inside of the chest cavity. They are used for forced breathing.
- The abdominal muscle can also contract, which pushes the contents of the abdominal cavity toward the diaphragm causing air to move out of the lungs. These muscles are also important for forced breathing.

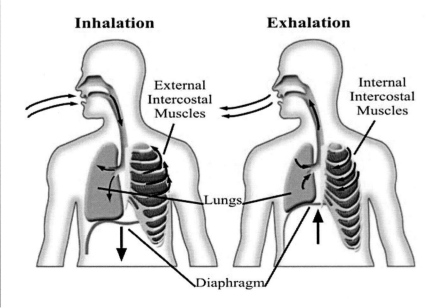

During the process of exhalation, the volume of the thoracic cavity decreases and the pressure increases to 267 pascals greater than the atmosphere. Air rushes out of the alveoli as it goes from an area of high pressure to an area of lower pressure.

## INHALATION

Just before inhalation, the air pressure in the alveoli is the same as the atmospheric pressure. For air to go into the lungs, the pressure must be lower on the inside of the chest and higher on the outside. Therefore, the air pressure must be actively decreased inside the chest. This low-pressure area is created by quickly changing the volume of the thoracic cavity. If the volume is increased, the air pressure decreases inside the chest. This is an active process, as it requires the contraction of muscles to increase the area of the thoracic cavity.
Your chest muscles pull your rib cage up and out. This is why breathing becomes difficult if there is pressure being placed against your ribcage

## MUSCLES OF INHALATION

The following muscles are responsible for breathing in

- The external intercostal muscles contract, which causes the ribcage to move up and out causing air to be sucked into the lungs.
- The diaphragm contracts, moves downward, and flattens, which causes air to be sucked into the lungs.

During the process of inhalation, the volume of the thoracic cavity increases and the pressure decreases to –267 pascals. Air rushes into the alveoli as it goes from an area of higher pressure to an area of lower pressure.

## HICCUPS

The muscles that control breathing are controlled and regulated by the nervous system. Sometimes nerves misfire and cause irregular contractions of the diaphragm. This interrupts the normal rhythm of breathing and causes air to rush in to the lungs unexpectedly. The brain immediately tries to correct this by causing the epiglottis to snap shut and close off the trachea. Air hits this closed opening, which is near the vocal cords, resulting in the 'hic' sound of the hiccup.

Hot liquids, carbonated drinks, or uncontrolled laughing can stimulate the irregular contraction of the diaphragm, which causes the hiccup.
The trick to getting rid of the hiccups is to interrupt the uncontrolled firing of the diaphragm. Everyone seems to have a different trick for doing this. One of the more common methods involves holding one's breath for three of four spasms, until the nerve tics subside.

# TRANSPORT OF OXYGEN

Oxygen is transported in two ways by the circulatory system. It is transported as a dissolved gas, but more importantly it is carried by a special red pigment in the blood called **hemoglobin**.

## TRANSPORT AS A DISSOLVED GAS

Oxygen dissolves directly into the plasma of oxygen-poor blood that circulates in the capillaries of alveoli. It does this because the oxygen in the alveoli exerts pressure in order to pass into the blood inside the capillaries.
 The internal oxygen pressure builds up in the capillaries as the blood moves along. This simple form of transport accounts for only one percent of the exchanged oxygen.

## TRANSPORT BY HEMOGLOBIN

Oxygen very easily combines with the red, iron-bearing heme of hemoglobin to produce **oxyhemoglobin**.
This occurs inside of the red blood cells and accounts for 99% of the oxygen transportation in the body. Atoms of oxygen combine with the hemoglobin molecule as indicated by the formula below. Oxygen is later released from the oxyhemoglobin molecule at the tissue level. After it is released, the newly freed hemoglobin molecule will return to the lungs to pick up more oxygen.
Formula:
$$\text{oxygen} + \text{hemoglobin} \rightleftharpoons \text{oxyhemoglobin} \rightleftharpoons \text{hemoglobin} + \text{oxygen}$$

## THE RELEASE OF OXYGEN FROM OXYHEMOGLOBIN

The bond between oxygen and hemoglobin is very strong as the two of them have a chemical attraction to each other. However, they still have to be able to break free of each other so that oxygen can be distributed to the parts of the body that require it. There are three factors that help hemoglobin release oxygen. These factors include temperature, acidity, and oxygen concentration.

1. **Temperature**

   Hemoglobin releases its oxygen faster as your body heats up. Increased body temperature will cause oxyhemoglobin to release oxygen so that the muscles can easily obtain the oxygen in order to produce more energy.

2. **Blood Acidity**

   Hemoglobin will release its oxygen faster as your blood becomes more acidic. Your blood becomes acidic from exercise or as a result of holding your breath. Both of these actions cause hydrogen ion concentration to build. The buildup of acid in the blood is explained below.

3. **Oxygen Concentration**

As the oxygen concentration decreases (**oxygen debit**) near body tissues, oxyhemoglobin will speed up its release of oxygen. On the other hand, if the supply of oxygen increases (**oxygen credit**)—such as in the capillaries of the lungs—hemoglobin picks up and holds on to oxygen molecules.

# TRANSPORT OF CARBON DIOXIDE

Carbon dioxide is transported in the circulatory system in three distinct ways. First, it is transported in a broken-down form in the cytoplasm of the red blood cell. Secondly, it is carried by the protein (**globin**) part of the hemoglobin molecules in the red blood cell. Finally, it is carried in a broken-down form outside of the red blood cell in the blood plasma.

## TRANSPORT IN THE BLOOD PLASMA.

Like oxygen, some of the carbon dioxide simply dissolves under pressure in the blood plasma. This is somewhat like the carbon dioxide that is dissolved in cola. The $CO_2$ that was packed in the beverage escapes the cola when you open it and releases the pressure into the atmosphere. Likewise, $CO_2$ is 'packed' in the blood tissues (under slight pressure). It is released when it enters the lungs. The lungs are designed to release this pressurized gas into the atmosphere. Only 7% of the $CO_2$ is transported in this fashion.

## TRANSPORT AS HYDROGEN IONS IN RED BLOOD CELLS

Most of the $CO_2$ moves from the blood plasma into the cytoplasm of red blood cells. The $CO_2$ breaks down (with the help of an enzyme called **carbonic anhydrase**) as it mixes with the water in and around blood cells. The enzyme, carbonic anhydrase, speeds up the reaction that is described by the formula that follows. This reaction allows $CO_2$ to be transported disguised as hydrogen ions and bicarbonate ions. Most of the hydrogen ions and bicarbonate ions are floating about in the cytoplasm of the blood cells. Some of the hydrogen ions, however, may attach to the globular protein on the hemoglobin molecule and be removed from circulation. Therefore, hemoglobin can act as a regulator of hydrogen ion concentration and is called a **buffer** as it controls the concentration of freely circulating hydrogen ions in the blood. The leftover bicarbonate ions remain floating in the cytoplasm. When the blood cells get to the lungs, these chemicals are released. The formula also works in the reverse direction, whereby the chemicals combine again to reform carbon dioxide and water. Carbon dioxide is then released out of the lungs as you exhale. Formula:

$$CO_2 + H_2O \rightleftharpoons H_2CO_3 \rightleftharpoons H^+ + HCO_3^-$$

carbon dioxide + water $\rightleftharpoons$ carbonic acid $\rightleftharpoons$ hydrogen ion + bicarbonate ion

About 70% of the total $CO_2$ is dissolved in this 'disguised' fashion.

## TRANSPORT BY HEMOGLOBIN (CARBAMINOHEMOGLOBIN)

The remaining portion of carbon dioxide does not break down in the cytoplasm in the same way it was explained above. Instead, it goes directly to the hemoglobin molecule, finds a spot on the outer protein (globin) portions, and hooks on for a 'free ride' to the lungs. When the $CO_2$ molecule joins with the outer protein structure of hemoglobin, the result is called **carbaminohemoglobin**. About 23% of the $CO_2$ is transported in the form of carbaminohemoglobin.

## REGULATION OF RESPIRATION

Breathing normally occurs at a regular rhythmic rate because of homeostatic control.

Breathing has both voluntary control and involuntary control. Involuntary control usually takes over if, for example, you hold your breath. Chemoreceptors are stimulated by $CO_2$ levels and hydrogen ion levels in the blood. If these levels are high, signals are sent to the medulla oblongata to increase the breathing rate, whether you want to or not.

The rate of respiration is closely tied to the acidity of the blood. The pH of arterial blood tends to be between 7.35 and 7.45, which is a very narrow range. The blood in the venous end will have a relatively lower pH, depending on the amount of carbon dioxide and the amount of hydrogen ions in the blood.

Hyperventilation, or breathing too quickly, causes your pH to increase, which makes the blood more alkaline.

Holding your breath or breathing too shallowly causes your blood pH to decrease, which makes it more acidic.

If the blood becomes too acidic, the rate of respiration will increase in order to breathe out $CO_2$, which causes the blood to become acidic. If the blood becomes too basic, the rate of respiration will decrease in order to allow the $CO_2$ to build up.

### Respiratory Acidosis

As carbon dioxide collects, it combines with water to produce carbonic acid, which is acidic. The carbonic acid then breaks apart into hydrogen ions and bicarbonate ions. As the hydrogen ions build-up, your blood becomes acidic (decreased pH). Too much $CO_2$, therefore, leads to acid build-up in your blood.

The buildup of hydrogen ions in the blood can be caused by conditions that interfere with gas exchange, such as pneumonia or emphysema.

### Respiratory Alkalosis

If an unusual amount of carbon dioxide is removed from the blood, it results in a decrease in hydrogen ions, which causes the blood to become too basic (high pH).

This can be caused by aspirin poisoning or by conditions that force an individual to breathe very rapidly (hyperventilation).

## GAS EXCHANGE

- External respiration is the exchange of gas between the alveoli and the blood in the capillaries of the lungs.
- Internal respiration is the exchange of gas between the blood of the systemic circulation and the cells of the body.

### The Composition of Atmospheric Air

Gas exchange occurs because gases exert partial pressures.

- The air we breathe in has an overall pressure of 101.325 kPa.
- The air is made up of several gases, such as nitrogen, oxygen, carbon dioxide, and others.
- Each of these gases has a different concentration in the air. Together, they account for only part of the total pressure (101.325 kPa). **Partial pressure** is the pressure exerted by a single gas in a mixture of gases.
- A gas with a higher concentration exerts a higher partial pressure; for example, oxygen makes up 20.9% of the air and therefore has a partial pressure of about 21.1 kPa of the total 101.325 kPa.

### The Composition of Inhaled Air

Inhaled air enters the respiratory tract with a partial pressure that is the same as in the atmosphere and has the following characteristics.

- Atmospheric pressure at sea level is equal to 101.325 kPa.
- Oxygen makes up 21% of the air, which is equal to $\dfrac{21.1}{101.325}$ kPa.
- $CO_2$ makes up 0.04% of the air, which is equal to $\dfrac{0.04}{101.325}$ kPa.
- Nitrogen makes up about 78% of the air.
- The remaining portion of air is made up of a variety of other gases.

### The Composition of Alveolar Air

Changes occur in these gas concentrations as you breathe; therefore, there is a change in the partial pressure of various gases as well.

Inhaled air mixes with the air that remains in the alveoli (the residual air volume).

The gas in the alveoli is always losing oxygen *to* the capillaries and picking up $CO_2$ *from* the capillaries. Therefore, the concentration of oxygen is lower and the concentration of $CO_2$ is high. Partial oxygen pressure will decrease. Partial $CO_2$ pressure will increase as compared to the inhaled air. This mixture of inhaled air and residual air is called the **alveolar gas** and has the following characteristics.

- Oxygen makes up 14.5% of this air, which is equal to about $\dfrac{14.7}{101.325}$ kPa.
- $CO_2$ makes up 5.5% of this air, which is equal to about $\dfrac{5.6}{101.325}$ kPa.
- Nitrogen makes up about 80% of this air.

NOTES

**The Composition of Exhaled Air**

Exhaled air is a mixture of alveolar gas and atmospheric air that remains in the trachea.

This air will be higher in oxygen and lower in $CO_2$ than the alveolar air. However, the mixed air will be lower in oxygen and higher in $CO_2$ when compared to atmospheric air.

Exhaled gas has the following characteristics.
- Oxygen makes up about 16% of this air, which is equal to about $\dfrac{16.2}{101.325}$ kPa.
- $CO_2$ makes up about 5% of this air, which is equal to about $\dfrac{5.1}{101.325}$ kPa.
- Nitrogen makes up about 78% of this air.

There is partial pressure of gases in the blood as well. Blood from the body that enters the capillaries of the lungs has an $O_2$ pressure of 5.3 kPa and $CO_2$ pressure of 6.0 kPa.

Leaving the lungs, the blood will have an increased concentration of oxygen and a decreased concentration of $CO_2$. Therefore, the partial pressure of oxygen is about 12.7 kPa, and the partial pressure of $CO_2$ is about 6.0 kPa.

There is also partial pressure of gases in the cellular tissues of the body that will vary depending on exercise and the type of tissue. The values for the pressures are as follows:
- Pressure of $O_2$ is equal to about 3.3 kPa.
- Pressure of $CO_2$ is equal to about 6.1 kPa.

Gases diffuse from an area of high partial pressure to an area of low partial pressure.

## RESPIRATORY DISORDERS

### THE BENDS

The blood and tissues of divers absorb extra amounts of gases because of the increased pressures under water. This is not a problem unless the individual comes to the surface too quickly. If this happens, the gases will bubble in the tissue like a can of cola will bubble when it is opened. This can cause dizziness, nausea, as well as muscle and joint pains. In extreme cases it can be fatal. This condition is called rapid decompression sickness, or the bends.

## SMOKER'S COUGH

Smoking causes the consistency of the mucus, thus making it less effective. The monocytes that protect you from infection and tumours are destroyed. The cilia, which are used to move the mucus away from the lungs and also help filter the air, become paralysed. Eventually, the ciliated cells die out. As a result, the lungs fill up with mucus secretions, and the smoker must cough to expel the mucus from of the lungs. Statistics show that a smoker who smokes a pack a day will reduce his or her life expectancy by approximately seven years. Lung cancer is also directly related to smoking.

## TUBERCULOSIS

Tuberculosis is a communicable disease among humans and animals that is caused by bacteria. It can manifest itself in the lungs, bone, urinary tract, brain, and other parts of the body. Tuberculosis affects the pulmonary system the most. It can cause mental illness and has a high infant death rate. Tuberculosis kills more people than all other communicable diseases combined. Symptoms include fatigue, abnormal sound in the lungs, afternoon fevers, and a buildup of blood in the lungs. It can be treated by collapsing the lung in order to rest it or surgically removing infected areas.

## PLEURISY

Any disease that causes inflammation of the pleural membranes in the lungs may result in pleurisy. Symptoms include chest pain in and fever. The inflamed pleura may collect fluids in the pleural space that separates the visceral pleura from the parietal pleura. This fluid buildup can cause the lung to collapse. A person suffering from this condition may require the fluid or air to be extracted with a needle.

## EMPHYSEMA

Emphysema causes the degradation of the elasticity of the bronchioles. Air can flow into the lungs but is unable to get out. Too much stale air collects in the lungs. As the pressure increases, the thin walls of the alveoli pop, and the ability for gas exchange is decreased. Shortness of breath occurs, and the breathing rate may increase as high as 40 breaths per minute. This disease is usually found in older people and may begin around the age of 40. This disease occurs four times more often among smokers than non-smokers.

## BRONCHITIS

Bronchitis is an infection of the airways (from the nose to the bronchioles).

## PNEUMONIA

Pneumonia is an acute or chronic disease that causes inflammation of the lungs. It can be caused by viruses, molds, bacteria, or chemicals.
This disease can sometimes be fatal, especially among elderly patients.
Chest pains and fever are among some of symptoms.

## PRACTICE EXERCISE

1. Explain how alveolar membranes are designed to increase the rate of diffusion.

2. Distinguish between internal and external respiration.

3. Explain how temperature, carbon dioxide concentration, and pH affect oxyhemoglobin.

4. Explain in detail how exhaled, inhaled, and alveolar air differs.

5. How is oxygen transported in the blood?

6. Where are chemoreceptors located? How do they help regulate breathing and blood pressure?

7. How do exercise and disease affect the rate of breathing? Include the effects of smoking.

**8.** Distinguish between respiratory acidosis and respiratory alkalosis.

**9.** Explain in detail how inspiration and expiration occur.

**10.** How do partial pressures of gases relate to gas exchange?

**11.** What is hyperventilation, and what effect does it have on the respiratory system?

**12.** How can the kidneys compensate for respiratory acidosis?

**13.** How does the right lung differ from the left lung?

## *Lesson 3  THE EXCRETORY SYSTEM*

Excretion involves the removal of metabolic wastes that are ingested or produced as the body works. If these wastes were to build up in the blood the body would be quickly poisoned. The entire body, therefore, works together to remove of wastes. The major organs involved in filtering the blood and excreting metabolic wastes include the skin, lungs, and kidneys. The digestive tract also is involved in the excretion of ingested wastes.

- The skin is designed to remove waste body heat, urea, and other wastes found in sweat.
- The lungs remove a very dangerous waste gas: $CO_2$.
- The kidneys remove urea, uric acid, extra water, and salts.
- The large intestine removes solid wastes and undigested materials.

### PARTS OF THE URINARY SYSTEM

### KIDNEYS

The body contains two kidneys on the back wall of the abdominal cavity. The functions of the kidneys include the following.

- Kidneys filter the blood by removing liquid wastes (urine).
- Potassium and salt levels in the blood are controlled by the kidneys.
- Water balance and blood acidity are also controlled by the kidneys.

Blood enters the kidney through the renal artery. It is filtered, and then the clean blood exits the kidney through the renal vein.

The functional unit of the kidneys is the nephron. Each kidney contains over a million nephrons. All of the blood in the body is filtered through the nephrons once every half hour. The fluids are filtered out of the blood as this occurs. This means that 180–200 litres of fluid is being filtered out of your blood each day. You obviously do not have that much fluid in your body; therefore, 99% of the water that has been filtered out must be recycled back into the blood. The nephron is explained in greater detail further on.

The materials filtered out of the blood collect as urine in the medulla of the kidney. The many metabolic waste products that make up urine include ammonium, uric acid, urea, ketones, urochrome, creatinine, as well as excess water, potassium, sodium, chlorine, hydrogen ions, and other trace elements. Glucose, amino acids, and other needed salts are re-absorbed into the blood from urine.

## MAJOR METABOLIC WASTES IN URINE

| Waste | Source of the Waste |
|---|---|
| Urea | Result of detoxifying ammonia in the liver |
| Uric acid | Result of breaking down nucleic acids that make up DNA |
| Ketones | Result of breaking down body fat |
| Ammonium | Result of breaking down protein |
| Urochrome | Pigment that makes urine yellow (from broken blood cells) |
| Creatinine | Comes from working muscles as they use up phosphocreatine |

## URETERS

The ureters are tiny tubes that are attached to the renal pelvis of the kidney and lead to the bladder. They transport freshly produced urine from the kidneys to the bladder. Ureters are about 25 cm long and are made of three different layers.

- The inner layer is made of a mucous membrane.
- The middle layer is composed of a muscular tissue.
- The outer layer is made of a protective fibrous tissue.

The muscles within the ureters are capable of producing peristaltic waves or contractions to move urine into the bladder.

## URINARY BLADDER

The bladder is a hollow stretchable bag. The bladder stores urine and is made of three muscular tissue layers.
The bladder is controlled by two valve-like structures called urinary sphincters.

## URETHRA

The urethra is a tube that leads from the bladder to the outside of the body. The urethra acts as a passageway for urine. It carries only urine in females, but it also carries urine and semen in males. Urine cannot be released at the same time as semen.
The deep, golden yellow colour of urine is caused by a pigment called **urochrome**. Urochrome is a pigment that comes from broken-down hemoglobin from worn-out red blood cells.

# THE NEPHRON

The nephron is the microscopic filter of the kidney. It does not work alone, as there are over one million of these nephrons in each kidney. The most important parts of the nephron (in terms of the filtering process) include the glomerulus, Bowman's capsule, proximal and distal convoluted tubules, loop of Henle, and the collecting duct. Each of these parts will be discussed in greater detail.

## PARTS OF THE NEPHRON

### Glomerulus

The glomerulus is a microscopic glob of capillaries that has blood circulating through it at an increased pressure. The increased blood pressure causes fluids to leak out of the capillaries. This process is called **filtration**. Filtration is a process in the nephrons of the kidney that forces materials out of the blood and into the nephron's tubules (where they are processed. Fluids and materials move out of the glomerulus and into the Bowman's capsule as a result of increased blood pressure.

The fluids and material of the blood or the filtrate contains nutrients and waste. Almost everything other than blood cells and large proteins is filtered out of the glomerulus. The filtrate, or exiting material, contains water, salts, sugars, amino acids, uric acid, urea, and other materials.

Two arterioles are involved in increasing the pressure of blood in the glomerulus. One is the **afferent arteriole** and the other is the **efferent arteriole**.

- The afferent arteriole controls blood flow *into* the glomerulus. It dilates to allow for increased blood flow volume into the glomerulus.
- The efferent arteriole controls blood flow *out of* the glomerulus. It constricts to increase the pressure as it backs up all the blood that the afferent arteriole has allowed in.
  Fluids are squeezed out, and the fluidless blood exits out of the glomerulus.

### Bowman's capsule

The Bowman's capsule is a cup-like structure that collects the filtrate from the glomerulus and sends it into a winding and connecting tube called the **proximal convoluted tubule**.

### Proximal convoluted tubule

The proximal convoluted tubule is responsible for the movement of filtrate *back into* the blood. This is called **tubular reabsorption**. The 'good' materials, or nutrients, are reabsorbed and most of the 'bad' materials are left behind. Waste or excess materials remain in the tubules and are thus destined to be excreted.

These waste or excess materials are in a closed exit chute and have a very slim chance of getting out before they are dumped out of the body. The much-needed materials, on the other hand—such as water, glucose, amino acids, vitamins, minerals, and some salts—are removed from the tubes back into the blood. The needed materials are rescued out of the water chute. It is very important to reabsorb some of these materials, so much so that this does not happen in a random, inorganic fashion, as is the case during the process of diffusion. Active transport is used to reabsorb glucose, amino acids, and some salts. Most of this is done with special carrier proteins and the use of ATP. The carrier proteins and the mitochondria that are needed to produce the ATP are located in the wall of the proximal convoluted tubule. Once the amino acids, glucose, and salts are transported out of the tube, they are left to diffuse into the capillaries, which circulate blood throughout the cortex of the kidney. The blood then becomes enriched with nutrients, while the waste remains in the tubules in order to be excreted. Approximately 70% of the reabsorption of nutrients in the kidneys occurs in the proximal convoluted tubules.

**Loop of Henle**

The loop of Henle is a long, microscopic tube that loops into the medulla area of the kidney and creates an environment that encourages water reabsorption. The loop creates a salty medulla that allows the kidney to draw out a little extra water from the other tubes running through this area. The extra water moves into the area via osmosis and is then returned to the blood. Animals that need to conserve water tend to have long loops of Henle. The action of the loop of Henle is further explained by the **counter current mechanism** described on the following page.

**Distal convoluted tubule**

The distal convoluted tubule is a winding tube that comes after the loop of Henle. Other items that still need to be reabsorbed into the blood are caught here. These tubules are thus also involved in reabsorption.

The distal convoluted tubule is able to aid in removing materials directly out of the blood supply at any time. Therefore, other unnecessary items that still need to be removed can be removed here. Materials such as hydrogen ions can be removed by the lining of the distal convoluted tubule in order to control the acidity of the blood. Any urea that may have escaped filtration can also be directly removed from the bloodstream. This process is called **tubular secretion**. Tubular secretion is the complete opposite of reabsorption. This process removes unneeded materials from the bloodstream into the tubules of the nephron so that they can be eliminated from the body.

The capillaries near the convoluted tubule aid in secretion as specific carrier proteins in the walls of the capillaries are transporting waste materials, such as left-over urea, out of the blood to be picked up by the distal convoluted tubule and the collecting duct.

NOTES

### Collecting duct

This is the final tube that takes the waste materials (that have not been reabsorbed) toward the centre of the kidney where they are 'dumped'. Tubular secretion also occurs between the collecting duct and the surrounding blood supply. Many collecting ducts from various regions of the kidney's cortex come together to form the renal pyramids of the kidney's medulla.

### THE COUNTER-CURRENT MECHANISM OF THE NEPHRON

The loop of Henle works toward the goal of water conservation. Animals that live in a terrestrial environment need to be careful not to waste water. If water were in short supply, it would be wasteful to release too much water with the urine. As a result, there needs to be a mechanism to encourage water out of the urine and back into the blood. The loop of Henle creates that mechanism in terrestrial animals.

There is no way to actively capture the water in the urine that passes through the collecting ducts. It would seem too late to reabsorb the water that is already on its way out of the body. However, the nephron creates a mechanism in the loop of Henle to get the water out of the collecting duct before it leaves the kidney. It does so by creating a salty environment in the medulla area of the kidney.

With the help of carrier proteins, the ascending loop of Henle actively transports chlorine ions out of the filtrate. Chlorine builds up in the fluids of the medulla as a result of active transport. Because it is a negative ion, it causes sodium ion, which is positive, to move out of the loop. Sodium exits via diffusion because of its ionic attraction to chlorine. The chlorine and the sodium ions collect and dominate the fluids outside the loop of Henle, which creates a salty environment. This salty environment 'attracts' the water that is passing through the nearby collecting duct. The collecting duct is permeable to water, but not permeable to salt. The salt creates an osmotic pressure that pulls the water out of the collecting duct via osmosis. Once the water is out of the duct, it is no longer destined for elimination; it can now be picked up by the nearby blood capillaries and returned to the different body systems.

The ascending loop will start running out of salt as this process takes place. However, the osmotic pump can continue because the descending loop is stealing back the salt that the ascending loop is so generously releasing. This helps keep a constant flow of salt inside the loop for the ascending loop to pump out. Because of the 'generosity' of the ascending loop and the 'frugality' of the descending loop, a salt trade, or salt current, is established as the salt moves out of the ascending loop and into the descending loop. This salt current established by the loop of Henle maintains an environment that attracts water out of the ducts and back into the blood.

This process is called the **counter current mechanism**.

## THE INFLUENCE OF HORMONES ON THE KIDNEYS

The kidneys need feedback and information regarding the water and salt needs of the body. The brain constantly monitors the blood and then sends messages directly to the kidneys. The brain also sends messages back to the adrenal glands that sit on top of the kidneys. These adrenal glands regulate or send orders to the kidneys after receiving their orders from the brain.

The kidneys are regulated by two hormones. One is produced in the adrenal glands: **aldosterone**. The other hormone is released from an important master gland in the brain known as the pituitary gland: **antidiuretic hormone (ADH)**.

### Aldosterone

Aldosterone is produced by the cortex area of the adrenal gland. This hormone causes the kidney tubules to become more permeable to sodium (salt). The salt will then leave the tubule and return to the body's blood. In other words, aldosterone is the messenger that orders the kidneys retrieve salt for the body. This messenger carries a second order: it requires the kidneys to secrete or kick out potassium from the blood and into the urine. Potassium ions basically act as replacements for the salts in the excretory process when this happens.

When too much aldosterone is released from the adrenal glands, the potassium ion concentration falls below normal and muscle paralysis or weakness develops. When not enough aldosterone is available, potassium ion concentration becomes too high. This causes cardiac toxicity and possibly cardiac arrest. It is very important that these messengers be carefully controlled. This is why the brain monitors the potassium levels.

### Antidiuretic Hormone (ADH) or (vasopressin)

Antidiuretic hormone is produced in the hypothalamus and stored in the posterior regions of the pituitary gland. Messages are sent by the hypothalamus when the osmoreceptors detect changes in the amount of water in the blood. When the blood is too concentrated (too thick), ADH is sent out to stimulate the distal convoluted tubules to become more permeable to water. Consequently, water can be reabsorbed from the urine into the blood. This in turn causes blood to become higher in water volume and less salty or concentrated. The higher volume of blood also increases blood pressure. In other words, this messenger instructs the kidneys to work hard at returning water to the blood. The more water that is returned, the higher the blood pressure.

# URINARY DISORDERS

## DEHYDRATION

If the kidneys are not functioning properly, they will not reabsorb water properly and your body will begin losing more water than it can replace. The body will begin to dry out and cells and tissues will die. Diuretics such as tea and alcohol can start the process of dehydration. Infants are more likely to suffer from dehydration, as their kidneys are not yet functioning to their fullest capacity. Dehydration due to kidney malfunction is accompanied by excessive urination; dehydration due to problems with the large intestine is not. Dehydration can occur if the large intestine is not reabsorbing water. Excessive dehydration can be fatal.

## WATER INTOXICATION

An excessive amount of ADH in the body can cause the retention of water. The osmotic balance will thus be out f balance, and the extra water will force its way into body cells, which will cause them to burst. Occasionally, water intoxication (like dehydration) can be caused by a psychiatric disorder that is typified by compulsive water consumption.

## EDEMA

Edema involves the collection of body fluids that are not picked up by the lymph vessels. Edema may also be caused by the retention of extra salt. The kidneys will make up for the extra salt by retaining water to prevent major changes in osmotic pressures.

## KIDNEY STONES

The kidneys also pass substances that will not completely dissolve in water, such as uric acid and calcium phosphates. Normally, these solids are not noticeable, as they are in such small quantities that they simply flow with the water that is being passed. These particles are also likely to be coated with special proteins produced by the body, which keep them from grouping into bigger particles. Some people do not have the ability to coat these urine solids. These solids can then group into what are called **kidney stones**. The formation of these stones can be extremely painful.

## NEPHRITIS (BRIGHT'S DISEASE)

Nephritis refers to a bacterial infection or other irritation and inflammation of the kidney. This can lead to the degeneration of the nephrons and eventually the malfunction and death of the kidney tissue.

## DIABETES INSIPIDUS

Diabetes insipidus is a disease in which ADH production is lower than it should be. The individual's kidneys are not getting the orders to reabsorb water from the urine. As a result, the volume of water released by urination greatly increases.

# PRACTICE EXERCISE

1. What are the functions of each of the following structures in the body?

   **a)** bladder

   **b)** ureters

   **c)** urethra

   **d)** kidney

   **e)** internal and external bladder sphincters

   **f)** renal medulla

   **g)** afferent arteriole

   **h)** efferent arteriole

   **i)** nephron

   **j)** renal cortex

   **k)** glomerulus

   **l)** Bowman's capsule

   **m)** distal convoluted tubule

   **n)** proximal convoluted tubule

   **o)** loop of Henle

   **p)** collecting duct

   **q)** renal artery

   **r)** renal vein

**2.** How does urine differ from glomerular filtrate?

**3.** What effect does blood pressure have on urination?

**4.** Define tubular filtration, tubular reabsorption, and tubular secretion.

**5.** In what ways does ADH control your blood pressure?

**6.** What may it indicate about the nephron if you were to find blood in your urine?

**7.** What are osmoreceptors? Where are they found? What is their significance?

**8.** Explain the importance of the loop of Henle.

**9.** How does active reabsorption differ from passive reabsorption?

**10.** What types of materials are actively reabsorbed and passively reabsorbed?

**11.** Glucose is not commonly found in urine. If it were found in urine, what would that indicate?

**12.** Why is uric acid (a waste) actively reabsorbed?

**13.** Explain how a hemodialysis machine works.

**14.** Draw a negative feedback cycle for aldosterone.

**15.** Diagram the kidneys, and explain the difference between the cortex and the medulla areas.

**16.** What is the effect of too much ADH? What is the effect of too much aldosterone on the body?

**17.** How do blood pressure and kidney function relate?

**18.** How are the kidneys involved in the acid regulation of the blood?

**19.** Why is urine yellow?

**20.** Explain how the urinary, digestive, and circulatory systems interrelate.

# *PRACTICE QUIZ*

1. What is the approximate length of the digestive tract?
   a) 1–2 metres
   b) 2–4 metres
   c) 4–8 metres
   d) 9–12 metres

2. The structure that helps separate air and food is called the
   a) epiglottis
   b) trachea
   c) larynx
   d) uvula

3. _____ is an inactive enzyme that is released by cells that line the stomach wall. This requires _____ to convert the enzyme into an active form.
   a) Pepsin, HCl
   b) Pepsinogen, HCl
   c) Rennin, bicarbonate
   d) Mucin, bicarbonate

4. The _____ manufactures bile, which is an emulsifier of lipids. The function of an emulsifier is to _____.
   a) liver, increase the surface area of fat
   b) stomach, act as an enzyme and digest fat
   c) gallbladder, act as an enzyme and digest fat
   d) small intestine, increase the surface area of fat

5. Pancreatic secretions require a pH level of approximately _____ . This pH is produced through the release of _____ into the duodenum.
   a) 8, sodium bicarbonate
   b) 8, Trypsinogen
   c) 2, pepsinogen
   d) 2, HCl

6. Glucose is a _____ . This _____ further enzymatic digestion prior to active transport across the epithelial layer of the small intestine.
   a) disaccharide, requires
   b) monosaccharide, requires
   c) disaccharide, does not require
   d) monosaccharide, does not require

7. Which of the following macromolecules diffuse across the epithelium of the small intestine?
   a) Lipids
   b) Glucose
   c) Maltose
   d) Amino acids

8. Which of the following can result from the inadequate production of mucin?

   **a)** Hepatitis
   **b)** Gallstones
   **c)** Peptic ulcers
   **d)** Cirrhosis of the liver

9. Which of the following structures uses ciliated cells to trap and remove particles?

   **a)** Nasal cavity
   **b)** Pharynx
   **c)** Trachea
   **d)** Larynx

10. Which structure prevents the lungs from collapsing?

    **a)** Muscle
    **b)** Alveoli
    **c)** Cartilage
    **d)** Pleural space

11. High $CO_2$ levels will cause an individual's breathing rate to _____. Chemoreceptors are most sensitive to the effects of _____ gas levels.

    **a)** increase, oxygen
    **b)** decrease, oxygen
    **c)** increase, carbon dioxide
    **d)** decrease, carbon dioxide

12. The greatest percentage of $CO_2$ is transported within the circulatory system in the form of

    **a)** carbonic acid
    **b)** carboxylic acid
    **c)** carbaminohemoglobin
    **d)** protons and bicarbonate

13. The functional unit of a kidney is the

    **a)** urethra
    **b)** nephron
    **c)** renal vein
    **d)** renal artery

14. Which of the following arrangements is the correct order for the excretion of urea?

    **a)** Urinary bladder, ureters, urethra, kidney
    **b)** Kidney, ureters, urethra, urinary bladder
    **c)** Kidney, ureters, urinary bladder, urethra
    **d)** Urethra, kidney, urinary bladder, ureters

**15.** _____ are reabsorbed at the proximal tubule.  This is achieved through _____ transport.

   **a)** Water and urea, active

   **b)** Water and urea, passive

   **c)** Glucose and amino acids, active

   **d)** Glucose and amino acids, passive

**16.** Which of the following conditions is a urinary disorder in which ADH production is lower than it should be?

   **a)** Edema

   **b)** Dehydration

   **c)** Kidney stones

   **d)** Diabetes insipidus

# Lesson 4  THE CIRCULATORY SYSTEM

The circulatory system of a human organism transports energy and matter to maintain equilibrium among the body systems as well as between the organism and its external environment.

- Human organisms must maintain an internal equilibrium with respect to organs and organ systems, as well as equilibrium with their external environment.
- The circulatory system aids in the digestive, excretory, and respiratory systems as it exchanges energy and matter with the environment.
- The body surface of an organism maintains equilibrium: temperature regulation, protection from pathogens, etc.
- The main components of blood—such as erythrocytes, leucocytes, platelets, and plasma—play a role in transport and in resisting the influence of pathogens.
- Cellular and non-cellular components of the human immune system—such as macrophages, helper T cells, B cells, killer T cells, suppressor T cells, and memory T cells—work together to defend the body from foreign substances such as pathogens.

## COMPARATIVE CARDIOVASCULAR PHYSIOLOGY

The movement of body fluids and blood is essential to living animals, just as the movement of water in a pond or lake is essential to the life of the ecosystem. Stagnant water brings death to a lake just as stagnant body fluids can be fatal to animals.

Fluids move differently in different species. In general, there are two systems of fluid circulation. One system involves large internal cavities (sinuses) where the blood freely bathes the tissues and organs. This type of system is referred to as an **open circulatory system**.

The other system involves the blood always moving through blood vessels. In this way, only the materials carried by the blood can pass in and out of capillaries. This is called a **closed circulatory system**. In a closed system, blood that leaks into a sinus (as it does during an internal hemorrhage) can cause severe physiological trauma, even death.

### Open Circulatory System

Invertebrates, such as arthropods and mollusks, generally have an open system. Interesting exceptions to this rule are the invertebrate annelids, or earthworms; they have a closed system. An open system is not as fast or as efficient as a closed system. The delivery of sugar to the tissues is the result of a hit-and-miss method, which in turn causes more waste. Insects require a lot of nutrients and oxygen for their body size.

Even with the high requirements, an open system is adequate in insects because insects do not rely on the circulatory system to deliver oxygen. Insects have a special tracheal system that delivers oxygen directly to the tissues in order to meet the needs of their high metabolism.

The grasshopper has a good example of an open circulation system. In an open circulation system, there is often a collection of vessels. The grasshopper, like most insects, has one dorsal vessel that contains several pumping regions or hearts. Blood is collected by the hearts and pumped forward, first into cavities (sinuses) in the head and then back through the body sinuses.
In a haphazard way, the blood returns to the dorsal vessel to be recirculated. The rate of blood flow is controlled by the movement of gut or body muscles.

**Closed Circulatory System**
All vertebrates such as fish, amphibians, birds, reptiles, and mammals have a closed system. There great variation in all the closed systems, ranging from very simple, linear, two-chamber systems to the four-chambered heart system of humans.

*Fish Circulation*
Of the vertebrates, fish have the simplest circulatory system. The system has one cycle pumped by a two-chamber heart.

The heart is situated immediately behind and below the gills. It consists of a folded tube with three or four enlargements in a linear sequence of chambers. Venous blood passes into an enlarged vein (sinus venosus) where it is held until it enters into a single auricle (atrium). The blood then enters a single, but strong ventricle and is pumped out through another enlargement called the **conus arteriosus**. The blood is pumped directly through the arteries to the capillaries of the gills. While passing through the gills, the blood picks up oxygen and then moves through the body tissues before it returns to the heart.

*Reptile and Amphibian Hearts*
Reptiles and amphibians have a more complicated circulatory system. A one-circuit system does not work well for land animals that require more oxygen and more blood pressure. Most reptiles and all amphibians have two circuits and a three-chamber hearts.

The frog's heart for example has two atria to collect incoming blood. The left atrium collects blood rich in oxygen from lung and skin tissue. The right atrium collects blood poor in oxygen from the body tissue.

Both atria dump the blood into one strong ventricle, which is the third chamber. The ventricle then pumps the blood out of two major arteries to the head, body, skin, and lungs.

The blood coming out of the ventricle has a mixture of oxygen-rich blood from the lungs and oxygen-poor blood from the body. Special valves and flaps prevent the complete mixture of these two types of blood.

Reptiles have a partial wall in the ventricle to further prevent mixing of blood. Crocodiles differ slightly from other reptiles in that the partition in the ventricles is complete. In other words, crocodiles have a four-chamber heart.

*Bird Circulation*
Birds have a complete four-chamber heart with two ventricles and two atria. Even though birds and mammals that have a four-chamber heart, their respective systems of circulation are distinctly different. Birds need to be light and need a good flow of oxygen for flight.

**Differences between Bird and Mammal Circulation**
- Red blood cells are oval and have nuclei, unlike those of mammals.
- Oxygenated blood leaves the ventricle by a right aortic arch (instead of the left, as it does in mammals).
- Bird hearts are larger compared to their body weight than the hearts of mammals.
- The normal heartbeat per minute of a resting bird is generally higher than that of a similar-sized mammal.

**Percentage of Heart Weight Compared to Body Weight**
- Goose            0.80%
- Raven            10.0%
- Hummingbird    20.0%

As a general rule, the larger the species of bird or mammal, the slower the heart rate.

Smaller birds have relatively larger hearts and faster heart rates than larger birds. The rate also tends to be lower for larger species.

**Heart Rates of Different Species at Rest (Per Minute)**
- Clam         2–20
- Elephant     25–40
- Horse        25–40
- Turkey       43
- Human        55–80
- Hare         64–200
- Rat          300–500
- Crow         342
- R            570

Great variations exist, depending on the age and fitness of the individual in each species.

## THE ANATOMY OF THE HUMAN HEART

### Syncytia of the Heart

The heart is the strongest, continuously working organ in the human body. The heart muscle contracts between 60 and 75 times each minute.

The heart is made of a unique muscle tissue that is unlike other muscle tissues in the body. The heart tissue is not made up of neatly packaged cells; instead, it is made up of a large mass of multi-nucleated protoplasm. In other words, the individual cellular divisions are missing among the community of cells that work together in heart tissue. This special type of tissue is called a **syncytium**.

The human heart is organized into two major syncytia, or two communities. Each community of the heart has its own electrical system that makes it self-stimulating or independent of the body. The syncytia are controlled by the electrical stimulators called **nodes**. One community is the atrial syncytium, which forms the upper part of the heart. The atria collect blood from the body and the lungs in two waiting rooms or chambers. The other community, the ventricular syncytium, is larger. It is located below (inferior to) the atria. The ventricles of the heart collect blood from each of the waiting chambers (atria) and pump it out of the heart. The ventricular syncytium has two chambers.
One chamber (the one on the right) will pump blood out to the lungs; the other (the one on the left) will pump blood out to the entire body. Therefore, each community has two chambers.

NOTES

Cardiac muscles are found in communities called **syncytia**.

### Chambers of the Heart

The heart has a total of four rooms or chambers. Each chamber of the heart has an entrance and exit, which are controlled by valves. Valves are flaps of thin tissue that control the flow of the blood by preventing it from going backward. The chambers are named as follows

*Heart Chambers*

| Chamber | Place | Function |
|---|---|---|
| Left atrium | Top left | Receives blood from the lungs |
| Right atrium | Top right | Receives blood from the entire body |
| Left ventricle | Bottom left | Sends blood to the entire body |
| Right ventricle | Bottom right | Sends blood directly to the lungs |

**Linings of the Heart**

The heart tissue is made up of several linings and layers. The smooth inner lining of the heart is called the **endocardium**. The endocardium provides a smooth surface for blood cells to slide through. The outer layer of the heart is called the **epicardium**. This is a smooth, tough, protective layer on the outside of the heart. Between the inner and outer linings is the strong cardiac muscle that is called the myocardium. The heart is contained in a separate sac of fluid for protection and for reduced friction as it works. The sac in which the heart is contained is called the **pericardium**.

**Valves of the Heart**

Valves of the heart work like trap doors that open in one direction but not the other. Valves open only in one direction in order to control the flow of blood. There are two types of valves in the heart.

Two **semilunar valves** are found between the left ventricle and the aorta, as well as between the right ventricle and the pulmonary artery.

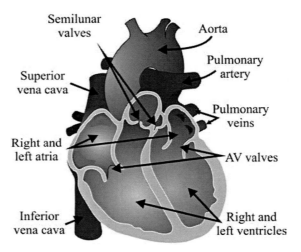

Two **atrioventricular valves** are found between the atria and the ventricles. The **bicuspid,** or **mitral valve** (named after a bishop's hat), is found between the left atrium and the left ventricle. The weaker tricuspid valve is found on the right side between the right atrium and the right ventricle. Small protruding muscles that are found inside of the ventricles operate these valves. These tiny protruding muscles are called **papillary muscles**. The valves are attached to these muscles by little string-like tissue called **chordae tendineae**.

## FUNCTION OF THE HEART

### Heart Rate

The heart rate is determined by the number of times the heart beats in one minute. The heart rate of an average adult is 60–75 beats per minute. An athlete will have a slower heart rate when that person is at rest. Athletes tend to have stronger hearts than a non-athlete. An athlete may have a heart rate as low as 45–50 beats per minute. This is because their hearts are more efficient and thus need to beat less often (slower rate) in order to deliver the same amount of blood to the body.

The heart rate of babies is much faster, between 120 to 140 contractions per minute. The weak heart of the infant must beat faster to move blood. There are many factors that affect the heart rate at a particular moment, such as exercise, emotional stress, sleep, body temperature, food, hormones, drugs, alcohol, and other chemicals in the blood.

### Stroke Volume (SV)

Stroke volume refers to the amount of blood that one contraction of the ventricle sends out to the body through the large artery called the **aorta**. It may also be used to refer to the volume of blood moving through the right ventricle and the pulmonary artery. A larger heart, with a larger left ventricle, will send out more blood per beat than a smaller heart.

The average heart pumps out 70-80 mL of blood to the aorta with each contraction.

Stroke volume will also depend on how much blood enters the ventricle in each beat and how much is left in the ventricle after the heart contracts.

### Cardiac Output (CO)

Cardiac output takes into account the heart rate and the stroke volume. Cardiac output refers to the amount of blood that is pumped out of the heart in one minute. If 80 mL are pumped out in one beat, and the heart beats at 70 beats per minute, the cardiac output would be calculated as follows:

Heart Rate × Stroke Volume = Cardiac Output
80 mL × 70 beats/minute = 5 600 mL/min
5 600 mL/min = 5.6 litres/min

At rest, an average human has a cardiac output of 5–6 litres/minute. During heavy exercise, the cardiac output can increase to 30–35 litres/minute. In order to get such an incredible increase in cardiac output, both the stroke volume and the heart rate increase during rigorous exercise.

### The Pacemaker

The heart has the unique ability of being independent of the nervous system. Almost all the organs of the body require instructions from the nervous system or the endocrine system in order to function in a regular fashion. The heart has its own nervous system of sorts and is therefore considered 'self stimulating'. In fact, the heart can taken out of the body and will still beat on its own and at the proper rate if it is kept moist with the correct fluids and salts.

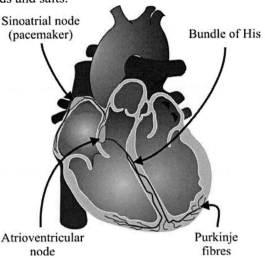

The main regulator or pacemaker of the heart is called the **sinoatrial node (SA node)**. This is a special area on the top right atrium that is able to develop an electrical charge that will then spread over the atrial syncytium and cause it to contract as a unit. Once this occurs, a sub-station called the **atrioventricular node (AV node)** at the border of the right atrium and the right ventricle detects the contraction. After a slight pause, it develops an electrical charge (**depolarization**) of its own. This charge is then passed through a bundle of conductive fibres called the **bundle of His** and distributed throughout the ventricles by smaller conductive fibres (called **purkinje fibres**) in the myocardium of the ventricles.

These microscopic fibres of the ventricles are able to quickly conduct an action potential (a nerve-like, electro-chemical impulse) in the heart so that all of the cells of the ventricle contract together.

### The Electrocardiogram

The charging and recharging of the tissue can be measured with a special machine that is called an **electrocardiogram (ECG)**. In the diagram of a normal electrocardiogram reading, the first wave, called the **P-wave**, indicates that the SA node is stimulated and becoming *depolarized*. The impulse spreads over the atria. The **QRS wave** then indicates that the AV node is stimulated or depolarized and that an impulse is beginning to spread over the ventricles. It is a much larger wave because the ventricles are much larger. The **T-wave** indicates that the ventricles have contracted and are preparing for **repolarization** (recharging) of the AV node, which has just discharged.

The atrium also needs to repolarize (recharge) and 'exhibits' a wave to indicate this; however, the QRS wave drowns out the appearance of this smaller wave.

**The Self-Regulated Electrochemical Impulse System of the Heart**
The heart pumps in a cycle of filling, contracting, and relaxing.
- The left and right atria fill.
- Both left and right atria contract at the same time, moving blood into the ventricles.
- The left and right ventricles fill while the atria relax.
- The left and right ventricles contract. As this occurs, the bicuspid and tricuspid valves snap shut. The blood is pushed out of the ventricles through the semilunar valves of the aorta and the pulmonary artery.
- Ventricular relaxation now occurs as the semilunar valves close so that the blood does not wash back into the relaxed ventricles.

**Heart Sounds:  Lub–Dub**
The heart muscle is a quiet machine; however, it has noisy valves. When the valves open, there is no sound, but when they slam shut, a distinctive sound is created.
LUB is the low-pitched booming sound caused by the snapping shut of the A-V valves (bicuspid and tricuspid). At the same time, the left and right ventricles contract, and the valves close in order to prevent the blood from backwashing into the atria. The LUB is a *systole sound* because it is created when the ventricles are contracting.

DUB is slightly higher-pitched and quicker than the LUB. It is a short and sharp sound. The sound is caused by the snapping shut of the semilunar valves (the valves that control the flow of blood into the aorta and the pulmonary artery). At the same time, the left and right ventricles relax and the semilunar valves close in order to prevent backwash from the aorta and the pulmonary artery into the ventricles. The DUB is a *diastole sound* because it is created when the ventricles relax.

A stethoscope is used to listen to the sounds of the heart. The sounds of the individual valves can be heard by placing the stethoscope at different locations on the chest.
Murmurs are caused by small amounts of blood backwashing into the atrium because the A-V valves have not closed properly. Usually murmurs are found in the mitral valve (bicuspid). A patient can survive with a murmur, but circulation is less efficient. That being said, not all murmurs indicate valve problems.

**Blood Vessels**
Blood is carried through tubes, or vessels, in the body. There are two different types of vessels that carry blood throughout the body.
A strong muscular vessel that carries blood away from the heart is called an **artery**. A softer and thinner vessel that carries blood toward the heart is called a **vein**.

The main purpose of the arteries and veins is to move fluids and blood cells through the body as they are needed.

There are many differences between arteries and veins. These differences are listed in the chart that follows.

**The Major Differences Between Arteries and Veins**

| Arteries | Veins |
|---|---|
| White colour | Bluish red colour |
| Carry blood away from the heart | Carry blood into the heart |
| Strong, thick, and muscular walls | Weak, thin, and non-muscular walls |
| Made up of three layers | Made up of three layers |
| Contain blood at high pressure (60 kPa) | Contain blood at low pressure (0–1.3 kPa |
| Have a pulse | Have no pulse |
| Carry bright red, oxygenated blood, except in the pulmonary artery | Carry non-oxygenated, bluish blood, except in the pulmonary vein |
| Contain no valves, as blood pressure is high enough and blood moves in one direction | Contain valves because pressure is low (these valves depend on skeletal muscle movement in order to work) |
| Are found deep below the surface | Many are found near the surface |

**Major Arteries and Veins of the Human Body**

| Artery | Location |
|---|---|
| Aorta | Largest artery that leads out of the heart (has a very high blood pressure) |
| Radial artery | Found in the wrist |
| Carotid artery | Left and right side of the neck |
| Dorsalis pedis | Artery in foot |
| Coronary artery | Small blood vessels in the heart tissue that supply blood for the metabolic needs of the heart's myocardium |

| Vein | Location |
|---|---|
| Superior vena cava | Large vein that leads into the heart from upper body (has a very low blood pressure) |
| Inferior vena cava | Large vein that leads into the heart with blood from lower body |
| External jugular vein | Large vein in neck |
| Coronary vein (coronary sinus) | Vein in the heart tissue itself that drains blood from the tissue of the heart |

### The Dimensions of Blood Vessels in the Human Body

| Vessel | Radius of Vessel (cm) | Number of Vessels in Body | Area of Vessel (cm²) | Average Blood Pressure (kPa) | Wall Thickness (cm) |
|---|---|---|---|---|---|
| Aorta | 1.25 | 1 | 4.5 | 14.7/10.0– 16.0/10.7 | 0.2 |
| Arteries | 0.2 | 159 | 20 | 12.0/8.0– 14.7–10.0 | 0.1 |
| Arterioles | $1.5 \times 10^{-3}$ | $5.7 \times 10^{7}$ | 400 | 4.7–8.0 | $2 \times 10^{-3}$ |
| Capillaries | $3 \times 10^{-4}$ | $1.6 \times 10^{10}$ | 4 500 | 4.7–1.3 | $1 \times 10^{-4}$ |
| Venules | $1 \times 10^{-3}$ | $1.3 \times 10^{9}$ | 4 000 | 1.3–0 | $2 \times 10^{-4}$ |
| Veins | 0.25 | 200 | 40 | 0 | 0.05 |
| Vena cava | 1.5 | 1 | 18 | 0 | 0.15 |

Data (except average pressures) taken from *Science*, August 31,1990, Vol. 249, pg. 993.

## MAJOR ARTERIES IN THE HUMAN BODY

1. Aorta
2. Carotid artery
3. Brachial artery
4. Descending aorta
5. Radial artery
6. Iliac artery
7. Femoral artery
8. Dorsalis pedis

### Pressure Points and Elevation

The lesion of an artery can be very serious, as it contains blood at high pressure. If a patient has a wound, it is important to slow down the loss of blood. There are major arteries in areas of the body that act as intersections of blood flow to the limbs. If there is severe bleeding in the arms or legs, you can slow down the loss of blood by elevating the wound and applying pressure to these areas. There are two major pressure point areas.

The brachial artery is a major artery located in the arm under the bicep muscle. The right and left external iliac arteries are major arteries located in the groin (between the legs and pelvic cavity).

### Blood Vessels and Their Pressures

*Aorta*

The aorta is the largest artery in the body. Blood moves through at 1.6 km an hour with pressure that fluctuates. The strongest pressure in the aorta is when the left ventricle of the heart is contracting. This strong pressure is called the **systolic blood pressure** and is typically measured at 60 kPa.

A weaker pressure is found in the aorta when the ventricle is relaxing and filling up. This weaker pressure is called the **diastolic blood pressure** and is measured at 10.7 kPa

NOTES

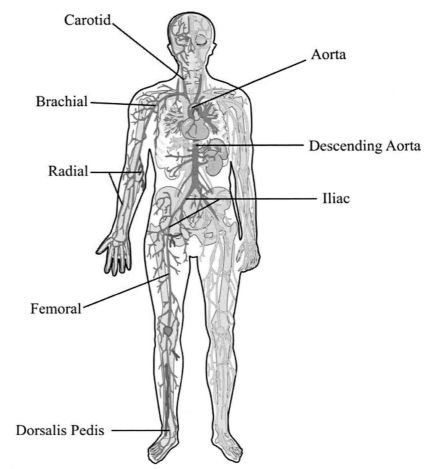

*Arteries*

The arteries carry oxygenated blood away from the aorta to the arterioles. Arteries have high pressure. The systolic pressure is about 14.7 kPa, and the diastolic pressure is about 10 kPa or lower.

*Arterioles*

The arterioles are no thicker than human hair and carry oxygenated blood away from the arteries into the capillaries. They are further away from the heart and smaller in diameter than the arteries, with a blood pressure of about 4.7–6.0 kPa. Because the arterioles are further from the heart, they are not affected by each contraction of the ventricles and thus have no systolic pressure.

*Capillaries*

The capillaries are tiny connecting bridges between arterioles and venules. Blood fluids exchange with fluids from the tissues of the body and the 'used', deoxygenated blood is sent back to the heart. Pressure starts at 4.7 kPa; by the time it gets to the end of the capillary, the pressure is 1.3 kPa. Capillaries are microscopic leaky blood vessels made of cells that are able to perform **pinocytosis**. Some fluids from the blood are drawn into capillary cells by pinocytosis and then moved across the capillary cells in a vesicle. It is finally released from the other end into tissue fluids.

## Capillaries

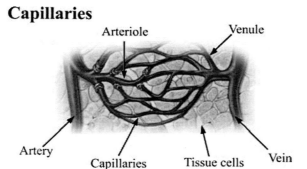

The capillaries allow gases and fluids to leak between the capillary cells and into the tissues. However, red blood cells are too big and rigid to move out of the capillaries. The capillaries allow only one red blood cell at a time through the centres of networking tunnels. Often, the RBCs will have to flatten out in order to get through the centres of the capillary tubes. There are about 99 000 km of capillaries in the average human body. That is enough to stretch around the world 2.5 times. Capillaries are no further than 50 microns from every cell.

Extra fat cells in the body need to be supplied with capillaries. For every pound of fat, there are over 200 miles (330 km) of capillaries. There are tiny muscles that control the flow of the blood in capillary beds, which are called **precapillary sphincters**. They can open and close the entrances into the capillary beds. During sleep, 10% of the capillaries in the body shut down for the night.

*Venules*

The venules carry deoxygenated blood back to the veins. They are further away from the heart and have a lower blood pressure of 0.7–1.3 kPa. They are larger in diameter (about the size of a human hair) and fewer in numbers than capillaries.

*Veins*

The veins carry deoxygenated blood back to the vena cava. They are further away from the heart and have no blood pressure (0 kPa). Veins are larger in diameter and fewer in numbers than venules. They rely on the contraction of skeletal muscles to provide the pressure to move the blood.

*Vena Cava*

This is the largest vein in the body. It takes blood from all of the body and dumps it into the right atrium of the heart. It also has a pressure equal to 0 kPa.

## BLOOD PRESSURE

Blood pressure is the measure of the force of blood in the circulatory vessels of the body. If the force of blood gets too high, it can rupture some of the vessels in the brain or heart. If the force of the blood is too low, your brain or heart can starve. Blood pressure can be increased or decreased by your body to meet ongoing demands. If your body wants more pressure, it 'tightens' the blood vessels, and if it wants less pressure it will 'loosen the tubes. It is similar to placing your thumb over the end of a garden hose in order to increase the water pressure.

Your kidneys can also regulate blood pressure. They can add more water to your blood if the pressure is too low, or they can remove water from if the pressure is too high. Your heart can also increase or decrease its output as needed.

The pressure of the blood in your arteries is directly influenced by five factors.

### Elasticity of the Artery

Arteries that are flexible and pliable maintain a lower blood pressure. Lower blood pressure usually means less wear and tear on your organs. High blood pressure is normally accompanied with the hardening of the arteries due to a high cholesterol diet (too much red meat and greasy foods, for example). Cholesterol can be reduced in two ways. The first way is by limiting the intake of fatty foods, and the second way is by exercising.

### Diameter of the Artery

The diameter of the arteries can cause higher or lower blood pressure. The wider the artery, the lower the blood pressure. Once again cholesterol and other fats can build up on the inner lining of the arteries and cause them to clog up and become narrower, which results in higher blood pressure.

A vasodilator causes arteries to expand as a result of autonomic nervous stimulation. A vasoconstrictor causes arteries to become constricted and narrower, which is also the result of nervous stimulation.

Hormones can affect the diameter of the arteries. The hormone produced in stressful situations causes the blood vessels to constrict. Smoking and drinking coffee artificially cause the release of the stress hormone **adrenalin**, which causes vasoconstriction and higher blood pressure.

Dr. Susan Jacobs-Kaufman from the University of Alberta has studied the relationship between hormones and blood pressure, as it relates to pregnant women. Her research is valuable because approximately 5% of all pregnant women exhibit high blood pressure during their pregnancy.

### Viscosity of the Blood

Thicker blood tends to resist normal flow. Blood is normally about five times thicker than water because of the blood cells and proteins that circulate in the plasma. The resistance to flow causes the heart to work harder; it also increases blood pressure. Certain diseases such as leukemia, a white blood cell disorder, can cause a change in the viscosity of the blood.

### Heart Rate

The speed at which the heart works also affects blood pressure. As your heart rate increases when you exercise, your blood pressure will also increase. When you sleep or relax, your heart rate will decrease, which helps lower blood pressure. An average heart rate should be between 65 and 75 beats per minute. The better the physical shape you are in, the lower your heart rate and blood pressure will be.

### Volume of Blood

A dramatic change in the volume of blood can cause a change in blood pressure. For example, if you have an accident and lose blood, your blood pressure will decrease. If it is too low, blood is unable to get to the brain and you may pass out or go into shock. If drinking fluids increases the blood volume, then your blood pressure may also increase.

### Blood Pressure Sensors

Specific centres of the medulla oblongata in the lowest region of the brain receive information from three different types of receptors. Receptors sense, detect, or receive information about the blood in arteries located throughout the body.
They then relay the information to a nerve that carries the information to the brain.

*Baroreceptors*

Baroreceptors are located in the carotid artery and the aorta. They receive information regarding pressure. These receptors are sensitive to the stretching of the arteries. Arteries will stretch more with increased power. Baroreceptors also can be called **stretch receptors**.

*Chemoreceptors*

Chemoreceptors are located in the carotid artery, the aorta, and the hypothalamus of the brain. They receive information regarding the concentration of chemicals such as hydrogen ions and carbon dioxide in the blood.

*Osmoreceptors*

Osmoreceptors monitor the amount of water that is in the blood. They are also located in the hypothalamus.

### The Blood Pressure Control Centre in the Brain

The medulla oblongata, a section of the brain stem, controls heart rate and blood pressure. It controls blood pressure with the help of three different areas of the medulla oblongata. The three centres in the medulla oblongata are described below.

### Cardiac Centre of the Medulla Oblongata

The cardiac centre sends signals to control the heart rate. If the heart rate is increased, then blood pressure will also increase.

Increased excitement or stress leads to increased blood pressure. Stimulation causes special nerve fibres (sympathetic nervous control) to release a special chemical called **epinephrine,** or **adrenalin**.
These chemicals stimulate automatic body functions including the rhythm at which the SA node (pacemaker) stimulates the atrial syncytium.
These nerve fibres increase both heart rate and blood pressure.

Increased blood pressure needs to be reduced sooner or later.
Baroreceptors will send information to the cardiac centre, which will then send impulses to the heart. This causes the heart rate to slow down (parasympathetic nervous control).

### Vasomotor Centre of the Medulla Oblongata

The vasomotor centre sends signals to the muscles that control the diameter of blood vessels. If the diameter of the blood vessels is decreased or constricted, then the pressure will also increase.

When blood pressure is too high, baroreceptors will send information to the vasomotor centre indicating that blood pressure is high. This can be very dangerous because it causes wear and tear on the circulatory and other body systems.
The depressor area of the vasomotor centre turns on and will inhibit constriction of the blood vessels so that they loosen up. This loosening will reduce the pressure in the blood vessels. The loosening and widening of the blood vessels is called **vasodilation**. The vasomotor centre will also cause the heart to slow down (to be inhibited), which helps lower blood pressure.

When $CO_2$ is in high concentration, chemoreceptors will send the information to the vasomotor centre.

This may be an indication that the body has begun to exercise and has collected too much poisonous $CO_2$. As well, the exercising muscle needs more blood flow and a higher blood pressure to supply the oxygen, glucose, and salts that it needs to work.

To meet the needs of the body, the pressor area of the vasomotor area turns on and stimulates the constriction of blood vessels, which causes them to tighten so that blood pressure can be increased. This is called **vasoconstriction**. Increased blood pressure will move the $CO_2$ toward the lungs at a faster rate. The centre will also cause the heart to speed up.

When blood pressure is too low, which can occur during hemorrhaging, the depressor area of the vasomotor centre will turn off and/or the pressor area will turn on. At the same time, the pressor area will tighten up the vessels. This causes the blood pressure to go up again.

The depressor area loosens up the vessels and lowers pressure.
The pressor area tightens up the vessels and raises pressure.

### Respiratory Centre of the Medulla Oblongata
The respiratory centre is part of the medulla that controls the rate and depth of breathing. It is indirectly related to blood pressure because often, as blood pressure increases to remove wastes produced during cellular respiration, the breathing rate will also have to increase to handle the extra workload.

## THE IMPORTANCE OF BLOOD
Blood has a variety of functions. Blood cells are important for moving oxygen and carbon dioxide between the lungs and the body tissues. Blood fluids transport food, hormones, water, heat, and waste products throughout the body.

A special variety of blood cells defend the body against bacterial infections, viral infections, and other foreign particles. Yet another cellular component of blood protects the body from excessive bleeding by forming clots.

### The Components of Blood
The blood is composed of four basic components: red blood cells, white blood cells, plasma, and platelets.

*Red Blood Cells - Erythrocytes*

Red blood cells (**erythrocytes**) can be considered the working class of the blood, as they work to deliver oxygen to the tissues of the body.

They make up about 45% of the total blood volume. They are simple cells that have no nucleus in their adult stage. Their average life span is 120 days. RBCs are produced in the bone marrow at a rate of 2 200 000 each second.

The bone marrow needs a rich supply of vitamin B12, iron, and folic acid in order to produce red blood cells. These components are normally supplied in a healthy, balanced diet.

Iron is important to produce the oxygen-carrying heme pigment that lodges a protein molecule called hemoglobin. Each blood cell can contain 300 million molecules of hemoglobin. RBCs have thin centres in order to expose the hemoglobin and allow for oxygen to diffuse easily. They are disk-shaped, so they can easily 'roll' through the capillaries.

*Plasma*

Plasma makes up about 55% of the blood volume. It is a pale yellow-coloured fluid that contains most of the nutrients and chemical needs of the body. Plasma does not include the cellular components of blood, such as red blood cells, white blood cells, and platelets. Cellular components will circulate with blood plasma, but are not considered to be a part of plasma.

Serum is the same yellow-coloured fluid as plasma except there are no clotting proteins in serum. Serum is the type of fluid that one could extract from body tissues.

**COMPONENTS OF BLOOD PLASMA**
- Water (hydrogen ions and hydroxyl ions)
- Nutrients (glucose and amino acids)
- Gases ($O_2$ and waste gas such as $CO_2$)
- Proteins
- Albumin (for transport)
- Fibrinogen (for clotting)
- Globulin (for antibodies)
- Prothrombin (for clotting)
- Ions (sodium, chlorine, and potassium)
- Hormones (insulin, androgens, and others)
- Vitamins and minerals

**Platelets (little plates) and Thrombocyte (platelet)**

Thrombocytes are commonly called **platelets**. Platelets are the smallest cells in the blood sample and are actually fragments of larger cells. Platelets aid in the formation of blood clots. They survive for around 10 days and then expire. About 200 billion new fragments are made each day in the bone marrow.

When there is a lesion, platelets rush to the broken tissue. The damaged tissue releases a substance that attracts the platelets. They then swell and stick to the tissue. The swollen platelets attract even more platelets; they all swell and stick together to form a plug. This process is referred to as the *extrinsic mechanism of blood clotting*.

Swollen platelets often break near the cut or damaged tissue and release hormones. One hormone (serotonin) causes the vessels around the cut to constrict. Other enzymes, such as thromboplastin, react with other proteins to speed up the clotting. A dry clot exposed to air is called a scab.

Thromboplastin is an important enzyme that works with clotting factors released by the platelets. These chemicals activate the plasma protein **prothrombin**. When prothrombin is activated, it converts into a highly active form called **thrombin**. Thrombin in turn reacts with another globular plasma protein called **fibrinogen**.

Fibrinogen globular plasma protein found in blood plasma aids in blood clotting. Fibrinogen converts into a strand-like protein called **fibrin** when all the other clotting factors are available. Fibrinogen also thickens the blood, as it is a colloid molecule.

The newly formed molecule called fibrin is a fibrous strand-like protein that is manufactured at the site of the injury. This protein is able to weave itself into a net that catches other blood cells and clotting substances. Fibrin strands create a dam in the flow of blood, which is commonly called a **clot**. This chemical process of clot formations is referred to as the *intrinsic mechanism of blood clotting*.

Calcium and vitamin K are very important for clot formation. The availability of these agents or chemicals in the blood has a direct effect on the ability of thrombin and fibrinogen to react and form the fibrin. Without calcium and vitamin K, no clots would form, and the person with the injury would continue to bleed.

## WHITE BLOOD CELLS – LEUKOCYTES

Leukocytes or white blood cells are the 'fighting elite'. These killer cells are important in defending the body against infections and foreign substances. Most white blood cells attack and eat a foreign substance through the process of phagocytosis. Some white blood cells produce proteins called **antibodies** that bind to foreign substances and render them useless. Still other white blood cells eject chemical substances that kill bacteria or viruses.

Granular
(polymorphonuclear
= 'many-shaped' nucleus)

Even though white blood cells are very large, they can squeeze out of the capillaries and hide in your tissue waiting for foreign invaders.
The process of changing the shape of the white blood cell so that it is able to squeeze out of the capillary is called **diapedesis**.

There are many different types of white blood cells, yet there are fewer white blood cells than red blood cells. There is only one white blood cell for every 600 red blood cells. In fact, white blood cells make up the smallest component of the total blood volume. They are nonetheless very potent and important. All WBCs are produced in the bone marrow. Most WBCs, except another type called the **monocytes**, live anywhere from one hour to four days.

**Two Groups of White Blood Cells.**
The most abundant type of granular white blood cell is the **neutrophil**, which makes up 62% of total WBCs. Neutrophils are fast-acting phagocytes. **Eosinophils** make up a much smaller portion of white blood cells (2.3%), but are very important because they fight allergic reactions. A total of 0.1 to 0.4% of white blood cells are **basophils**. These cells fight allergic reactions in the tissues and have an anticoagulant called **heparin** that prevents the over-clotting of the blood. Heparin is found abundantly in the liver.

Lymphocytes comprise approximately 30% of white blood cells. There are 10 000 to 100 000 different types of lymphocytes that hide in the lymph glands, waiting to combat 'foreign invasions'. They wait and reproduce when needed. They also control the body's immune system.

There are two groups of lymphocytes: T cells (Thymus cells) and B cells (Bursa cells). Both of these cells are produced by the bone marrow; however, they mature in different locations and function differently.

**The Process of Diapedesis and Phagocytosis by White Blood Cells**
T cells mature in the thymus gland of the human body. These cells will rapidly reproduce and work to kill an invading organism by having the correct antibody embedded on their plasma membranes. The T cells will come into direct contact with the invading organisms.

Dr. Linda M. Pilarski from the University of Alberta is currently an expert in T cell development. She studies the specific roles of the human thymus gland and T cells in certain types of cancer and other immunodeficiency diseases.

Agranular
(mononuclear = one
nucleus)

B cells mature in some unknown location in the human body. The B cells get their name because in chickens, they are found maturing in lymph tissue called *bursa of fabricus*. B cells produce and secrete antibodies against an invading antigen. The B cells then do not have to come in direct contact with the invading organism. Much is still unknown about these B cells.

Another type of agranular white blood cell is the monocyte, which makes up 5.3% of all WBCs. These cells are slow acting. They also clean up cellular debris and become giants, swelling up to five times larger than normal at the site of an injury. As monocytes become active and swell up, they are called **macrophages**. Through the process of phagocytosis, these cells can eat up to 100 bacteria at a time and can even eat small parasites. Although they can live for years, they die quickly in battle.

**Monocytes** also work together with lymphocytes. The monocyte will activate or initiate the reproduction of the lymphocytes. After it is activated, a lymphocyte bears or secretes the antibodies that are best able to combat the antigen of the invader (infection).

A drug-induced disease called **agranulocytosis** involves a decrease of these granular white blood cells (**leukocytes**). This disease is accompanied by a high fever and damaged mucous membranes (called **lesions**).

### White Blood Cells

| Cell Name | Percent of WBC | Functions |
|---|---|---|
| Monocyte | 5.3% | Removes cellular debris by phagocytosis |
| Lymphocyte | 30% | Antibody production |
| Neutrophil | 62% | Fights infections via phagocytosis |
| Eosinophil | 2.3% | Fights parasites and allergies |
| Basophil | 0.4% | Anti-clotting and combats allergies and inflammation |

## BLOOD TYPES AND BLOOD TRANSFUSIONS

Dr. Karl Landsteiner, a physician from Venice, first discovered human blood groups in 1900. He reported that red blood cells could be classified into four basic blood types (Type A, Type B, Type O, and Type AB). These blood types are unique and tend to cause difficulties in blood transfusions.

When a large volume of blood is lost, the body will immediately respond by conserving water to restore the volume. It may take six to eight weeks, however, to get the red blood cell count back to normal.

If more than 40% (more than 1.5–2 litres) of the blood is lost, it is traumatic for the body. Organs will begin to starve and the brain may not get the supplies that it needs. This is because the blood pressure drops dramatically, and the body is unable to compensate. A blood transfusion is usually needed in this case.

NOTES

Many people died from blood loss during conflicts prior to the 20th century. Desperate attempts were made to transfuse blood into injured military and civilian casualties. First, syringes were used to take blood from donors and inject it into injured patients. However, it became evident that not just anyone's blood could be used for a particular patient. Blood from some donors would sometimes clump when added to a patient. This clumping (called **agglutination)** was obvious, as a patient's blood seemed to curdle in its rejection to the foreign blood that was being transfused. However, in other cases, agglutination did not occur.

In order to do a blood transfusion, doctors realized that they first needed to mix the blood of the donor and the patient outside of the body. If it clumped (agglutinated), then the donor blood could not be used.

The methods of transfusions eventually improved. Syringes were very inefficient because they could draw blood fast enough from the donors. Special suction devices and bottles to collect the blood were developed. Pumps were also added to the system.

An understanding of these different blood types progressed during the First World War. It was determined that blood cells have uniquely different identifying proteins on the cell's membrane. These special identifying proteins that distinguish different types of cells are called **antigens**. Antigens can cause an immune response to occur if a foreign antigen is introduced into a body. Blood antigens are specifically called **agglutinogens**. The lymphatic system of the body will produce a protein that can combat the foreign antigens. This protein is an **antibody**. Antibodies are usually transported in the blood plasma and are specifically called **agglutinins**.

It was determined that A blood has an A-type antigen on its cell membrane. B blood has a B-type antigen on its cell membrane. AB blood has A and B type proteins on its membrane. Blood type O has no antigens on its membrane.

Antigens are not the only concern in blood transfusions. Transfusions are also subject to viral infections that may lead to serious complications or death.

**Type O Blood - Universal Donor**

Because O blood has no antigens, it can be given to anyone without worry of triggering an immune response. As a result, a person with type O blood is considered a **universal donor**.

On the other hand, a person with type O blood will react to any type of blood antigen that is received. This is true because all blood antigens are foreign to O blood. Type O blood can only receive O blood from donors. The antibodies of the type O patient reject all other types of blood. Blood type O is the most common blood type (45%) and is very useful to the Red Cross, as it can be given to almost all patients.

**Type AB Blood - Universal Recipient**

Type AB blood cells have both A and B antigens on their membranes. As a result, the body that has this blood produces none of its own blood antibodies. If it did produce antibodies, then its own blood would agglutinate. Because an individual that has AB blood produces no blood antibodies, it can receive blood from anyone without an immune reaction. As a result, a person with type AB blood is considered a **universal recipient**.

AB blood cannot be given to anyone because it has both antigens and will evoke an immune reaction in anyone who receives the AB blood. AB blood is very rare among Caucasians. AB blood accounts for 4% of the North American population.

**Type A Blood**

Type A blood cells have the A antigen on their cell membranes. Therefore, an individual with this blood will not, therefore, produce A antibodies. The individual's immune system would produce B antibodies that would react against invading B or AB blood cells, which causes agglutination.

An individual with A blood cells can receive transfusions only from A and type-O donors.

Type A is the second most common blood type among Caucasians. It accounts for 41% of the population.

**Type B Blood**

Type B blood cells have the B antigen on their cell membranes. An individual with this blood will not, therefore, produce any B antibodies. However, the individual's immune system produces A antibodies that would react against invading A or AB blood cells, which causes agglutination.

An individual with B blood cells can receive transfusions only from donors with blood type B and O.

B blood type is the second least common blood type among Caucasians. It accounts for 10% of the population.

**Rh Factor**

Rh factor is a term for another important antigen found on some blood cells. Rh stands for *rhesus*, so named because researchers first isolated the antigen in the rhesus monkey. Not all people are born with this antigen on their red blood cells. If the blood cells have the antigen, the blood is labelled **Rh-positive**. Blood cells that do not have the antigen are labelled **Rh-negative**.

NOTES

In blood transfusions, it is important that doctors match the Rh factor. If a person has Rh-negative blood, they must have an Rh-negative blood transfusion. If this person gets Rh-positive blood by mistake, their body's immune system will prepare antibodies that will combat the newly transfused blood and cause it to agglutinate or clump.

People with Rh-positive blood have it a little easier. They do not produce antibodies against the Rh factor. Therefore, they can take blood from Rh-positive donors or Rh-negative donors without any problem.

Rh factor is a serious concern for couples wishing to have children. If the mother is Rh-positive, there is no concern even if the baby is Rh-negative, because the mother cannot produce the harmful antibodies. The baby's blood cannot harm the mother because it does not mix with the mother's and because it is not yet able to produce antibodies against the mother's blood.
There is a concern if the mother has Rh-negative blood and produces Rh antibodies because there is a possibility that these antibodies could cross the placenta and cause agglutination of the fetus's blood. If the fetus survives, it is born with a blue colour, as its blood will not carry oxygen properly. This condition is called **erythroblastosis fetalis**.

Erythroblastosis fetalis will not occur in the first pregnancy because the mother would not have produced any antibodies against the baby's blood. There is no mixing of the mother's and baby's blood thanks to the design of the placenta. Fluids and nutrients can cross the placenta membrane, but blood cells cannot.

When the mother gives birth in the first pregnancy, her placenta rips and the baby's blood mixes with her own blood. When they mix, the mother becomes sensitized and begins to produce antibodies. This will not harm the baby because the baby is already born. It also will not harm the mother because the mother has Rh-negative blood. The problem arises in the second pregnancy. If the fetus is Rh-positive, the mother's antibodies that were produced during labor in the first pregnancy can endanger the fetus in the second pregnancy as antibodies pass through the placenta.
The antibodies thus attack the Rh-positive blood of the fetus.

Doctors can treat this problem by injecting the mother with a competitive inhibitor that will inactivate the fetal antigens that entered her body. They must do this within 72 hours of the delivery of the baby in the first pregnancy. This must be done within this time limit so that she does not have a chance to produce her own antibodies. Then, during the second pregnancy, the female will not have the antibodies that could harm the fetus.

**RED BLOOD CELL (ERYTHROCYTE) PRODUCTION, ERYTHROPOIESIS (EE-RITH-ROH-POY-EE-SIS)**

Erythropoiesis is the production of red blood cells. Red blood cells are produced in the bone marrow of bones such as the skull, ribs, and vertebrae. RBCs tend to live approximately 120 days and move through nearly 1 200 km of blood vessels during their lifetime. Every day, blood cells are destroyed as they travel and age. Their remains are collected by the spleen and the liver. Needless to say, the body's bones constantly need to produce red blood cells. Each second, they produce about 2 200 000 blood cells.

The speed at which the body makes RBCs can vary. The bone's marrow determines the speed according to the amount of oxygen that is supplied to the bones. If the bones are not getting enough oxygen, the bone marrow will step up RBC production.

Iron is a very important mineral that is required for the production of hemoglobin, which is part of the red blood cell. Vitamin B12 and folic acid are also important for the production of hemoglobin in red blood cells.

**Blood Reservoirs**

Blood is stored in the spleen and liver and released in case of an emergency such as a sudden loss of blood.

**Anemia**

Anemia is the lack of red blood cells or hemoglobin. One RBC can have up to 270 000 000 hemoglobin molecules in it. Each hemoglobin molecule can carry four molecules of oxygen. This makes the RBCs an efficient carrier of oxygen. Water could be used to carry oxygen; however, blood carries 70 times more oxygen than water can. An anemic person is usually tired and pale because not enough oxygen is being delivered to the cells to create ATP.

**Polycythemia**

Polycythemia (pol-ee-sy-thee-mee-uh) is the over-production of RBCs. Blood becomes thick and sticky. As a result, circulation becomes difficult. Polycythemia can be caused by a slower supply of blood to the bone marrow. Bones are thus 'fooled' into producing more cells than are actually needed.

**White Blood Cell (Leukocyte) Production**

All white blood cells are produced in bone marrow; however, some very important blood cells called lymphocytes mature and are stored in lymph tissue such as the thymus gland and in lymph nodes in the neck, under the arms, and in the groin area.

Production varies for WBCs as it does for RBCs. If there is an infection in the body, the number of neutrophils increases by nearly five times. Lymph nodes also swell as they actively produce more WBCs.

NOTES

Some types of cancer increase the production of WBCs without limit. The white blood cells will attack the body's own tissues. This disease is called **leukemia**.

### Capillary Fluid Exchange

Fluid has to move into and out of the capillaries in order to keep the surrounding tissues healthy (supplied with gases and nutrients). The exchange of body fluids between the body tissues and the blood stream is called **capillary fluid exchange**.

Red blood cells are not part of this exchange, as they stay within the capillaries. These cells are too large and inflexible to freely move between the interior of the capillary tube and the exterior tissues. The red blood cell, however, transports the important oxygen atoms that the tissues need; the cell must release the oxygen into the plasma before the plasma rushes back to the heart and lungs to pick up more oxygen. The fluid then moves out of the capillaries with the oxygen and delivers this important gas and other nutrients to the tissues.

Fluids move into and out of the capillaries with the help of two types of pressures. One type of pressure is caused by the heart pushing on the fluids in the blood vessels, which causes the fluids to be pushed out of the capillaries. This pressure is called **hydrostatic pressure**. The other type of pressure is the 'sucking' of fluid back into the capillaries as water moves from an area of high concentration in the tissues to an area of low concentration that now exists in the capillaries. This pressure is called **osmotic (oncotic) pressure**.

### Hydrostatic Pressure

Hydrostatic pressure is the 'pushing-out' pressure in the capillaries. Hydrostatic pressure is the blood pressure that is caused by the constant pumping of the heart. The pressure at the arterial end is about 4.7 kPa. This pressure will push the fluid out of the capillaries. By the time it reaches the venous end of the capillary, the pressure drops because of the resistance to flow. It drops to about 2.1 kPa.

### Osmotic Pressure

Osmotic pressure is the 'pulling-in pressure in the capillaries. Osmotic pressure is created by the *colloid suspension* (particulate materials or tiny solid particles floating in a fluid). Proteins that are floating in blood plasma create this osmotic pressure. This pressure draws extracellular fluid into the capillaries because of the movement of water from an area of high concentration to an area of low concentration. Water is in low concentration in the capillaries because of the colloid suspension; therefore, fluid moves in via osmosis. This pressure remains constant at about 3.3 kPa at both the arterial and venous ends of the capillaries.

### Pressures at the Arterial End of a Capillary

At the arterial end of the capillaries, there is a net pressure on the fluid pushing out of the capillaries at 1.3 kPa (net outward pressure). This is because fluid is being pushed out of the capillaries at 4.7 kPa into the surrounding tissue and because at the same time fluid is being reabsorbed back into the capillaries at only 3.3 kPa.

### Pressures at the Venous End of a Capillary

At the venous (vein) end of the capillaries there is a net pressure on the fluid pulling back into the capillaries of 1.2 kPa (net inward pressure) because 2.1 kPa pushes out into the surrounding tissue, and 3.3 kPa of pressure is being applied to the fluid going back into the capillaries.

### Overall Pressure Dynamics

The net outward pressure at the arterial end of the capillary is greater than the net inward pressure at the venous end. This means that there is a 'leak' in the capillaries. Overall, more fluid is pushed out than is reabsorbed.

With the net outward pressure being greater than the net inward pressure, more fluid is lost to the tissue than is reabsorbed to the blood stream. This difference is accounted for by the lymphatic system, which is also involved with body fluid circulation.

## LYMPHATIC SYSTEM

### Lymph

All body tissues need to be bathed in a fresh fluid that is rich in nutrients, minerals, vitamins, and salts. Tissues are not bathed in blood as many think they are. Instead, they are supplied with a constant fresh supply of clear plasma-like fluid from the blood.

The tissues of the body are constantly supplied with fresh fluid; however, more fluid leaves the blood capillaries than returns to them. This extra interstitial fluid called **lymph** is picked up at the capillary bed by blind-end lymph capillaries. Lymph is a clear, watery fluid that contains a special protein, white blood cells, and lipids that have been absorbed from the digestive system.

Lymph is transported in a completely different network of vessels that run parallel to the blood vessels. These lymph vessels are somewhat like veins in that they have valves.

The lymphatic system not only transports the extra fluids that are booted out of the capillaries but also other components. Lipids and proteins from the liver and intestine are added to the lymph. The system also adds a special type of white blood cells from structures called lymph nodes.

This cleansing fluid circulates in special lymph vessels that return it to the blood at two large draining areas in the left and right sides of the body. The upper left side and lower regions of the body drain lymph into the **great thoracic duct**, and the upper right side drains lymph into the right **lymphatic duct**. These ducts then drip the fluid back into the blood at special entry points of the subclavian veins and the left jugular vein. These veins are located in the neck and shoulder regions and are protected by the clavicle bone.

### Lymph Nodes

Lymphocytes (lymph cells) are added to the lymph fluid that circulates from the lymph nodes to the rest of the body. Lymph nodes or lymph glands are small oval or round bodies located on lymph vessels, which supply lymphocytes to lymph fluids. Lymphocytes are produced in bone marrow and are stored and possibly mature in the lymph nodes.

There are two types of lymphocytes. One type is called a B cell, and the other type is called a T cell. B cells are released from lymph glands throughout the body, and T cells are released from a special gland called the thymus gland. The lymph nodes also seem to contain a specialized cell called a **dendritic cell** that is involved in immune responses.

There are many lymph nodes throughout the body. There is a group of them under the jaw, under the arms, and in the groin area. They are also abundant in the intestinal area. The spleen and the tonsils are large collections of lymph nodes. Tonsils that are found in the pharynx region are called **adenoids**. The lymph nodes are located strategically to produce the white blood cells needed for certain areas of the body. The nodes in the groin area normally take care of infections in the legs or pelvic region. If an infection is present, the nodes will often swell.

Over 24 hours, 2–4 litres of lymph (interstitial) fluid circulates and is returned to the blood.

## CARDIOVASCULAR DISORDERS

### Edema

If the lymphatic system fails, fluid accumulates in the tissues and swelling occurs. Lymph vessels have valves for unidirectional flow and require muscular movement to move the fluid. Therefore, if muscles are not moved, fluid can collect in the tissues. This is an important consideration for those that are confined to a bed.

### Varicose Veins

Weak valves in the veins allow the blood to flow back, which causes it to collect in the distal regions of the vein. The extra pressure causes the walls to push out. The veins become over-stretched and lose their elasticity. Varicose veins can be caused by pregnancy and by standing for long periods of time. Hemorrhoids are a type of varicose vein in the anal area. They can be removed with a new technique called **cryosurgery** (freezing using liquid nitrogen).

### Hypertension

Hypertension is medical term for high blood pressure. Blood pressure of 18.7/12.0 kPa for extended periods of time can lead to heart failure, kidney damage, blockage, or rupture of a cerebral artery (stroke).

### Shock

Sudden emotional stimuli can cause the sympathetic division of the nervous system to be suppressed. As a result, blood pressure and heart rate will decrease as insufficient cardiac output results, a condition called **shock**. Patients in shock need to lie down with feet slightly elevated. They also should be kept warm. Decreased cardiac output can also be caused by an excessive loss of blood.

### Hemorrhage

A hemorrhage is a term that refers to the excessive loss of blood. Blood can be lost externally as you bleed from a bad cut or lesion, or it can be lost internally as blood vessels on the inside of the body are ruptured. The loss of blood lowers blood pressure and thus leads to the constriction of blood vessels. Shock can result. Internal hemorrhaging can cause shock as well. Coughed-up blood and blood in stool can be an indication of internal hemorrhaging. Internal hemorrhaging can also be detected by feeling the injured area for hard swelling (in areas that are normally soft).

### Stroke

A blockage (occlusion) or rupture of a blood vessel in the brain is called a **stroke**. A stroke can cause death or paralysis. Occlusions may often occur in the carotid arteries. Some occlusions can be corrected by surgery.

### Atherosclerosis and Arteriosclerosis

Atherosclerosis is a disease in which cholesterol and other lipid materials build up inside large arteries. These deposits may restrict blood flow, which can cause malnutrition in nearby tissues.

Atherosclerosis can progress into a more serious condition as calcium precipitates with the lipids. This causes the deposits to harden. The arterial wall can also begin to degenerate. At this stage, the disease is called **arteriosclerosis**. This may lead to high blood pressure or angina. People often develop blood clots as a result of the hardening of the arteries, which can completely stop the flow of blood in the coronary arteries or the brain.

### Heart Attack – Myocardial Infarction

A heart attack is caused by the occlusion of a coronary artery. When the blood supply is cut off, myocardial cells are deprived of the oxygen and nutrients they need to work and live. Heart attacks can occur over 4–8 hours. They are often mistaken as indigestion. A patient may have poor circulation and slightly blue skin while experiencing a heart attack.

NOTES

As the blood supply begins to be reduced because of blocked or constricted vessels in the heart tissue, the patient begins to feel severe pain. This is called angina pectoris, a condition that is less serious than a heart attack but certainly should serve as an early warning of a failing heart. Nitroglycerine tablets are given to reduce the pain, as they cause blood vessels to dilate so that the heart tissue can receive more blood.

Sometimes tiny clots can lodge in a coronary artery that has narrowed as a result of fat deposits. An enzyme called **tissue plasminogen activator (tPA)** dissolves these clots so that the coronary artery is once again open and thus allows blood to move through.

At times, another non-surgical method called **angioplasty** can be used to treat a blocked artery.
An endoscope is inserted into an artery in the arm and then wiggled into the heart through the coronary arteries. Once in place, a small balloon at the tip of the endoscope is inflated, which compresses the fatty deposits and enlarges the artery so that more blood can get through.

Finally, if all else fails, a coronary bypass operation may be required. In this type of operation, unneeded blood vessels from another part of the body (such as the legs) are used to create a pass around the blocked coronary artery. This operation can be very dangerous.

It is possible to recover from a heart attack; however, in order to prevent a re-occurrence, it requires a healthier life style that includes stress reduction and a proper diet with light, but regular exercise.

### Septal Defect

Septal defect is caused when the opening (foramen ovale) between the left and right atrium does not close off after birth. As a result, some of the oxygenated blood is lost out of the left atrium, and the patient does not get enough oxygen. Openings can also be found between the ventricles, which can be sewn shut with synthetic patches.

### Aneurysm

An aneurysm is a blood-filled sac that is formed by the ballooning or separating of an arterial wall. This can occur in the brain (cerebral artery), in a ventricle of a heart, or in the aorta. Aneurysms are most common in the aorta. They need to be cut out and replaced with synthetic gortex arteries before they rupture. Lipid deposits called **atheromatous plaques** build up inside the artery. These deposits are rich in cholesterol and can restrict the flow of blood. Often blood clots can form in these restricted passageways, which can cause the degeneration of nearby tissues.

# PRACTICE EXERCISE

1. Define the following terms.

   **a)** Capillaries                              **b)** Coronary arteries

   **c)** Hypertension                             **d)** Myocardium

   **e)** Stroke volume                            **f)** Cardiac output

   **g)** Heart rate

2. Describe the pathway blood takes when entering the heart through the vena cava.

3. An Rh− female gives birth to her first child, who is Rh+. What is the expected result?

4. Explain what a heart attack is and why a person's diet can play a major role in the prevention of a heart attack.

5. If lymph fluid cannot be collected in your lymph vessels, what will the result be?

**6.** How does lymph differ from blood plasma?

**7.** What is the lymphatic system responsible for?

**8.** How does the lymphatic system relate to the circulatory system?

**9.** Explain the structure of a lymph vessel.

**10.** What is edema?

**11.** What is the function of the spleen?

**12.** What is the importance of a leukocyte?

**13.** How does the circulatory system interrelate with the endocrine system?

**14.** What is the average heart rate at birth? What is the average heart rate in adulthood?

**15.** What is the name of the fibrous sac that covers the heart?

**16.** What is the specific name for heart muscle?

**17.** What does the lub/dub sound represent?

**18.** What is the responsibility of the left ventricle?

**19.** How would the heart of an adult athlete differ from the heart of a non-active adult?

**20.** What are possible causes of a heart attack (myocardial infarction)?

**21.** What are the three sequential steps of a single cycle of the heart pump?

**22.** What is hypertension?

**23.** What effect does epinephrine have on the heart?

**24.** What is the importance of capillary fluid exchange?

**25.** Define systolic and diastolic pressure.

**26** What are the two types of pressure that allow for capillary fluid exchange?

**27.** What are three major functions of blood?

**28.** What are four major components of blood?

**29.** What increases RBC (red blood cell) production?

**30.** How do antibodies and antigens affect each other?

**31.** What is the cause of agglutination in blood transfusions?

**32.** What type of blood is considered to be the universal donor? What type of blood is considered the universal acceptor?

**33.** A patient with type A blood needs a blood transfusion. What type of blood can she or he be given?

## Lesson 5  THE MOTOR SYSTEM

### ORIGINS

The evolution of single celled aquatic organisms into complex land-dwelling and multicellular organisms required a significant number of highly interdependent adaptations. These ranged from solving how to pull oxygen out of a non-water environment to multicellular movement without the supportive buoyancy of water. Organisms evolved into a number of distinct directions. The environment dictated the survival of some organisms. Existence, for the most part, would depend on what the environment offered within a fixed location. Other organisms developed simple to complex systems that enabled them to choose their environment through movement. Plants would grow where conditions were favorable. They developed systems of gas and nutrient exchange, with the stomata being the organelle of choice for the controlled flow of gases and water. These tiny openings not only allowed plants to 'breathe' but also provided the enormous forces necessary to pull hundreds of kilograms of water to the tips of trees that measured up to 115 metres in height. (This is the height currently recognized as the tallest living tree in the world [*Sequoia sempervirens* – California Redwood]). Other organisms, such as the poriferans (sponges), evolved as sessile (stationary) animals.
With the advent of DNA-based research, sponges, considered among the simplest organism within the kingdom Animalia, appear to have lost this designation. Recent research by Dunn et al. 2008. "Broad phylogenomic sampling improves resolution of the animal tree of life." Nature 06614 found that the phylum Ctenophora (the comb jellies of which the sea gooseberry is a member) may now represent the most basic form of animal life.

Organisms unwilling to remain in one particular location would have to evolve the means to move and obtain nutrients. Unicellular organisms would use simple diffusion in conjunction with passive and active transport. Efficient ingestion and egestion, at a unicellular level, would require a high surface to volume ratio (the smaller, the better).

Locomotion initially depended upon relatively simple structures. Unicellular organisms evolved external tube-like structures that would either rotate (flagella) or bend (cilia) and bring the organism closer to a preferred environment. The use of internal microtubules also allowed for the reshaping of an organism's membrane. Amoeboid-type motion used these internal structures to create pseudpods (membrane extensions) to complete the three methods of locomotion used by unicellular organisms. However, hidden underneath the surface of the amoeba's pseudopod membrane is a glimpse of a protein interaction that would prove critical for a dramatic evolutionary leap forward. The polymerization of the protein actin and its interaction with the protein myosin (and its associated microtubules) would form the basis of an incredibly strong contraction process that enabled the rapid movement of multicellular organisms in water, over land, and eventually high up into the skies.

The unique needs of large multicellular organisms would require proteins that allowed for a long list of critical processes. Complex systems would have to be dedicated to respiration, digestion, circulation, excretion, and movement. Each system would be dependent upon this new group of contracting proteins and collectively would be called muscle. Muscle is categorized as being either being smooth or striated. Striated muscle, initially used for locomotion, would further evolve into proteins dedicated to cardiac (heart) function. Smooth muscle is composed of spindle shaped fibres that contain a single nucleus.

They lacked visible striations (lines), hence the term *smooth muscle*. Smooth muscle is regulated by the autonomic nervous system and does not require conscious control. The stimulus for contraction is either a nerve impulse or chemical signals sent by neighboring cells (paracrine control).

Multicellular organisms must distribute nutrients to a large number of specialized cells. This requires an efficient mechanism for ingestion, digestion, and excretion of relatively large quantities of food. This is achieved through the use of smooth muscle. The mammalian digestive system evolved into a long muscular tube that churns and moves food along its length in a series of slow rhythmic smooth muscle contractions (peristalsis). Large quantities of food and water are physically and chemically digested without the need for conscious control.

These contractions require minimal amounts of energy. This explains the low number of ATP-producing mitochondria located within each smooth muscle. Despite the efficiency of this digestive process, another system would be required to distribute nutrients to each individual cell.

The distribution of food in a unicellular organism is dependent upon basic structures and organelles that enveloped, digested, and excreted nutrients. Larger organisms would need a system that provided nutrients and gases to each cell. The mammalian circulatory system solved this distribution of nutrients and gases by evolving mechanisms that were dependent upon a high velocity liquid (blood) enclosed within kilometres of blood vessels (approximately 100 000 in an average human adult). This system was also entirely dependent upon a continuously beating muscle that pumps approximately 9 500 L of blood per day. Although an open circulatory system developed within a number of organisms, the culminating achievement of endothermic, multicellular organisms would be the closed circulatory system.

The human circulatory system is dependent upon smooth muscle enveloping all blood vessels except capillaries. Smooth muscle helps the body regulate blood flow through the vasodilation and vasoconstriction of blood vessels, whereas skeletal muscle supports the return of blood to the heart through contractions around veins containing one-way valves.

The driving force of this vast system of blood vessels is a unique form of striated muscle, similar to skeletal muscle, but highly modified to work as a single cohesive unit.

Cardiac muscle (myocardial) evolved to function without external nervous control. A unique bundle of nerves (the SA node) provides the heart with an internal and regular source of nerve impulses that triggers a coordinated heart contraction. Cardiac muscle is so highly evolved to work as a coordinated unit that separate muscle cells, with separate and uncoordinated contractions, will attain a unified rhythmic contraction. Myocardial muscle has evolved regions between muscle cells called **gap junctions**. These communicating gap junctions allow for the spread of one **action potential** (nerve signal) to each individual muscle cell. Single muscle cells (a myofibril) contain one centrally located nucleus. Myofibrils branch off and connect with other myofibrils through adheres junctions, which hold separate myofibrils together. This creates a network of interconnected myofibrils that form a branch-like structure.

The contraction of cardiac muscle generates the force necessary to pump blood toward the upper and lower parts of the body as well as to the lungs.

Unicellular organisms rely on their high surface-to-volume ratio for another essential process: cellular respiration. The intake of oxygen allows for aerobic organisms to generate ATP. This act of breathing occurs as a result of simple diffusion of oxygen across a unicellular organism's membrane. Because the individual cells of a multicellular organism also require a constant supply of oxygen, a much more efficient system of obtaining oxygen had to evolve.

The essential dilemma that needed to be solved was the following: how can a multicellular organism obtain oxygen without the benefit of an external membrane in contact with dissolved gases? The solution was elegant. Instead of discarding this primary process of diffusion, the system was moved inside an air-breathing organism. The diffusion of gases (and the water necessary for this process) moved inside a large set of protective organs (the lungs). Because efficient diffusion still required a large surface area, high numbers of circularly shaped structures (alveoli) generated the maximized surface area necessary for efficient diffusion. One problem still remained, however. A mechanism was required to allow for a constant flow of fresh oxygen and the removal of waste gases.

The solution required a muscle that could be placed under both involuntary and voluntary nervous control. The muscle that allowed for this process was a striated skeletal muscle. This muscle type looks very similar to myocardial. In fact, it is believed that skeletal muscle was the evolutionary template for the evolution of myocardial muscle. Yet, how could muscle be used to generate airflow? The process relied on the generation of low air pressure within a cavity or space created by the careful placement of mammalian bone. The mammalian skeleton evolved a rib cage that is able to expand while skeletal muscle contracts.

An upward and outward movement of the ribcage is achieved through the intercostal muscle group. This process also required another muscle group to pull downward. This is achieved through the diaphragm, a large muscle that is located at the bottom of this thoracic space. It is curved when relaxed and flattened when contracted. Neither the intercostals nor the

diaphragm requires conscious control. Breathing is accomplished by the contraction of both groups in a rhythmic manner. Breathing in becomes the generation of a large space into which air flows, whereas breathing out is the simple relaxation of muscle.
This reduces the space and forces air out of the lungs.

Although this mechanism solved the exchange of gases, muscle was to play one more role. The pathways leading to the alveoli had to be able to expel unwanted liquids and particles. This expulsion is known as a cough, a sudden contraction of the respiratory muscles that pushes air, particles, and liquids out of the lungs. This rush of air travels through pathways that are surrounded by smooth muscle. It had been assumed that these muscles served a necessary function. However, recent research proposes that this muscle may be vestigial (of no known function).

With digestive, respiratory, and circulatory systems in place, the multicellular organism still had one other major hurdle to overcome. If a sessile existence (one in which the adult is anchored to a particular supportive foundation) was not selectively advantageous, a means of locomotion had to evolve.

Unicellular organisms could use flagella, cilia, or a pseudopod. Unfortunately, these were dependent upon a small cellular size as well as an existence within a water-based environment. The solution would depend upon muscle and, in the case of mammals, a strong bone structure called the skeleton.

The evolution of skeletons moved into three distinct directions: the hydroskeleton, endoskeleton, and the exoskeleton. The hydroskeleton is a 'skeleton' that does not have bone or chitin. Certain invertebrates, such as jellyfish and starfish, use an interplay of muscle and fluid to produce locomotion. This process works well within an aquatic environment, but it is mechanically inadequate for large land-dwelling organisms. These organisms required a system of muscle supported by either exoskeletons or endoskeletons.

The evolution of the exoskeleton dates back approximately 550 million years. The strong outer shell made it possible for small to moderately sized organisms (primarily the arthropods) to flourish in water environments, move onto land, and eventually fly. Because of physical limitations imposed by a hard external shell, the largest arthropods were limited to an aquatic environment. The largest arthropod fossil on record is that of the sea scorpion, which measures between 2.5 to 2.6 metres. The largest living arthropods are the American lobster and the Japanese spider crab.

NOTES

The most successful land-dwelling arthropods belong to the class insecta. A determination of the largest insect is difficult to achieve because drying and other factors greatly influence the measurement of dead specimens. The general consensus is that, on average, the heaviest species is the giant scarab. The family Scarabaeidae is native to Africa and weigh in the range of 25 grams; however, a *Deinacrida heteracantha* from New Zealand was measured at 71 g, making it the heaviest insect on record.

The jointed exoskeleton, composed of a polysaccharide called **chitin**, serves as both a hard shell and a flexible material located at the joints of each appendage. The exoskeleton depended upon internal striated muscle but had a number of major disadvantages compared to the endoskeleton (internal skeleton). Growth was a process that required a **molt** (shedding of the exoskeleton). This places a major constraint on the physiology of appendages. It also leaves the organism in a particularly vulnerable state during this shedding. Recent studies suggest that a land-dwelling arthropod's respiratory system is too inefficient to support large arthropoda. It has been proposed that gigantic insects that existed during the late Paleozoic era were able to do so only because of high atmospheric oxygen levels. Because of these limitations, a large land-dwelling organism requires an internal skeleton.

The endoskeleton relies on a system of bone, cartilage, tendon, and vertebrate muscle. Skeletal muscle evolved into two distinct types: fast and slow skeletal muscle. Fast and slow skeletal muscle have a different initial contraction speed and duration. This often lends itself to the use of the terms 'fast-twitch' and 'slow-twitch' muscles. Skeletal muscle is under conscious control and attached to the skeleton by tendon. Skeletal muscle appears to have lines (striations) and is subdivided into two categories: Type I and Type II fibres. Type I is the slow-twitch variety. They have high numbers of mitochondria, are resistant to fatigue, and are rich in a special oxygen carrying protein called myoglobin. The Type II fibres are described as fast-twitch. They fatigue easily, have low numbers of mitochondria, and are the dominant muscle used for fast movement. Skeletal muscle is multi-nucleated as a result of the fusion of single nucleated muscle cells early in the embryo's development. This suggests that striated muscle cells are an evolutionary step forward from single nucleated smooth muscle cells.

Type I muscle fibres = slow-twitch

Type II muscle fibres = fast-twitch

Skeletal muscle consists of bundles of contracting muscle fibres, or myofibres, that lie parallel to one another. Each muscle fibre's surface area is covered with a sarcolemma that contains channels that permit the transmission of an action potential (nerve impulse). Each muscle fibre is composed of five to 10 000 multi-nucleated myofibrils. A myofibril is a continuous strand of repeating sarcomeres placed end-to-end.. Each myofibril is enclosed within an outer-covering called the **sarcoplasmic reticulum**. This network of pathways is essential for the regulation of calcium, which, in its ionic form, is a key component of a muscle contraction.

The model currently used to describe a muscle contraction is the 'Sliding Filament Model'. This model was first proposed by independent studies carried out by Hugh Huxley and Allan Huxley and published in *Nature*, May 1954. Further research helped determine that the contraction of a muscle cell is an 'all-or-nothing' event. Each cell carries out a maximal contraction once it is triggered by an incoming signal. However, a graded response is possible since the number of myofibrils that are recruited is based upon the amount of force needed for a particular muscular contraction.

Each sarcomere is composed of four types of proteins, two of which are the filaments **actin** and **myosin**. According to the model, actin proteins slide in between myosin proteins and pull the two Z-lines of the sarcomere together. The term *Z-lines* originates from the German *Zwischenscheibe*, which means "the band in between." The 'in-between' region is the I band, which extends over each Z-line. Actin filaments attached to a band at the Z-line extend halfway toward the next Z-line. The space between these extended actin filaments is called the H **zone**. At the center of the H zone is the central portion of the sarcomere called the M **band**.

## Actin, Myosin, and Cell Movement

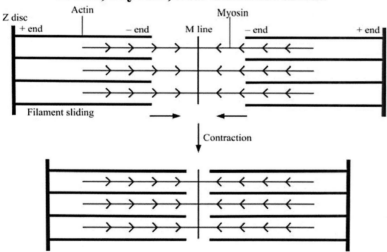

If a voluntary muscle contraction is required, a nerve signal is sent to the muscle. Each nerve branches off into separate neuron terminals. These can separate and connect with up to 2 000 separate muscle fibres. Each fibre that receives a signal will contract. This group of contracting fibres forms a motor unit. The graduated muscle contraction is dependent upon the number of motor units that are activated. A muscle at rest still undergoes a contraction of a small number of muscle fibres. This is called **tonus**.

The 'signal' is an action potential that travels the length of a nerve cell, which causes the release of a neurotransmitter (acetylcholine). This neurotransmitter travels across a gap (synapse) and then binds to receptor sites on the muscle membrane. This triggers a depolarization of ions, which results in an electrical signal spreading along the surface of the muscle cell. This signal enters T-tubules that extend deep into each muscle fibre. Calcium, stored within the sarcoplasmic reticulum, flows into the sarcomere and results in a chain of events that includes a shortening of the sarcomere.

Of the two filaments found within the sarcomeres, myosin is the more complex of the two. Myosin II is composed of six strands of protein filaments. Two heavy strands are coiled around each other and are joined at a 'head' region by four light chains. These light chains bind the two heads so that they extend outward. Myosin filaments are bundled together with the heads facing outward. These heads contain two binding sites. One site allows for the binding and hydrolysis of ATP, while the other site binds to actin. During the relaxed muscle phase, a the bundle of myosin heads are in contact with a three-subunit tropinin complex that forms a bridge between the myosin heads, a tropomyosin filament, and the actin filament.

The actin thin filament is a chain of globular proteins joined as two helically twisted strands. Tropinin rests on tropomyosin, which 'hides' myosin-binding sites located along the actin filament. These myosin heads, in a resting muscle, are in a 'cocked' position. This position could be compared to the potential energy stored within the spring of a 'set' mousetrap.

Once an action potential arrives, it travels along the muscle fibre surface (the sarcolemmal membrane) and enters the muscle fibre via a series of T-tubules. This T System allows the action potential to travel deep into the fibre to terminal areas that contain $Ca^{2+}$. When an action potential arrives in this region, it produces a reversal of the polarity at the ends of these tubes. This induces the release of $Ca^{2+}$ from the sarcoplasmic reticulum.

$Ca^{2+}$ binds to the troponin complex at the calcium-binding troponin subunit (TnC). The complex and the attached tropomyosin shift, which exposes the myosin-binding sites located along the actin filament. A power stroke occurs when the cocked myosin heads releases ADP and a phosphate while contracting into a relaxed position. This pulls the myosin filaments along the actin filaments. As the action potential passes, the $Ca^{2+}$ gates are closed, and $Ca^{2+}$ is pumped back into the sarcoplasmic reticulum. ATP then causes the heads to release from the myosin-binding sites along the actin. Using the energy available from ATP, the heads are then again cocked. If no further contraction is required, the myosin-binding sites are again covered by tropomyosin, and the myosin heads are again bridged by the troponin complex. Another key function of muscle, besides its contractile properties, is the generation of heat, especially within endotherms.

Skeletal muscle, even at rest, generates heat. This is the result of the ATP used by the muscle's sodium/potassium pumps (needed to maintain adequate concentrations for nerve transmission), ATP's role in the cocking myosin heads, and the recharging of $Ca^{2+}$ stores within the sarcoplasmic reticulum. Heat is also generated within resting muscle because small numbers of fibres are constantly cycling through contractions. These involuntary muscle contractions are also essential for the maintenance of posture and balance. The process is described as **tonus (muscle tone)**. This term is not used in the same context as a descriptor of an individual's muscle mass or appearance. During muscular contractions, ATP use increases. This produces a corresponding increase in the amount of heat generated.

Finally, recalling that all muscle tissue can only contract, a further modification of muscle activity was required.

The physiological limitation of a 'contraction-only system' requires the coordinated movement of opposing or paired muscle groups. The process of antagonism allows for multiple direction movement. An example is the bicep/tricep pairing that allows for movement of the forearm in an up and down motion.

**Extended**

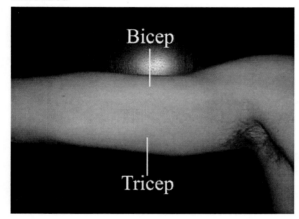

**Flexed**

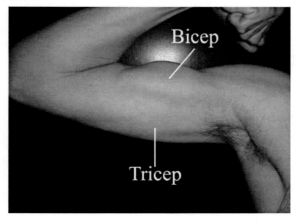

# PRACTICE EXERCISE

1. Describe the two types of muscle

2. Name and describe the process by which unicellular organisms generate cellular energy.

3. Describe gas exchange in mammals.

4. List the three means of locomotion that can be employed by unicellular organisms.

5. List and describe the three distinct forms of skeleton.

**6.** How do Type I and Type II muscle fibres differ?

**7.** Explain the current model used to describe a muscle contraction.

**8.** Explain the process of muscle contraction.

**9.** Name two types of proteins of the four that comprise sarcomeres.

**10.** How does skeletal muscle generate heat?

# *REVIEW SUMMARY*

- The human digestive system is made up of the mouth, esophagus, stomach, liver, pancreas, gall bladder, small intestine, and large intestine.

- Food goes from the mouth, down through the esophagus to the stomach via peristaltic wave movement.

- The stomach stores food, mixes gastric juices, and sets the rate of digestion. Enzymes produced by the stomach include pepsinogen and rennin.

- Bile, used to break down fats and neutralize strong acids from the stomach, is produced in the liver and stored in a concentrated form in the gall bladder. The pancreas produces hormones and enzymes that aid in digestion.

- The majority of digestion and absorption occurs in the small intestine. The inside layer of the small intestine contains finger-like projections called microvilli that increase the surface area available for absorption. A special vessel filled with lymph fluid (called a lacteal) runs through the interior of the villi and is responsible for the absorption of digested lipids.

- The large intestine—which is made up of the transverse colon, ascending colon, and descending colon—absorbs water, minerals, and salts into the blood stream; decomposes organic material with the help of bacteria; produces vitamin B, vitamin K, and folic acid; and stores and eliminates solid waste.

- The nasal cavity, pharynx, larynx, trachea, bronchi, bronchioles, alveolar sacs, and lungs make up the respiratory structures.

- In order to exhale, pressure must be higher on the inside of the lungs than on the outside. Relaxing the external intercostal muscles, relaxing the diaphragm, and contracting the internal intercostal muscles can force exhalation.

- In order to inhale, the external intercostal muscles contract; the diaphragm contracts and flattens.

- Oxygen can dissolve directly into the plasma of oxygen-poor blood or combine with the iron-bearing part of the hemoglobin molecule. Carbon dioxide can be transported in blood plasma by hemoglobin or as hydrogen ions in red blood cells.

- Respiration rate is closely tied to blood acidity. As blood becomes acidic, respiration rate increases in order to remove more $CO_2$; as blood becomes basic, respiration rate decreases.

- The major organs involved in excretion include the skin, digestive tract, lungs, and kidneys.

- Kidneys filter blood by removing liquid wastes. They also control water balance, blood acidity, and potassium and salt levels in blood. The material filtered out of the blood collects in the medulla of the kidney as urine. Ureters transport urine from the kidney to the urinary bladder and outside of the body via the urethra.

- The functional unit of the kidney is the nephron, which is made up of the glomerulus, Bowman's capsule, proximal and distal convoluted tubules, the loop of Henle, and the collecting duct.

- Aldosterone and antidiuretic hormone (ADH) regulate the kidneys. Aldosterone causes the kidneys to become more permeable to sodium, and ADH stimulates the distal convoluted tubules to become more permeable to water.

- The heart is made up of the left and right atrium, the left and right ventricle, two semilunar valves, and two atrioventricular valves.

- The heart beats in a cycle of filling, contracting, and relaxing. The heart rate is determined by the number of times the heart beats in one minute.

- Blood vessels carry blood throughout the body. Vessels carrying blood away from the heart are called arteries and vessels carrying blood toward the heart are called veins. The coronary artery and vein only transport blood within the heart tissue.

- Capillaries are tiny blood vessels and are the main site of gas and fluid exchange between blood and tissues.

- Blood pressure is the measure of the force of blood in vessels

- Blood is composed of red and white blood cells, plasma, and platelets.

- Red blood cells deliver oxygen to tissues. Plasma is a fluid that contains most of the nutrients needed by the body. Platelets are fragments of larger cells and help in the formation of blood clots. White blood cells defend the body against infections and foreign substances.

- Red blood cells can be classified into four basic blood types: type A, B, O, and AB. The blood type is determined by the presence of identifying proteins called antigens. A antigens produce antibodies against B antigens, and B antigens produce antibodies against A antigens.

- Blood cells that have the Rh factor antigen are labelled Rh-positive, and blood cells that do not have the antigen are labelled Rh-negative.

- Lymph fluid contains proteins, white blood cells, and lipids. Two types of lymphocytes, B cells and T cells, are involved in immune responses.

- Muscle is categorized as smooth, striated, or cardiac. Smooth muscle controls peristaltic movement, vasodilation, and vasoconstriction. Striated skeletal muscle is involved in respiration, and voluntary muscle controls and generates heat, even at rest. Contraction of cardiac muscle generates the force necessary to pump blood toward the upper and lower parts of the body as well as to the lungs.

- The "Sliding Filament Model" of actin and myosin describes muscle contraction.

# *PRACTICE TEST*

1. The process that increases the surface area of food without breaking molecular bonds is called
   a) mechanical digestion
   b) chemical digestion
   c) peristalsis
   d) ingestion

2. Which of the following statements about the digestive process is rue?
   a) The stomach requires less than one hour to process most foods.
   b) Peristalsis does not occur within the stomach.
   c) The stomach converts a bolus into chyme.
   d) Alcohol digestion requires up to 24 hours.

3. The hormone _____ is triggered by the presence of food in the stomach. The hormone is released into the _____ and targets cells lining the stomach, which then release gastric juices.
   a) gastrin, stomach
   b) somatostatin, stomach
   c) gastrin, circulatory system
   d) somatostatin, circulatory system

4. The hormone _____ causes the gallbladder to release bile in response to the presence of fat in the _____.
   a) gastrin, stomach
   b) insulin, pancreas
   c) somatostatin, small intestine
   d) cholecystokinin, small intestine

5. The lining of the small intestine contains small structures called _____. Their primary function is to _____.
   a) villi, increase surface area
   b) lacteals, actively absorb lipids
   c) epithelial layers, passively absorb all nutrients
   d) Brunner's glands, secrete enzymes into the lumen of the small intestine.

6. Which of the following hormones is correctly matched with its target?
   a) Secretin/pancreas
   b) Gastrin/gallbladder
   c) CCK/small intestine
   d) Somatostatin/large intestine

7. The primary function of the large intestine is the
   a) increase of macromolecule surface area
   b) absorption of nutrient macromolecules
   c) enzymatic breakdown of proteins
   d) reabsorption of water

8. Which of the following structures allows for the exchange of gases between the respiratory system and the circulatory system?
   a) Alveoli
   b) Trachea
   c) Bronchi
   d) Bronchioles

9. During inhalation, the diaphragm will _____ and assume a _____ shape.
   a) relax, curved
   b) relax, flattened
   c) contract, curved
   d) contract, flattened

10. The pH of normal arterial blood is approximately _____. A pH lower than this will result in _____ in respiration rate.

a) 7.30, a decrease

b) 7.30, an increase

c) 6.30, a decrease

d) 6.30, an increase

11. _____ is a respiratory disease that involves a hardening of the bronchioles and bursting of alveoli.

a) Emphysema

b) Pneumonia

c) Bronchitis

d) Pleurisy

12. Which of the following substances is reabsorbed back into the circulatory system?

a) Urea

b) Creatine

c) Ammonia

d) Amino acids

13. Which of the following arrangements is the correct pathway for the excretion of urine?

a) Bowman's capsule, distal convoluted tubule, Loop of Henle

b) Loop of Henle, distal convoluted tubule, Bowman's capsule

c) Proximal convoluted tubule, Loop of Henle, collecting duct

d) Glomerulus, distal convoluted tubule, Loop of Henle

14. Which of the following hormones allows for an increased reabsorption of water within the kidneys?

a) CCK

b) Gastrin

c) Secretin

d) Aldosterone

15. Which of the following best describes key functions of the kidney?

a) The filtering of blood

b) The regulation of bodily water levels

c) The removal of waste such as urea

d) All of the above

16. Humans have _____ circulatory system. This is necessary because _____.

a) an open, an open system efficiently delivers nutrients and oxygen

b) closed, a closed system efficiently delivers nutrients and oxygen

c) closed, closed systems require very few blood vessels

d) open, a closed system is an inefficient system

17. Cardiac muscle cells are unique because they

a) contain no nucleus

b) require no external nerve stimulation.

c) each beat independently and separately

d) require low levels of oxygen and glucose

**18.** The pericardium is essential for proper heart function because it

    **a)** anchors the AV valve to the bottom of the ventricle

    **b)** is a one-way valve located between the atrium and ventricle

    **c)** provides a nerve impulse that allows for a proper heart rhythm

    **d)** is a separate fluid-filled sac that provides protection and friction reduction

**19.** The correct pathway for blood flow beginning at the vena cava is

    **a)** right ventricle, right atrium, pulmonary artery, and pulmonary vein

    **b)** right atrium, pulmonary artery, pulmonary vein, and aorta

    **c)** left atrium, pulmonary vein, pulmonary artery, and aorta

    **d)** left ventricle, AV valve, left atrium, and aorta

**20.** The LUB sound is caused by the

    **a)** semi-lunar valves opening

    **b)** semi-lunar valves closing

    **c)** AV valves opening

    **d)** AV valves closing

**21.** The only blood vessels that allows for the exchange of nutrients and gases between the circulatory system and cells are the

    **a)** veins

    **b)** arteries

    **c)** arterioles

    **d)** capillaries

**22.** Which blood vessel contains structures that prevent backflow?

    **a)** Capillaries

    **b)** Arterioles

    **c)** Arteries

    **d)** Veins

**23.** The _____ are sensitive to the stretching of the arteries. These are located in _____ .

    **a)** osmoreceptors, carotid arteries, the aorta, and the hypothalamus

    **b)** baroreceptors, carotid arteries, the aorta, and the hypothalamus.

    **c)** osmoreceptors, corotid arteries and the aorta

    **d)** baroreceptors, carotid arteries and the aorta

**24.** Arteries are best defined as blood vessels that carry _____ . The largest of these is the _____ .

    **a)** oxygenated blood, aorta

    **b)** oxygenated blood, vena cava

    **c)** blood away from the heart, aorta

    **d)** blood away from the heart, vena cava

25. _____ binds oxygen and carries it throughout the circulatory system. These proteins _____ a nucleus.

   a) Red blood cells, contain
   b) White blood cells, contain
   c) Red blood cells, do not contain
   d) White blood cells, do not contain

26. Platelets prevent the leakage of blood through a 'cascade' event. This process, although very quick, requires a complex series of steps. A general overview of the correct sequence is

   a) thrombin, prothrombin, fibrin, fibrinogen
   b) fibrin, fibrinogen, thrombin, prothrombin
   c) prothrombin, thrombin, fibrinogen, fibrin
   d) fibrinogen, fibrin, prothrombin, thrombin

27. Leukocytes are responsible for _____. These make up the _____ number blood proteins.

   a) blood clotting, largest
   b) oxygen transportation, smallest
   c) combating foreign invaders, largest
   d) combating foreign invaders, smallest

28. Human blood is categorized by _____ on the surface of red blood cells. According to the ABO system, an individual with blood type AB has _____ blood antibodies within their blood plasma.

   a) antibodies, no A or B
   b) antibodies, A and B
   c) antigens, no A or B
   d) antigens, A and B

29. The lymph system contain _____ within their vessels. These transport a variety of substances that include _____.

   a) no one-way valves, red blood cells
   b) one-way valves, red blood cells
   c) no one-way valves, lipids
   d) one-way valves, lipids

30. Which muscle type is spindle-shaped, contains a single nucleus in each cell, and is under autonomic control?

   a) Smooth muscle
   b) Striated Type I muscle
   c) Striated Type II muscle
   d) Cardiac (myogenic) muscle

**31.** Vasodilation and vasoconstriction are terms associated with _____ muscle activity directly affecting _____.

    **a)** striated, the heart

    **b)** smooth, blood vessels

    **c)** smooth, the digestive tract

    **d)** myogenic, skeletal muscle

**32.** Myocardial muscle is unique because it

    **a)** has no myosin or actin

    **b)** does not require calcium

    **c)** does not contain sarcomeres

    **d)** requires no external nervous control

**33.** Respiration is dependent upon _____ muscle. The muscle groups involved are the _____.

    **a)** smooth muscle, diaphragm and the intercostals

    **b)** skeletal muscle, diaphragm and the intercostals **c)** smooth muscle, alveoli and capillaries

    **d)** skeletal muscle, alveoli and capillaries

**34.** Skeletal muscle is _____. This suggests that it evolved from _____.

    **a)** mono-nucleated, cardiac muscle

    **b)** mono-nucleated, smooth muscle

    **c)** multi-nucleated, cardiac muscle

    **d)** multi-nucleated, smooth muscle

**35.** The sliding filament model is based upon the _____ contractile unit. This requires that _____ heads are cocked through the hydrolysis of ATP.

    **a)** sarcomere, actin

    **b)** sarcomere, myosin

    **c)** tropomyosin, actin

    **d)** tropomyosin, myosin

**36.** Prior to a muscle contraction, calcium is stored in the ?

    **a)** Z-line

    **b)** T-tubule

    **c)** sarcoplasmic reticulum

    **d)** sarcolemmal membrane

**37.** The generation of heat by a muscle

    **a)** rarely occurs because it requires a muscle contraction

    **b)** occurs constantly, but requires a muscle contraction

    **c)** is a byproduct of friction between actin and myosin

    **d)** occurs constantly as a result of tonus and ATP use

# Answers

# and

# Solutions

**Castle Rock**
Research Corp

# NOTES

# THE BIOSPHERE

## Lesson 1—The Biosphere

### PRACTICE EXERCISE—
### ANSWERS AND SOLUTIONS

1. **D.**
   The three divisions of the biosphere are the lithosphere, the hydrosphere, and the atmosphere.

3. **B.**
   An autotroph can also be termed a photosynthesizer and a producer.

5. **A.**
   The organelles that perform photosynthetic operations are called chloroplasts.

7. **A.**
   Endergonic means that energy has gone into the reaction and has been stored in chemical bonds. Organic, catabolic, and exothermic all refer to reactions that break molecules apart in order to release chemical energy from sub-molecular bonds.

## Lesson 2—The Biosphere and Energy

### PRACTICE EXERCISE—
### ANSWERS AND SOLUTIONS

1. **B.**
   Motility refers to self-generated biological movement.

3. **B.**
   Carbon is a necessary component for a compound to be considered organic.

5. **C.**
   Water vapour has the highest specific heat capacity of the options listed. Therefore, it is the best storage agent for heat in the atmosphere.

7. **C.**
   The five guilds of lifeforms are photosynthesizers, herbivores, carnivores, scavengers, and decomposers. Xerotrophs live on rocks and sand and help break rocks down into soil. However, they are not considered a separate guild by the *Gaia Hypothesis*. Xerotrophs photosynthesize. Therefore, the correct answer is **C**.

## Lesson 3—The Carbon Cycle

### PRACTICE EXERCISE—
### ANSWERS AND SOLUTIONS

1. **C.**
   Respiration is the only biotic process listed. Combustion is involved whenever something is burned. Erosion is the process by which landforms are changed by wind or water, and precipitation involves the formation water from water vapour.

3. **A.**
   The polymerization of glucose involves a process known as dehydration synthesis. Dehydration synthesis always produces excess water molecules.

5. **A.**
   Carbon fixation is performed during photosynthesis. Carbon dioxide is taken from the air and bonded with water to form larger organic molecules. The type of organism able to perform photosynthesis is a producer.

7. **C.**
   Glucose molecules have a chain structure wherein one side of the molecule has a hydroxyl group $(OH^-)$ and the other side has a hydrogen ion $(H^+)$. These two ions can break away from glucose to form $H_2O$, or water. The removal of water molecules from glucose during polymerization is known as dehydration synthesis.

## Lesson 4—The Nitrogen Cycle

### PRACTICE EXERCISE— ANSWERS AND SOLUTIONS

1. **A.**
Fixation is performed by bacteria in nodules attached to plant roots. It is therefore a biotic factor. Photosynthesis is not a process that uses nitrogen. Phosphorylation is the addition of a phosphate group to a protein molecule or other small molecule, and respiration is a biotic factor, but it is not part of the nitrogen cycle.

3. **A.**
Because animals are unable to fix nitrogen from the atmosphere directly, they can only assimilate nitrogenous compounds by consuming plant matter that has metabolized nitrogen that has been ammonified and then nitrogenated. During inhalation and respiration, animals exchange nitrogen, but they are unable to create any biotic reactions with it. Ammonification is performed by bacteria and microbes. Animals cannot metabolize the products of this reaction either.

5. **D.**
Aqua regia can dissolve solid heavier metals that other, less reactive acidic substances cannot. Precious metals such as gold and platinum can be dissolved by aqua regia, though not by hydrochloric acid or nitric acid independently.

7. **A.**
The products of nitrogenation are nitrate and nitrite. Nitrous oxide and nucleotides are formed in different processes. Ammonia and ammonium are produced through ammonification, whereas ATP and carbon dioxide are the products of cellular respiration.

## Lesson 5—The Phosphorus Cycle

### PRACTICE EXERCISE— ANSWERS AND SOLUTIONS

1. **D .**
The answer is decomposition. Decomposing plant and animal matter return phosphates to the soil for reuse. Since phosphates do not tend to form airborne or gaseous compounds, respiration and fixation are neither possible nor necessary for the cycling of the material. Erosion is not a biotic process.

3. **D. Deleted question.**
Since phosphates are found in all cell membranes, appears as calcium phosphate in bones, and appears in ATP and ADP molecules wherever energy is expended (like muscles), all of the choices in this question are valid places to find phosphorus.

5. **B.**
Nucleic acids are used to store genetic information and to transmit that information during the process of cellular division and reproduction. DNA and RNA are two important types of molecules within the reproductive cycles of all living things. Both DNA and RNA are composed of nucleic acids.

7. **A.**
Like nitrogen, animals cannot metabolize phosphorus through their lungs or gills, so answer **A** is incorrect. Decomposition and perspiration are processes that do not involve consumers assimilating nutrients. Therefore, answer **B** is correct. Animals can only intake these nutrients through the processes of eating and digestion.

## PRACTICE QUIZ

### ANSWERS AND SOLUTIONS

1. **B.**
Free nitrogen gas makes up approximately 78% of air content. Oxygen makes up the next largest proportion at approximately 21%.

3. **A.**
Combustion is not a biotic process that takes place in producers. Decomposition does not necessarily require oxygen because there can be anaerobic decomposition. All of these processes, however, produce a net amount of heat.

5. **D.**
Heat is lost from the biosphere to outer space in order to balance the solar energy that is entering the system. All organic life does contain carbon. Carbon is an essential component of all living structures. Greenhouse gases do trap heat within the atmosphere. The only untrue statement given is **D**. The albedo of the polar caps reduces the amount of heat Earth's surface receives from direct sunlight. It does not create $CO_2$.

**7. C.**
Plants are autotrophs and producers precisely because they are photosynthesizers. The correct answer is **C**. Plants are not defined as consumers.

**9. C.**
Fullerenes are found in trace amounts within soot and candle residue, but not within living tissue. Sulfur dioxide is a key component of acid rain, but it is not involved in the formation of any cellular structure. The cells of some decomposers may produce ammonia, but it is not a necessary component of living cells. The correct answer is **B**. Phospholipids are integral parts of all cellular membranes, such as the surface of organelles.

**11. C.**
Free nitrogen has a very stable triple bond structure and thus requires a large amount of energy to form other compounds. The powerful electrical discharge of lightning can create nitrates, which are then washed into the soil by rainfall.

**13. B.**
Photosynthesis uses carbon dioxide and water to form glucose and oxygen within plants. Digestion breaks down nutrients from ingested food into component parts that can be absorbed by the bodies of consumers. Cellular respiration takes place in all organic life for the purpose of producing metabolic energy. The only process that does not take place within the bodies and cells of living beings is combustion.

**15. A.**
Phosphorus is generally found in the lithosphere in the form of phosphate rocks and as sediment in the hydrosphere. The vast majority of water (97%) on Earth is stored in the oceans. Nitrogen is predominantly found in a free nitrogen state in the atmosphere. All organic life contains carbon. It is also found in carbon dioxide in the atmosphere, and carbon sinks in the lithosphere. They are not present in aqueous ions.

**17.** A steady state equilibrium is a self-maintaining, self-regulating system that uses balanced opposite reactions and processes to keep itself functioning indefinitely in exactly the same way.

**19.** The greenhouse effect is a delicately balanced system that traps thermal energy in the atmosphere, which in turn heats the biosphere. Gaseous water vapour forms the most significant component of the greenhouse effect, but other gases such as methane and carbon dioxide can make a significant contribution. Living things depend on the greenhouse effect to keep the planet's surface at a habitable temperature. Without the greenhouse effect, most living things on Earth would likely freeze. However, there is the danger of intensifying the greenhouse effect. If the effect becomes too strong, there is the possibility that the polar ice caps could melt, which would reduce the albedo of the biosphere and raise sea levels to dangerous heights.

## Lesson 6—Water

### PRACTICE EXERCISE— ANSWERS AND SOLUTIONS

**1. B.**
Water can form ionic bonds, particularly when reacting to an acid or a base. Water can also form covalent bonds with other non-metals, as well as forming hydrogen bonds with other water molecules. This versatility of bonds is what causes a large number of substances to dissolve in water. That is why water is sometimes called the universal solvent. Isotopic bonds deal with subatomic structure and has no bearing on a biological discussion at this level.

**3. B.**
Energy is released from a molecule of ATP when a water molecule splits in two to separate one phosphate group from the rest of the molecule. The resulting ADP molecule is then said to have been dephosphorylated. Because this was caused by a water molecule, the process is referred to as hydrolysis. Fusion and vaporization refer to a change in state, not molecular reaction, and dehydration synthesis actually produces excess water.

**5. B.**

The pH of a neutral substance, or a substance that does not demonstrate any characteristics of either an acid or a base, is 7. Pure distilled water is a pH neutral substance and thus is not acidic (6), basic (8), or very alkaline (15.2). Water is rarely found in this form, however, because any substance that dissolves in water will change its pH.

**7. B.**

Increasing the gaseous temperature of one gram of water vapour by one degree would only require 0.5 calories. To melt ice to water, one would need to add 80 calories. To raise the temperature of liquid water by 10°C, one would need 10 calories per gram multiplied by 10 degrees, which is equal to 100 calories. However, in order to make one gram of water evaporate into a gram of water vapour, 540 calories would be required. The correct answer is **B**.

## Lesson 7—The Hydrologic Cycle

### PRACTICE EXERCISE—
### ANSWERS AND SOLUTIONS

**1. B.**

Water does evaporate into the atmosphere as water vapour and then condenses into precipitation that falls back to Earth, where it can runoff the surface of the lithosphere. Erosion may be a by-product of runoff, but it is not a direct process within the hydrologic cycle.

**3. A.**

Because solid ice has only 10% of the density of sea water, only 10% of the iceberg should appear above the surface of the water.
The correct answer is **D**.

**5. C.**

A gently sloped area with absorbent soil and vascular plant life that could intercept rain would be the ideal place to observe low or decreased surface runoff from precipitation. Steeply sloped land would increase surface runoff. Hard rocky ground or a paved urban landscape would not be very absorbent. Therefore, a thickly wooded forest would act as a watershed and retain water much more efficiently than the other three alternatives.

**7. B.**

Water is stored in the lithosphere in stone, rock, or clay repositories known as aquifers.
The answer is therefore **B**. A geode is a hollow, crystalline rock. An aqualung is a kind of SCUBA equipment, and the arctic seas are not part of the lithosphere.

## Lesson 8—Energy and Matter

### PRACTICE EXERCISE—
### ANSWERS AND SOLUTIONS

**1. C.**

Aeolian processes strictly deal with actions of the wind. The three aeolian processes are erosion, transportation, and deposition.
This means that the only process listed that is not an aeolian process is precipitation, which is part of the hydrologic cycle.

**3. B.**

The troposphere is the layer of the atmosphere found closest to the surface of Earth and extends upward 11 km. It represents the intersection of the biosphere and the atmosphere.
The ionosphere, stratosphere, and the thermosphere have such low air pressure that there are no naturally occurring life forms in these areas.
The troposphere has 75% of the mass of the atmosphere.

**5. D.**

Freezing does not cause the formation of water molecules. It is simply a changing of state, where water goes from a liquid to a solid. Photosynthesis uses water molecules to form glucose and oxygen. In fact, photosynthetic processes actually break apart water molecules. Aeolian deposition is the process by which the wind deposits material in a new location. There are no chemical reactions involved in this process. The correct answer is **D**. Cellular respiration results in the end products of carbon dioxide, water, and ATP.

**7. D.**

Nitrogen as an element tends toward an $N_2$ structure, which is most commonly found in its gaseous state. In order to find nitrogen in any state other than a gas, it would have to be 195.79°C or colder. Free nitrogen is very stable, and it tends toward a gaseous state. Therefore, because nitrogen comprises 78% of the air we breathe, the atmosphere is the likeliest place to find it.

## *Lesson 9—Maintaining the Balance*

### PRACTICE EXERCISE—
### ANSWERS AND SOLUTIONS

**1. A.**

Water vapour, carbon dioxide, and nitrous oxide are all greenhouse gases. Only ammonia does not function as a greenhouse gas.

**3. C.**

Greenhouse gases contribute to a greater amount of heat conserved in the biosphere.
An increased amount of greenhouse gas content in the atmosphere would most likely cause the average global temperature to rise, which would cause the melting and shrinking of the polar ice caps. This would in turn increase the volume of the oceans and raise sea levels. An increase in greenhouse gas composition of the atmosphere, however, would not increase the planetary albedo. In fact, the albedo would decrease as the ice caps retreated or melted. Ice and snow are responsible for a lot of high reflectivity of solar energy.

**5. C.**

Of all the greenhouse gases, the one that has the single greatest impact on the climate of the biosphere is water vapour. This is a result of its high specific heat capacity.

**7. B.**

Methane is primarily produced through two processes: digestion and anaerobic decomposition.
Anaerobic decomposition generally happens in wet areas, where water cuts off the oxygen from the decomposers involved. Because neither a forest fire nor a desert has much standing water, **A** and **C** are incorrect.
In general, a swamp will have more decaying and rotten biomass than a freshwater lake.

Dead vegetation that is very moist or submerged is very likely to produce a lot of methane as it decomposes. Although there is some methane production from lakes, it is not until a lake becomes a fen or a swamp that methane production really increases. Therefore, the best answer is **B**.

## *PRACTICE TEST*

### ANSWERS AND SOLUTIONS

**1. B.**

Fermentation has virtually nothing to do with water and nutrient transportation within vascular plants. Water and nutrients are moved through a plant as osmotic root pressure pushes water into the base of the plant. Transpiration, on the other hand, allows water to evaporate from the stoma in leaves. Capillary action enables the cohesive quality of water to maintain a steady stream through the narrow tubes and vessels within the plant.

**3. B.**

Nitrogen fixation is actually performed by bacteria and microbes, but some plants form nodules on their roots and create a symbiotic relationship with nitrogen fixing bacteria. Plants of this type are called legumes. The other responses refer to different varieties of photosynthetic producers, but none of them are directly involved in nitrogen fixations.

**5. C.**

A lithospheric zone of infiltration is found at ground level. Here, water is still available for absorption by plant roots, but it is no longer able to interact with the atmosphere. Water in that zone is referred to as ground water. Therefore, **D** is not the correct answer.

The zone of aeration is the layer of ground where water can still freely evaporate back into the atmosphere. Water in this zone is referred to as soil water. Therefore, **A** cannot be the right answer.
The zone of saturation indicates the depth at which the vast majority of plant roots can no longer reach the water, and the water is effectively out of range of biotic interaction. Water at this depth is called the water table of the area, and therefore, **C** is the correct response.

Technically, there is no such thing as a zone of hydration, but the term could be used to describe any area with moisture or humidity. Because it is not as specific as the previous answer, **B** is not the best response.

7. **B.**
Two of the responses essentially mean the same thing. Boiling and evaporation are synonymous terms. Therefore, neither of these two alternatives can be right.
Condensation refers to the change of state between gas and liquid. Sublimation involves a change of from a solid directly to a gas. The intermediary liquid state is skipped during sublimation. Because this involves adding the latent heat of fusion and the latent heat of vaporization together, this process requires more energy.

9. **D.**
Considering that precipitation landing on a hill will runoff downward, it is logical to think that the nutrients on the top level of the soil or on the vegetation will be carried downward. In short, consider that more water will arrive at the base of the hill having dissolved more nutrients than water that stays at the top of the hill.
Nutrient-rich soil will have more micro- and macrobiotic life, and this will help with soil consistency, making it thicker or loamier.
The question asks what is most likely true because there could be factors such as wind and slow runoff that might change the situation, but the best answer in this case is **D.**

11. **D.**
The approximate percentage of free nitrogen in the air by volume is 78%, but the question is asking for both free nitrogen and free oxygen. In fact, nitrogen comprises 78.084% of the atmosphere.
The approximate percentage of free oxygen in the air by volume is 21%. Oxygen comprises 20.946% of the atmosphere.
Adding the two values together yields a total of 99.03%.
Therefore, if the portion of the atmosphere composed of nitrogen and oxygen is removed, the net volume of the atmosphere remaining is 0.97%, or a little bit less than 1%.

13. **B.**
The following are the chemical formulae of the given alternatives:
**A.** $NO_3$
**B.** $NH_3$
**C.** $HNO_3$
**D.** $N_2O$
The only formula without oxygen is **B.**

15. **C.**
Root pressure operates by having more dissolved materials in aqueous solution than an aqueous solution on the other side of a membrane. Water will try and equalize the concentrations on both sides of the membrane. Water will therefore push through the membrane until the concentrations are balanced.
The force that water exerts in this case is called osmotic pressure. The membranes of plant roots use the force of osmosis to push water through the vascular systems of plants.
Root pressure is therefore a type of osmotic pressure.

17. The biosphere is considered an energetically open system. What this means is that matter is conserved, but energy is not. Matter generally does not enter or leave the biosphere, but sunlight constantly showers radiation on it. Geothermal energy can also inject energy into the biosphere. In addition, low-wave radiation in the form of heat is constantly bleeding off into space, which means that Earth is constantly giving and taking energy from something outside the system. When there are exchanges between a system and something beyond the system, it is considered open.
Matter exchanges, however, principally take place within the biosphere, which is why there are matter cycles to constantly reuse the resources available. Sustaining life on Earth is not dependent on meteorites entering the biosphere from space, for example.
The steady state equilibrium of the biosphere is maintained through an essentially closed system of matter and an open system of energy.
If no energy came from somewhere beyond the planet, the biosphere as a whole would perish. The same holds true if heat did not leave the biosphere. All living things would perish if the heat as the sun continued to add more and more heat and energy into the system. This is the fundamental concept of the biosphere as an open system.

**19.** Many scientific models, including those of the Intergovernmental Panel on Climate Change, speculate that carbon dioxide emissions from human activities may cause an increase in the greenhouse effect.

This means that more heat—both from surface albedo reflected directly and from existing atmospheric heat—will be conserved within the troposphere. The result of this effect would be an increased temperature of the global climate.

– First, an increased $CO_2$ level in the atmosphere would trigger a tremendous amount of blue-green algae, phytoplankton, and cyanobacteria activity. An increased $CO_2$ concentration in the air means there are more dissolved aqueous nutrients available for aquatic photosynthesizers. This causes these organisms to produce more oxygen.

– Next, an increased global temperature would involve an acceleration of the water cycle, as evapotranspiration would increase. More heat means that more water will evaporate, and a greater amount of water would be in the form of vapour. A cloudier atmosphere means less direct sunlight and a greater albedo for the planet, which reduces the amount of solar energy.

– Increased temperatures may also lead to the melting of the polar ice caps. As ice sheets thaw and melt into the oceans, several things may occur. Lower immediate temperatures will increase the concentration of $CO_2$ in the oceans because the carbon dioxide is dissolved from the air, which reduces the amount of airborne $CO_2$.

–If the polar ice melts into the oceans, this will decrease the salinity of seawater, which will in turn have several effects. Fresh water has a lower boiling point and thus is more likely to evaporate. According to the Geological Survey of Canada, it could also change the circulation of ocean currents. Finally, it would raise sea levels worldwide, which would threaten many human settlements, including populated islands.

– Rising sea levels might threaten major populated areas, but on a world-wide scale, agricultural floodplains that would be lost to future harvests are actually an enormous contributor of methane to the atmosphere.

The central idea here is that all of the components of the biosphere are interconnected and a number of cycles maintain a steady state equilibrium by adapting and cope with change. The biosphere is filled with checks and balances that work to sustain stability.

# ECOSYSTEMS AND POPULATION CHANGE

## Lesson 1—Ecosystems

### PRACTICE EXERCISE—ANSWERS AND SOLUTIONS

**1.  B.**
Climatic components of an ecosystem are defined as those related to weather. Weather patterns can influence ecosystems through the availability of water, oxygen, and sunlight. Latitude, however, is defined independent of weather. Latitude is a physiographic factor in an ecosystem because it is defined by how far north or south an ecosystem is located on the globe, not by how the weather affects it.

**3.  A.**
Commensalism is a biotic component of an ecosystem because it refers to the interaction of organisms with one another. In particular, commensalism is a situation in which one organism is given a competitive advantage by another type of organism without affecting the advantages possessed by the latter organism. Structuralism is a school of thought that deals with creating a system within which all biological systems are based on a greater conception of matter as a whole. It does not form a component part of an ecosystem's dynamic. Salinity and turbidity refer to abiotic factors present in aquatic ecosystems.

**5.  D.**
Trees release nutrients into the soil by shedding leaves, needles, or spines, which are then broken down into basic chemical components by decomposers. Living trees generally do not secrete or release nutrients through their roots. In fact, roots are the means by which trees are able to withdraw nutrients from the soil. Animals excrete wastes that are broken down by decomposers into chemical nutrients, but they do not need to live in trees in order to do so. Although trees provide shade for the soil and although shade is generally good for decomposers, there is no direct link between the nutrients found in trees and the nutrients returned to the soil.

**7. A.**

Ecology is the study of relationships between organisms and the environment in which they inhabit. Biology is the broad name for the study of living organisms. Chemistry looks at the composition, structure and properties of matter, and ergonomics is the discipline that is concerned with designing things according to human needs.

**9. A.**

A habitat would represent the smallest biological division of an area, as it is the typical environment for a single species. An example might be Great Bear Lake, which contains a number of species of fish not found elsewhere. A biome is a climatically and geographically defined area of similar organisms and communities. An example could be tundra, which is a treeless plain that has permanently frozen subsoil. A biome may contain a number of habitats. The biosphere encapsulates all of the regions on Earth that can support life and includes all biomes. The order of terms from smallest to largest is habitat, biome, and biosphere.

**11. B.**

Any location defined as a region specific to a particular organism is referred to as the habitat of that organism. As general similarities are found between habitats and the communities of organisms that dwell within them, greater classifications for those climatic and geographic areas—such as biome and ecosystem—are applied. The biosphere encompasses all life-bearing areas on Earth.

**13. D.**

Of the four options given, all four could potentially reduce the size of a bird population. What is important to consider is the relationship between these destructive and lethal scenarios and the density of the population that they affect. A large mudslide would destroy habitat and interfere with nesting and breeding, as well as the availability of food. However, a mudslide would inconvenience and threaten a small population as well as a large one. The amount of individuals per unit of space is largely irrelevant. Alternative **B** is therefore incorrect, and so are **A** and **C**. The size of the population does not impact the degree of lethality that these conditions impose.

Alternative **D** is the best answer because as a bird population becomes more densely-packed and crowded, there is a greater likelihood that an airborne virus could spread to more members of the population as it increases.

## *Lesson 2—Biomes*

### PRACTICE EXERCISE—
### ANSWERS AND SOLUTIONS

**1. A.**

Biomes are characterized by distinctive plants, animals, and climate. The boundaries of biomes are often the transition areas of one biome and another. Habitats are specific areas that support a specific type of organism. Populations are interbreeding members of a species that are found in a specific area at a particular time. A community defines a systemic interaction between different species.

**3. D.**

Biodiversity is used to describe the number of different organisms found within a particular area. Tropical rainforests contain the greatest biodiversity per square meter. A key term that truly defines the tropical rainforest is stratification. This vertical layering of organisms within the rainforest results in numerous co-existing communities. High humidity and temperatures, combined with rapid and plentiful decomposition, create a swift cycling of matter and energy through complex and plentiful communities of organisms.

**5. C.**

Grasslands are areas characterized by large ungulates, four seasons, and deep, rich soil. Of the four alternatives, only grassland and taiga biomes have four seasons. Tropical rainforests generally only have wet and dry seasons, and deserts have little variation in rainfall and temperature over the course of a year. Of the remaining two options, taiga has poor soil because of the low temperatures, low soil pH levels, and low rates of decomposition. Therefore, the correct answer is grassland. Rich soil is the accumulation of biomass that are formed from nutrients that remain within the soil. Low precipitation reduces the washing away of soil. There is also limited tree growth as a result of overall cooler temperatures and longer winters,.

A unique characteristic of grasses is blade growth from the base or crown, which allows for ungulates to browse on grasses without killing the plants. No matter how close to the ground a cow bites off a grass plant, the grass is still able to regrow its leaves. This also selects against the growth of trees since leaf browsing stops growth until the next growth period (not of the tree as a whole but at the site of the leaf stem.

6.  **A.**

The plant life within taiga biomes are characterized by coniferous trees that shed acidic needles rather than leaves. The lower temperatures reduce the rate of decomposition, which makes the layer of fertile soil very thin. This greatly limits the types of plants that can successfully compete for nutrients.
In addition, the majority of precipitation that falls on taiga tends to be in the form of snow or ice. Neither of these is immediately usable, which explains the preponderance of water-conserving morphologies within this biome.

7.  **B.**

The key to this question is the word permafrost. Permafrost is permanently frozen soil, which is characteristic of tundra.

8.  **C.**

Primary succession occurs when new life grows where none had previously existed. Lichens are pioneer plants: they can colonize and survive on barren rock. A forest fire does not remove or destroy the soil community. Nutrients are often cycled into the soil, which allows for the rapid regeneration of producers. Farming normally attempts to remove only the surface plant material. The cycling of the remaining matter is necessary for the maintenance of topsoil levels as well as soil nutrients. Shrubs and trees growing in an area of grassland is a sign of secondary succession, not primary succession.

## Lesson 3—Food Chains, Food Webs, and Pyramids

### PRACTICE EXERCISE—
### ANSWERS AND SOLUTIONS

1.  **C.**
Food chains are a simplified and linear form of energy flow. A food chain is normally characterized as having up to five organisms. Each organism eats only one other type of organism.

3.  **D.**
An organism's trophic level describes how it obtains its energy within an ecosystem. A niche is the role an organism has within a particular environment. This is not limited to how it obtains energy. A community describes the interaction of populations, while a population **D** describes members of a species that occupy the same area at the same time.

5.  **B.**
Earthworms and maggots are examples of detritivores. These organisms help to recycle matter by feeding on waste and decaying plants and animals.

7.  **B.**
A food web is more complex than a food chain. The complexity is a result of the interconnectedness of numerous food chains. A diagram of a food web thus contains a much greater number of organisms than a diagram of a food chain.

## PRACTICE QUIZ

### ANSWERS AND SOLUTIONS

1. **B.**
   Water is an abiotic (non-living) component of an ecosystem. Plants, bacteria, and detritivores are all biotic (living) components.

3. **D.**
   A habitat is the specific area an organism occupies, including the biotic and abiotic factors that provide a viable environment for the organism.

5. **C.**
   An ecosystem consists of all the interacting biotic and abiotic factors found within its boundaries. A habitat refers to the biotic and abiotic factors necessary for the survival of an organism. A community is the interaction of populations within a given area, and a biome is a large area characterized by unique biotic and abiotic factors.

7. **D.**
   Stratification refers to the five layers of autotroph growth within tropical rainforests. This layering is one reason that such biodiversity exists within the relatively small surface area of a tropical rainforest biome.

9. **A.**
   Large producers adapted to cool temperatures and acidic soil conditions are found in the taiga biome. Most conifers have small leaves that are in the shape of needles. These needles are covered with wax to minimize water loss and to allow snow to slide off more easily. Many also have deep green pigmentation, which ensures maximum absorption of useable light energy. This is necessary given the taiga's low to moderate light energy levels. Fallen needles are responsible for the acidity of the soil. The acidity helps suppress or kill competing producers and thus minimizes the competition for light, water, and soil nutrients.

11. **B.**
    Secondary succession can occur only on land with soil (humus) or existing communities that support autotrophs. Soil is normally not sterile, and the pre-existing communities aid in the progression and maturation of an ecosystem. Lifeless, barren land is characteristic of primary, not secondary, succession. Lava flow is molten, sterile rock that solidifies and offers the foundation for primary succession. Fires do not normally sterilize or destroy soil; in fact, they often provide ideal conditions for the growth of autotrophs and the recycling of nutrients.

13. **C.**
    The trophic level to which an organism belongs is determined by how it obtains energy. Primary producers obtain their energy from the sun or from deep-sea geothermal vents. Primary consumers feed on primary producers. Secondary consumers feed on primary consumers, and so on.

15. **A.**
    A food web is a series of interacting food chains. Food chains are normally limited to approximately five organisms. They are characterized by a chain that consists of one organism eating or being eaten by another organism. This chain is linear, whereas a food web allows multiple pathways of energy distribution. Autotrophs are essential components of a food web (and chain). They are the only pathway through which light or chemical energy can enter an ecosystem.

17. **Similarities:** Food chains, food webs, and pyramids are diagrams that illustrate the flow of energy through a portion of an ecosystem. They each separate organisms according to how they obtain energy. This is defined as an organism's trophic level. They each begin with autotrophs, and they do not show the sun as the original source of energy, although this is indeed required as an energy source (except in the case of chemosynthetic autotrophs). Relationships are simplified in that either a small number of individual organisms are named or in that their general role in energy transfer is used.

**Differences:** Food chains and food webs do not normally indicate the quantity of organisms, their biomass, or the amount of energy relative to each trophic level. This is particularly important with ecosystems that have fewer individual autotrophs than primary consumers. The pyramid takes on the form of a normal pyramid supported by a smaller producer-trophic level. This may appear to be incorrect because only 10% of energy is transferred up to the next trophic level. For example, a large tree is counted as a single autotroph, but it can support large numbers of organisms. A pyramid of biomass can also assume this shape. Pyramids illustrate each trophic level as a clear and separate area within the diagram. This simplifies identification of an organism's role in an ecosystem. Although food webs also include a number of different examples of organisms within each trophic level, their identification of trophic level is not as clear. The web describes a large number of energy transfers that do not easily lend themselves to trophic level identification. However, a web is a more realistic illustration of the biotic factors within an environment.

## Lesson 4—Variation in Populations

### PRACTICE EXERCISE—
### ANSWERS AND SOLUTIONS

1. **C.**
Variation describes differences between individuals, which increases biodiversity. Although most variations do not increase the fitness of an individual, each slight change adds to a populations overall genetic diversity. Also, most variations are not extreme in their difference to the population average. The majority of a population falls within this 'average' range, with extremes occurring with less frequency outside of this range.

3. **B.**
Asexual reproduction produces the least variation. This is because there is no crossing over of chromosomes or random fertilization. A benefit of asexual reproduction is comparatively high rates of replication (the rapid and consistent reproduction of one cell type).

5. **D.**
Bacteria and yeast reproduce asexually. Processes such as binary fission allow bacteria to replicate, while budding is a proccess carried out by yeast. Humans, birds, and flowering plants reproduce sexually.

7. **A.**
Eye colour is an example of an inherited trait. This is determined by the random assortment of parental chromosomes. Emphysema is an acquired disease that is associated with environmental pollutants. A spoken language is an acquired skill that is dependant upon environmental learning. Although it is often seen that certain individuals have the ability to acquire a proficiency in a number of languages, the language itself requires study and practice. This is also the case with tennis. The genetic makeup of an individual does not guarantee proficiency in any given sport. It is an acquired skill that requires instruction and practice.

## Lesson 5—Taxonomy and Binomial Nomenclature

### PRACTICE EXERCISE—
### ANSWERS AND SOLUTIONS

1. **B.**
The kingdom Monera encompasses all of the life forms that are unicellular and prokaryotic. There are approximately $5 \times 10^{30}$ organisms on Earth that can be classified as monerans.

3. **D.**
The three domains are Archaea, Eukaryota, and Bacteria. Because Protista is not a domain, this alternative is incorrect. A golden chanterelle muchroom is multicellular, which means that it is excluded from the domains Archaea and Bacteria. The correct answer is therefore Eukaryota.

5. **A.**

Phylogeny deals with the genetic development, organization, and evolution of living beings. Taxonomy is a field of study concerned with classifying individuals according to various characteristics, including morphology, reproduction, and modes of nutrition. Alternatives **B**, **C**, and **D** deal with the classification of species in terms of physiological or behavioural qualities. Although this demonstrates a taxonomic process of classification, only alternative **A** contains information relevant to the expression of genetic information within the cellular structure of organisms.

7. **C.**

There are indeed plants that consume other living organisms. An example is the Venus flytrap. Plants such as mosses and ferns reproduce using spores. Therefore, alternative **B** is incorrect. Although there are some species of plant that have no chlorophyll, all plants have chloroplast organelles. The kingdom Plantae is definied phylogenetically. Therefore, all plants have the same cellular structure, even though some have since developed into species that no longer photosynthesize. Alternative **D** is therefore incorrect. The correct answer is **C**. The Ginkgo tree is the only representative of the phylum Ginkgophyta in existence.

## Lesson 6—Evolution and Natural Selection

### PRACTICE EXERCISE— ANSWERS AND SOLUTIONS

1. **A.**

Evolution is the gradual appearance of new characteristics within a species from generation to generation. This is a long-term process that is dependent upon beneficial changes to a population's genes. Natural selection is the process whereby the fitness of particular trait is tested by environmental pressures. These pressures may include competition within a species (intraspecific competition) or other biotic and abiotic factors that have an impact upon a species. Adaptation is the process an organism undergoes whereby a trait has been selected for and is then transferred to future generations. Survival of the fittest is the phrase often attributed to Charles Darwin. The British economist Herbert Spencer is actually credited with the phrase, although this was apparently based upon his reading of Charles Darwin's writings.

3. **D.**

Fitness is the ability of an organism to obtain food and have surviving offspring. The level of fitness is directly related to how well adapted an organism is to its environment's biotic and abiotic factors. The longevity of an organism may not indicate fitness because the organism might be sterile. Breeding by itself, is also not a sign of fitness, since most or all offspring may fall to predation, disease, or other environmental pressures.

5. **B.**

Darwin proposed the theory of natural selection. His theory was based upon observations made during a lengthy voyage as a naturalist aboard the HMS Beagle. Creationism is the proposed origin of species as put forward by many faiths. Punctuated equilibrium theorizes not a gradual evolution, but rather short and dramatic leaps in the adaptations of a species followed by long periods of relatively stability. Convergent evolution is the evolving of two different species so that both are best able to survive within the same type of environment.

**7. A.**

DNA is the biochemical evidence for evolution. It is remarkable that all living organisms use DNA as a template for cellular replication and protein manufacture. This evidence is considered indirect evidence supporting the theory of evolution. It cannot be quantitatively measured in the same was radioactive dating in conjunction with fossil evidence can be quantitatively measured. However, it is a strong argument for a common ancestor.

## *PRACTICE TEST*

### ANSWERS AND SOLUTIONS

**1. A.**

Variation provides a wider range of traits available to a species. This increases the overall stability of an ecosystem. Although this also increases the chances of detrimental or non-favourable variations, the changes that can occur within an environment over long periods of time can be great. A narrower range of beneficial traits may allow for higher survival rates initially, but this greatly reduces the adaptability of a species to changing environmental conditions.

**3. B.**

Cells use asexual reproduction to rapidly produce identical copies of the parent. Bacterial copies are called daughter cells, which are produced through the process of binary fission. It is a very efficient process that can produce copies within minutes. Prior to fertilization, sexual reproduction requires the development of gametes that are a chromosomal half-copy of the complete chromosomal karyotype. Fission and budding are strategies used by bacteria and yeast during asexual reproduction.

**5. C.**

Flowers allow for the fertilization of ova through the transfer of pollen by flying organisms. Bees and other organisms serve as pollinators. Anthers and holding sperm transfer pollen to the bodies of these organisms. Pollen is then passed to the stigma of another flower. The stigma contains the ovum, which is subsequently fertilized. This is only one method of fertilization by plants. Certain plants can self-fertilize, while others pollinate using wind and airborne pollen.

**7. B.**

The pigment found in hair is an inherited trait. Hair colour can be passed on to offspring. The role of recessive and dominant alleles determines the hair colour of an individual. This is the result of the random assortment of chromosomes donated by both parents. This variation is dependant upon the probability of a hair colour appearing.

**8. B.**

The darkening of skin pigment is an acquired characteristic caused by exposure to light energy. This darkening requires an environmental stimulus. A tan, which is caused by the production of melanin by cells called melanocytes, is a response to UV energy. The tan cannot be passed on to offspring. What can be passed on is the number of melanocytes and their inherent activity level.

**9. A.**

Plant height demonstrates continuous variation. It is the result of polygenic control and is often dependent on genetics combined with environmental factors. When measured from a large enough sample group, plant height will exhibit a bell curve distribution. The sex of an organism will normally be either male or female. Usually, there is no gradient of sexes between these two. Human blood type exhibits discontinuous variation. Human blood types are based upon the ABO system of blood type antigen. There will no variation between the four possible blood types. A pea being either smooth or wrinkled is also discontinuous. There is no gradient from smooth to wrinkled.

**10. B.**

The most observable evolution is microevolution. It is supported by more empirical evidence than macroevolution. This type of evolution has a shorter timeline. Because many different species that originated from a common species are still alive, the collection of empirical evidence is relatively easy. Macroevolution is the occurrence of change over much longer periods of time. The adaptations observed can be dramatic; however, empirical evidence is largely based upon fossilized remains and these are not as common for many species. This is due to the very particular conditions needed to adequately preserve traces of an organism.

**11. B.**

Although strength is often seen as a key determinant of male breeding among herbivores and carnivores, by itself, it does not assure natural selection. The organism best adapted to its environment will normally survive. This may or may not include characteristics such as strength.

**12. A.**

Bat echolocation and evasive moth strategies are an example of co-evolution. The evolving of adaptive moth behaviours is a direct result of evolving bat hunting strategies, which include echolocation, nocturnal predation, and near silent flight. Divergent evolution is the development of different species from a common ancestor. The Galapagos Finches are an example. Convergent evolution is the adaptation of different species to common environmental pressures. Punctuated equilibrium is the rapid evolution of species followed by lengthy periods of little evolutionary change.

**13. A.**

Directional selection chooses members of a population that are on either extreme of a bell curve. These are the non-average members. Stabilizing selection chooses members that are within the range of the average. The term *stabilizing* suggests that such a process helps maintain the longterm survival of a population and is also the result of an environment that supports the most common traits. Disruptive selection is a process that shifts between stabilizing selection (the average) and directional selection (the extremes). This is often seen in environments that undergo substantial changes in environmental pressures. Natural selection is the force that selects population members that are best adapted for the selective pressures of an environment. These pressures may select for the most common traits, or they can select for extreme variations.

**15. D.**

Similarities in the embryonic stages of different species are considered indirect evidence in support of the theory of evolution. Commonalities observed are gill-like structures and protruding or extended vertebrae (tails). Direct evidence would be fossil evidence or radioactive dating. Although webbed hands are evident during embryonic development, these are not accompanied by fins.

**16.** Sexual reproduction is dependant upon the union of gametes from both parents. The union of two haploid cells provides random fertilization, which greatly increases the variation among offspring. Prior to this, there is an independent assortment of chromosomes and a crossing over of chromosomal DNA during meiosis.

**17.** Natural selection is dependent upon environmental pressure to select for and against variations within a population. An organism's fitness is demonstrated through a series of essential 'steps'. Charles Darwin proposed the following:

-   Offspring are required to compete for limited resources.
-   There must be variation among offspring. This variation helps selects those indivduals that are best adapted to environmental conditions.
-   These offspring must reproduce and pass on these beneficial variations.

# PHOTOSYNTHESIS AND CELLULAR RESPIRATION

## Lesson 1—Photosynthesis

### PRACTICE EXERCISE—
### ANSWERS AND SOLUTIONS

1. **C.**
Chlorophyll *a* is found in the reaction centre. Antennae pigments such as chlorophyll *b* are located within a photosystem that surrounds the reaction center. These photosystems are imbedded in the thylakoid membrane.

3. **A.**
Water is the source of oxygen. The removal of oxygen occurs during photolysis.

5. **C.**
RuBisCO is an enzyme involved in the fixation of a carbon to RuBP. This process occurs within the light-independent Calvin-Benson cycle.

7. **C.**
Phycoerythrin and phycocyanin are antenna pigments associated with Photosystems II and I.

## Lesson 2—Light-Dependent Photosynthesis

### PRACTICE EXERCISE—
### ANSWERS AND SOLUTIONS

1. **A.**
Photolysis donates electrons to Photosystem II. This occurs as a result of the excitation of electrons within the reaction centre of Photosystem II. As these are transferred to the electron transport chain, they are replaced by electrons from water.

3. **D.**
The reduction of $NADP^+$ to NADPH occurs after PS I, not PS II. This process requires the enzyme $NADP^+$ reductase.

5. **B.**
P stands for pigment. Therefore, P700 represents pigment whose absorption of light peaks at 700 nm.

7. **B.**
The energy for the phosphorylation of ADP is provided by chemiosmosis. A proton gradient forces $H^+$ ions through ATP synthase (from the thylakoid space), across the thylakoid membrane, and into the stroma.

## Lesson 3—Light-Independent Photosynthesis

### PRACTICE EXERCISE—
### ANSWERS AND SOLUTIONS

1. **A.**
The Calvin-Benson cycle occurs within the stroma. Structures associated with PS II, PS I, and the electron transport chains are located within the thylakoid membrane. Photolysis occurs within the thylakoid space.

3. **B.**
The light-independent reaction can occur in both light and dark conditions. Dark photosynthesis would indicate a process that requires darkness. This is not the case.

5. **B.**
The Calvin-Benson cycle must fix six molecules of carbon dioxide to form one molecule of glucose.

7. **D.**
ATP and NADPH provide phosphate and $H^+$ to the Calvin-Benson cycle. ADP, $NADP^+$ and glucose are products from the cycle. $O_2$ is produced as a by-product of photolysis, a light-dependent reaction.

## PRACTICE QUIZ

### ANSWERS AND SOLUTIONS

1. **D.**
The conversion of light energy into chemical energy is the result of both light-dependent and light-independent reactions. Light-dependent reactions use light energy and water to generate NADPH, ATP, and oxygen gas.
Both NADPH and ATP are subsequently used by the light-independent reaction in order to generate glucose.

3. **C.**

Chlorophyll *a* and *b* pigments reflect green and absorb red, blue, and orange. Although chlorophyll absorbs very little light energy within green's wavelength of 490–560 nm, pigments such as phycoerythrin and phycocyanin can absorb light energy within this range.

5. **B.**

The immediate effect is a stoppage of electron excitation. Electron excitation occurs as a direct result of light energy being absorbed by pigments located within the thylakoid membrane. The Calvin-Benson cycle can continue as long as ATP, NADPH, and carbon dioxide (or modified forms found in CAM plants) are available. Antennae pigments allow for photosystems to use a wider range of light energy.

7. **A.**

RuBisCO is an enzyme that 'floats' in the stroma. Because it acts as a catalyst for carbon fixation, it must be in the same location as the Calvin-Benson cycle.

9. **D.**

ATP synthase is imbedded in the thylakoid membrane. The generation of a proton gradient in the thylakoid space forces protons through this protein, which uses this flow of protons to generate ATP.

11. **D.**

Each water molecule allows for the transfer of two electrons to PS II and then two electrons to PS I. These electrons are transferred to $NADP^+$. $NADP^+$ reductase is the enzyme that catalyzes the reaction of $NADP^+ + H^+ + 2e^-$ to form nicotinamide adenine dinucleotide (NADPH).

13. **A.**

The term carbon fixation is used to describe the addition of a carbon molecule to RuBP. The key final product of this reaction is glucose. ATP and NADPH are used to drive the Calvin-Benson cycle by donating the phosphates and hydrogen ions. Electron excitation provides the energy, which allows for the transfer of electrons along the photosystems.

15. **D.**

RuBisCO is an enzyme that is required to catalyze the addition of carbon dioxide to RuBP at the 'start' of the Calvin-Benson cycle. The rate at which this occurs is approximately 3 $CO_2$ per second. This is considered slow for an enzyme. However, the large concentration of this enzyme allows for an overall rapid fixation of $CO_2$.

17. Both PS II and PS I are located within the thylakoid membrane. The key function of PS II is the excitation of electrons via the transfer of light energy by certain plant pigments. The photolysis of water provides replacement electrons. PS I accepts electrons from PS II through the reduction and oxidation of cyctochromes that form the electron transport chain. PS I transfers these electrons to $NADP^+$ and $H^+$ to form NADPH.

Photolysis occurs in the lumen (thylakoid space). It provides electrons to PS II and $H^+$ for the generation of a proton concentration gradient. This gradient forms the bases of the force necessary to generate ATP. A by-product of this reaction is also oxygen; however, this "waste" is essential for aerobic cellular respiration. ATP synthase is a protein that is imbedded in the thylakoid membrane. Its key function is to act as a proton channel for the flow of $H^+$ as it travels down a concentration gradient from the lumen (thylakoid space), through ATP synthase, and out into the stroma. ATP synthase has binding sites that accept ADP and $P_i$. The change in shape, initiated by proton flow, forces the binding of ADP + $P_i$ to form ATP. This process is repeated. Calvin-Benson cycle occurs in the stroma. Its key function is the generation of glucose molecule through the fixation of carbon dioxide. ATP and NADPH drive the cycle. These molecules originate from the light-dependent reactions. It requires 6 molecules of $CO_2$ to generate 1 molecule of glucose. The cycle is also described as the light-independent reaction, which indicates that it does not require light energy.

**19.** The Calvin-Benson cycle relies upon the light-dependent reactions for ATP and NADPH. These are available during light conditions because of the transfer of light energy to pigments. Once light energy is no longer available, the processes occurring at PS II and PS I stop. As ATP and NADPH supplies are reduced, the fixation of $CO_2$ by RuBisCO is also greatly reduced. $C_3$ plants conserve water by closing stomata during the night. This greatly reduces the available amount of $CO_2$ for carbon fixation during darkness.

## Lesson 4—Cellular Respiration

### PRACTICE EXERCISE—
### ANSWERS AND SOLUTIONS

**1. D.**
Light energy is converted and stored as chemical energy through the process of photosynthesis. The resulting chemical energy can take the form of glucose, which can be used by organisms during cellular respiration.

**3. A.**
A cell will initially attempt to access other sugars. If these are not available, fat is the next molecule that is used as an energy source. This is then followed by protein. Both water and oxygen offer no energy in this process.

**5. C.**
$C_6H_{12}O_6 + 6O_2 \rightarrow 6CO_2 + 6H_2O + 36ATP$.

**7. A.**
Endobiosis is a theory that describes the relationship developed between host cells, mitochondria, and chloroplasts. This symbiotic relationship is of benefit to the cell and to both mitochondria and chloroplasts. It is important to note that both mitochondria and chloroplasts contain their own DNA, which is one of the criteria that lends support to this theory.

## Lesson 5—Anaerobic Respiration

### PRACTICE EXERCISE—
### ANSWERS AND SOLUTIONS

**1. D.**
Anaerobic respiration occurs in low oxygen conditions. Because oxygen is virtually absent, the required final acceptor for the electrons that are being transferred along through the electron transport chain is absent. This forces cells to use the alternate fermentative pathway for ATP synthesis.

**3. B.**
Glucose must be oxidized prior to fermentation. This oxidative pathway is described as glycolysis. This requires the input of 2 ATP resulting in the generation of 4 ATP. The net ATP produced is 2. Oxidation occurs through the transfer of electrons and protons to $NAD^+$.

**5. B.**
Under anaerobic conditions, a muscle cell will produce lactic acid and 2 ATP. This allows for a limited production of ATP and the oxidation of NADH to $NAD^+$. Lactic acid can be converted into pyruvate if the anaerobic conditions change to aerobic conditions. Therefore, lactic acid is a temporary stored form of pyruvate within the muscle cell. Pyruvate is not an end product of fermentation, and the production of 36ATP occurs only as a result of aerobic cellular respiration.

**7. B.**
Glycolysis is required prior to fermentation. Pyruvate is the substrate necessary for the production of either ethanol and $CO_2$ or lactic acid. Glycolysis can occur in either aerobic or anaerobic conditions. This allows for a substrate that can be used under varying conditions. The Krebs cycle, oxidative phosphorylation, and a proton gradient are all processes involved in aerobic cellular respiration.

## Lesson 6—Aerobic Respiration

### PRACTICE EXERCISE—
### ANSWERS AND SOLUTIONS

1. **A.**
Aerobic respiration requires the oxidation of glucose. This happens during glycolysis, which produces 2-pyruvate that then enter the mitochondria during aerobic conditions. Oxidative decarboxylation describes the removal of carbon ($CO_2$) as pyruvate is converted into acetyl-CoA.
The Krebs cycle accepts acetyl-CoA, which results in the formation of citric ccid. Oxidative phosphorylation occurs as a result of the proton gradient created by the Krebs cycle generating NADH and $FADH_2$.

3. **D.**
Glycolysis does not require oxygen as an electron acceptor. This process occurs outside of the mitochondria and can occur in both aerobic and anaerobic conditions. Oxidative decarboxylation, oxidative phosphorylation, and the Krebs cycle occur within the mitochondria. Each directly or indirectly requires oxygen.

5. **B.**
Glycolysis produces a net amount of two ATP. This amount takes into account that glycolysis uses two ATP prior to producing four ATP.
A total of 36 ATP are produced by the aerobic cellular respiration of one molecule of glucose.

7. **D.**
The Krebs cycle uses carbon derived from glucose to generate NADH and $FADH_2$. These proton carriers are the reduced forms of $NAD^+$ and FAD. These carriers transfer protons and electrons to the electron transport chain which produced the proton gradient necessary to carry out oxidative phosphorylation.

## PRACTICE TEST

### ANSWERS AND SOLUTIONS

1. **D.**
Fructose is an isomer of glucose, whereas galactose is an epimer. All three are monosaccharides, which are described by the formula $C_6H_{12}O_6$. Fructose is an isomer that has a 5-carbon cyclic structure with an attached 6-carbon. Galactose is an epimer because it has the same 6-carbon structure as glucose; however, at carbon 4 (C4), there is a structural change.

3. **D.**
Through the process of hydrolysis, ATP has a phosphate group removed, which converts ATP to ADP. The removal of the third phosphate and the resultant energy is essential for supplying energy for cellular processes. Alternative **D**, which represents the gamma phosphate group, is the correct answer.

5. **A.**
The complete formula for aerobic cellular respiration is $C_6H_{12}O_6 + 6O_2 \rightarrow 6CO_2 + 6H_2O$ (plus 36 ATP and heat). The electrons that are transferred along the electron transport chain are accepted by $O_2$ (final acceptor). These combine with protons to produce water. Heat is a byproduct of cellular respiration, with amounts of approximately 50–61% heat loss in birds and mammals. This is necessary for the maintenance of body temperature.

7. **B.**
The greatest number of mitochondria would be found in muscle cells. Muscle contraction is dependent upon ready access to ATP. This compound is the source of energy needed to bring about muscle fibre contractions. The sliding movement of filaments is dependent upon the use of ATP and the 'recharging' of ADP through oxidative phosphorylation. Most eukaryotic cells contain mitochondria. Bacteria fall under the category of prokaryotes, which lack a membrane-enclosed nucleus as well as organelles such as mitochondria. Tendon is a connective tissue formed between muscle and bone. It functions as a very strong fibrous tissue with few, if any, nerve fibres within its main section. This results in little need for the energy supplied by ATP.

**9. C.**

Glycolysis occurs in both aerobic and anaerobic conditions. This is essential because the key product, pyruvate, can be used by two pathways. Aerobic conditions allow for the movement of pyruvate across the outer and inner mitochondrial membranes. This necessitates the oxidative decarboxylation of pyruvate, which results in a final product of acetyl-CoA. The eventual complete oxidation of one molecule of glucose produces a net amount of 36 ATP. If conditions are anaerobic, two ATP can still be produced through the use of the fermentative pathway.

**11. A.**

A final product of aerobic cellular respiration is 36 ATP. It should be noted that the main production of ATP occurs as a result of oxidative phosphorylation. Lactic acid and ethanol are final products of the fermentative pathway. Pyruvic acid (pyruvate) is the final product of glycolysis.

**13 C.**

The conversion of pyruvate to acetyl-CoA occurs within the intermembrane space of the mitochondria. The conversion is necessary to allow pyruvate to be transferred into the Krebs cycle in the form of acetyl-CoA. The oxidation of glucose into 2 pyruvate occurs during glycolysis within the cytoplasm. The donation of two carbons in the form of acetyl-CoA occurs within the matrix, whereas the oxidation of glucose into lactic acid occurs within the cytoplasm under anaerobic conditions.

**15.** Oxidative phosphorylation describes the synthesis of ATP through the proton motive force generated by the transfer of electrons in the electron transport system. The term oxidative applies to both electrons and protons oxidized from glucose. The generation of ATP depends upon a proton gradient within the intermembrane space. This is a result of proton carriers (NADH and $FADH_2$) transferring $H^+$ and electrons to proteins imbedded within the mitochondrial inner membrane. These proteins are collectively called an electron transport chain. Electrons provide the energy through a series of oxidative and reductive electron transfers that provide the energy necessary to shuttle $H^+$ through these proteins and into the mitochondrial intermembrane space. This proton gradient eventually forces $H^+$ through ATP synthase, which is also imbedded in the mitochondrial inner membrane.

The flow of $H^+$ is described as the proton motive force necessary to carry out the phosphorylation of $ADP + P_i \rightarrow ATP$ by ATP synthase.

Substrate-level phosphorylation describes the synthesis of ATP using a phosphate transferred from a substrate. The process requires that a substrate have a phosphate bonded to it.

It also requires an enzyme that can remove the phosphate and transfer this to ADP. These reactions are not the principal source of ATP during aerobic cellular respiration. These reactions occur during glycolysis and the Krebs cycle. During glycolysis, the enzyme pyruvate kinase removes a phosphate from phophoenolpyruvate. The phosphate is transferred to ADP, which results in the phosphorylation of ADP to produce ATP. Within the Krebs cycle, the enzyme nucleoside diphosphokinase carries out the transfer of phosphate from GTP. GTP has removed a phosphate from succinyl-CoA and acts as a intermediary phosphate carrier. The phosphate is then transferred to ADP and results in the phosphorylated ADP producing ATP.

**17. Similarities**

Both chloroplasts and mitochondria use membranes to separate areas of high and low proton concentrations. Chloroplasts utilize the thylakoid membrane to create a proton gradient. Mitochondria utilize the inner membrane to do the same.

Both rely on $H^+$ as a proton motive force to generate ATP through oxidative phosphorylation carried out by ATP synthase. A model of ATP synthase suggests that the flow of protons causes a rotational movement of subunits within ATP synthase. The resultant motion allows for the conformational changes necessary for the attachment and conversion of ADP to ATP.

**Differences**

The area of greatest proton concentration in a chloroplast is within the thylakoid space. This forces $H^+$ to go out across the thylakoid membrane and into the stroma. The area of greatest proton concentration in mitochondria is in the intermembrane space. This forces protons across the inner membrane into the matrix. Thus, the direction of proton flow is opposite.

Although both chloroplasts and mitochondria produce ATP, the primary role of mitochondria is to produce an end product of 36 ATP. Chloroplasts convert light energy into the chemical potential energy of glucose and also generate ATP, but these ATP molecules are used to drive the Calvin-Benson cycle during the formation of each glucose molecule. The net production of 36 ATP by mitochondria compares to the use of approximately 18 ATP to produce one molecule of glucose.

# HUMAN SYSTEMS

## Lesson 1—The Digestive System

### PRACTICE EXERCISE—
### ANSWERS AND SOLUTIONS

1. Digestion is achieved through both chemical and mechanical processes that function within the human body, independent of the influence of gravity.

Mechanical digestion is achieved first by chewing food in order to form a bolus, which then passes from the mouth to the stomach through peristaltic movement within the esophagus. Further mechanical digestion takes place within the stomach via the combined efforts of involuntary muscular, wave-like contractions and the folds of rugae, which are responsible for the mixing and breakdown of complex food particles into smaller molecules that are easily absorbed into the blood.

Chemical digestion is achieved through the combined efforts of hormonal regulation, acidic secretions, and a number of digestive enzymes that are secreted from the mouth, stomach, and small intestine as well as some auxiliary digestive organs such as the liver and pancreas.

Movement through the digestive system is involuntary and determined by smooth muscle contractions along the entire length of the alimentary canal (GI tract). Backflow of material is restricted at numerous sites within the digestive tube through the presence of one-way valves and sphincters. These valves and sphincters prevent the flow of material in the opposite direction. In a zero-gravity environment, these valves would prevent the gastric juices from the stomach from 'floating' into the esophagus, for example.

3. **a)** Ingestion is the consumption of food or beverage through the mouth.

**b)** Digestion is the breakdown of large, complex molecules into smaller molecules that can be transported into the blood via cellular processes. Digestion includes both chemical digestion (acidic and enzymatic action) and mechanical digestion (chewing and the mixing action of the involuntary smooth muscle contractions of the stomach).

c)   Absorption is the transport of small molecules (nutrients) and water from the stomach, small intestine, and large intestine into the blood plasma (as facilitated by the cellular lining of these organs).

5.   As a result of its biological design, the movement of material is slowed as it passes through the large intestine. This permits the following.

   a)   Absorption of excess water and important salts (sodium and chloride)
   b)   Decomposition of remaining organic material in conjunction with resident intestinal bacteria
   c)   Production of vitamins B and K as well as folic acid
   d)   Storage and elimination of fecal matter

7.   The three primary processes that occur in the digestive system are the following: ingestion, digestion, and absorption.

9.   Three different types of ingested materials that can change the rate of digestion include the following:
   1.   Fats slow down the rate of digestion and muscular contraction.
   2.   Cold food slows down the rate of digestion and muscular contraction.
   3.   Alcohol speeds up the rate of digestion by stimulating acids and digestive enzymes.

11.   Three components that are necessary for the digestion of protein are proteolytic enzymes (such astrypsinogen and pepsinogen), acidic secretions of HCl, and activation enzymes (such as gastrin and enteropeptidase).

## Lesson 2—The Respiratory System

### PRACTICE EXERCISE
### ANSWERS AND SOLUTIONS

1.   Alveolar membranes are designed to increase the rate of diffusion in a number of ways.  They are massive in number (300–600 million sacs), which thereby increases the surface area of the lungs by 300 times.  This increased surface area equates to an increased number of gas and fluid exchange sites and thus an increased rate of diffusion.  Furthermore, the alveolar membranes are moist and very thin (0.2 microns). They therefore provide little resistance to the movement of gas and fluid from the lung space into the blood.  Finally, the alveolar sacs are surrounded by an extensive web-like network of capillaries that permits rapid uptake of dissolved materials into the blood stream.

3.   Temperature:  An increase in temperature increases the rate of oxygen release from the oxyhemoglobin molecule.

   pH: A decrease in blood pH (which is equal to an increase in blood acidity) due to an increase in hydrogen ion concentration increases the rate of oxygen release from the oxyhemoglobin molecule.

   Carbon dioxide concentration:  As carbon dioxide concentration increases, so does the concentration of hydrogen ions in the blood. This is due to the mechanism of carbon dioxide transport in the blood that involves the action of the enzyme carbonic anhydrase.  This enzyme speeds up the conversion of carbon dioxide in the presence of water into hydrogen ions and bicarbonate ions so that it may more easily be transported by the red blood cells.  We therefore see an increase in hydrogen ions in the blood, which results in an increase in blood acidity and a decrease in blood pH.  A decrease in blood pH results in an increase in the rate of oxygen release from the oxyhemoglobin molecule.

5.   Oxygen is transported in the blood in two different ways.

   1)   It is transported as a dissolved gas within the blood plasma and accounts for 1% of oxygen transport in the body.

**2)** It is also transported as oxyhemoglobin within the red blood cells. Oxygen combines with the red, iron-bearing heme portion of the hemoglobin molecule to form oxyhemoglobin and accounts for 99% of oxygen transport in the body.

**7.** Physical activity increases the breathing rate (the number of times you need to breathe each minute) because it increases the buildup of carbon dioxide in the blood. It does this to avoid an increase in blood acidity.

Disease of any type will interfere with the normal functioning of the lungs and typically increases the rate of breathing to compensate for inefficiency at the exchange sites. For example, emphysema and pneumonia interfere gas exchange and can result in respiratory acidosis because carbon dioxide is not being adequately expelled from the lungs. Emphysema is a condition directly related to smoking. Another effect of smoking on the rate of breathing is the change in the consistency of the protective mucus coating of the respiratory system. Smoking causes this protective mucus coating to become less effective and can paralyze the cilia responsible for filtering air and moving the mucus away from the lungs.

**9.** Air will move from and areas of high pressure to areas of low pressure.

For inspiration to occur, the air pressure must be lower on the inside of the chest relative to the outside. To accomplish this, the air pressure within the lungs must be actively decreased and is done so by quickly changing the volume of the thoracic cavity. The muscles involved in increasing the thoracic volume include the external intercostals (which contract and cause the rib cage to move upward) and the diaphragm (which contracts and flattens).

For expiration to occur, the pressure must be higher on the inside of the chest relative to the outside. To create this high-pressure area within the lungs, the volume of the thoracic cavity is decreased, which results in a subsequent expulsion of air.

Expiration is a primarily passive process that occurs as the muscles of inhalation relax, which moves the ribcage back down and forces the diaphragm back up. Exhalation can occur with greater force by also involving the internal intercostals and the abdominal muscles, which help to rapidly decrease the thoracic volume.

**11.** Hyperventilation is the action of breathing too quickly. It results in the increased expulsion of carbon dioxide from the respiratory system. If enough carbon dioxide is removed, it will result in a decrease in hydrogen ions and a concurrent increase in the alkalinity of the blood (increased blood pH). This condition is referred to as respiratory alkalosis.

**13.** The right lung has three lobes, whereas the left lung only has two lobes. The right lung is also larger than the left lung. These differences in the left lung relative to the right are to accommodate the space required by the heart.

## *Lesson 3—The Excretory System*

### PRACTICE EXERCISE
### ANSWERS AND SOLUTIONS

**1.** What are the functions of each of the following?

**a)** The bladder is a hollow, stretchable bag that stores urine.

**b)** The ureters transport urine from the kidneys to the bladder via peristaltic contractions.

**c)** The urethra carries urine from the bladder to the outside world. In females, it only transports urine. In males, both urine and semen are transported by the urethra, but never at the same time.

**d)** The kidneys produce urine by filtering the blood and by removing liquid wastes. They also control the potassium and salt levels, water balance, and the acidity of the blood.

**e)** The internal and external bladder sphincters control the discharge of urine into the urethra (involuntary control) and to the outside world (voluntary control).

**f)** The renal medulla is the inner portion of the kidney. It is arranged into a series of triangular structures called renal pyramids and contains the nephrons.

**g)** The afferent arteriole controls blood flow into the glomerulus. It increases blood flow or volume into the glomerulus in order to increase blood pressure.

**h)** The efferent arteriole controls blood flow out of the glomerulus. It constricts to back up the blood exiting the glomerulus in order to further increase the pressure in the glomerulus.

**i)** The nephron is the functional filtering unit of the kidney.

**j)** The renal cortex is the outer portion of the kidney. It contains portions of the kidney's nephrons.

**k)** The glomerulus is a complex capillary cluster that functions as the initial filtering point in the nephron. Materials under high pressure exit the blood through the capillaries of the glomerulus into Bowman's capsule.

**l)** The Bowman's capsule collects the filtrate from the glomerulus and transports it to the proximal convoluted tubule.

**m)** The distal convoluted tubule collects filtrate from the loop of Henle and aids in reabsorption and in tubular secretion directly from the blood stream. It is the last line of action for both filtration from the blood and reabsorption from the filtrate.

**n)** The proximal convoluted tubule collects from the Bowman's capsule and functions to move the nutrients in the glomerular filtrate (such as water, glucose, amino acids, vitamins, minerals, and some salts) back into the blood.

**o)** The loop of Henle collects from the proximal convoluted tubule and functions to increase the salinity within the renal medulla, which promotes osmotic water retention from the nephron ducts passing through this region of the kidney.

**p)** The collecting duct receives the filtrate from the distal tubules of many nephrons and empties into the renal pelvis.

**q)** The renal artery helps bring blood to the kidney.

**r)** The renal vein helps carry blood away from the kidney.

3. Blood pressure determines the rate of filtration at the glomerulus and therefore the rate of urine production. An increase in blood pressure would result in an increase in the amount of fluid and material moved out of the glomerulus into the Bowman's capsule, which would increase urine production.

5. Antidiuretic hormone is activated by the hypothalamus (under conditions of concentrated or thick blood) to stimulate the distal convoluted tubule of the nephron to become more permeable to water. This permits for a greater rate of reabsorption of water into the blood. The higher water volume in the blood causes the blood to become less concentrated and higher in pressure.

7. Osmoreceptors are located in the hypothalamus of the brain. They monitor the water content of the blood by monitoring blood pressure. When the osmoreceptors detect that the blood is too thick (not enough water), then the hypothalamus signals the release of ADH from the posterior pituitary.
   The ADH in turn stimulates the distal convoluted tubule of the nephron to become more permeable to water, a measure that allows more water to be reabsorbed from the urine into the blood, thus increasing blood pressure.

9. Active reabsorption requires the use of carrier proteins and mitochondrial ATP. These carrier proteins and mitochondria are located within the walls of the tubules. Passive reabsorption typically refers to transport that does not require the use of ATP and includes the processes of diffusion and osmosis.

11. If glucose were found in urine it would likely mean that there were excessively high levels of glucose in the blood (hyperglycemia), which is indicative of diabetes mellitus. It may also indicate that the kidneys are malfunctioning and not properly reabsorbing the glucose that is in the filtrate.

**13.** Hemodialysis is a method used to remove wastes and excess water from the blood when the kidneys are in renal failure. In hemodialysis, a person is hooked up to a machine that will filter their blood, a few ounces at a time, and then return the clean blood back to their body. This process can take 3–5 hours and needs to be repeated a minimum of three times per week to ensure that all of the waste products are effectively being removed from the blood. The machine passes the affected person's blood past a semi-permeable filter and typically uses a counter-current flow of dialysate to maintain the concentration gradient across the membrane at a maximum and increase the efficiency of diffusion of unwanted materials from the blood into the dialysis solution.

**15.** Diagram the kidneys, and explain the difference between the cortex and the medulla areas.

## Diagram of Kidney

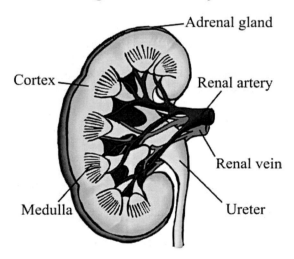

The cortex area of the kidney is the outer portion of the kidney that houses the main body of the nephrons including the glomerular apparatus, Bowman's capsule, proximal convoluted tubule and distal convoluted tubule. It is within the cortex that glomerular filtrate is produced and around the bulk of the tubular reabsorption and tubular secretion occurs. The renal medulla is the inner portion of the kidney and it is arranged into a series of triangular-shaped sections or pyramids.

The renal medulla primarily houses the loops of Henle and collecting ducts. It is within the medullary pyramids that the bulk of water reabsorption occurs and the final urine product is collected.

**17.** Increased blood pressure increases the rate at which glomerular filtrate is produced and subsequently the rate at which this filtrate moves through the nephron to the collecting ducts. Additionally, blood pressure has feedback mechanisms that trigger the release of hormones such as aldosterone and ADH that directly impact kidney function.

**19.** The yellow color of urine is caused by a pigment called urochrome, which is the remnant of the broken-down hemoglobin of expended red blood cells.

## PRACTICE QUIZ

### ANSWERS AND SOLUTIONS

**1. D.**
The entire digestive tract is between 9–12 meters. The longest section is the small intestine, which is named for its small diameter. The entire digestive tract consists of the esophagus, stomach, small intestine, and large intestine.

**3. B.**
Pepsinogen is an inactive enzyme that requires HCl to convert it into its active form, pepsin. Inactive enzymes are described as zymogens. These require an alteration in their structure to make their active sites available for substrate interaction. Mucin is released to protect the walls of the stomach from enzymatic digestion (proteolysis). Bicarbonate, which is released by the pancreas, neutralizes HCl inside the first section of the small intestine. This is necessary to prevent proteolysis of the intestinal wall and for the proper functioning of enzymes released into small intestine.

**5. A.**
A pH of approximately 8 is required for secretions from the pancreas and the small intestine to function effectively. This environment is generated by the release of sodium bicarbonate from the pancreas into the small intestine via the pancreatic duct. HCl creates a pH of approximately 2 within the stomach. This is far too acidic for secretions within the duodenum. Trypsinogen and pepsinogen are inactive enzymes (zymogens) that require activation prior to their hydrolysis protein. They are not responsible for altering pH.

**7. A.**

Lipids diffuse across the epithelium of the small intestine. They are then transferred into close-ended lymph vessels. Amino acids and glucose require active transport, whereas maltose must be enzymatically hydrolyzed prior to active transport.

**9. D.**

The trachea is lined with ciliated cells that help remove small particles. These cells work in conjunction with mucus. The nasal cavity uses hair and mucus to trap particles. The pharynx is a passageway that contains the epiglottis, which is responsible for food and air separation between esophagus and the trachea.

**11. C.**

High $CO_2$ levels will cause an individual's breathing rate to increase. Chemoreceptors are most sensitive to $CO_2$ levels. Although oxygen levels are monitored, $CO_2$ entering the blood stream is combined with water to form carbonic acid. This is quickly converted into protons and bicarbonate. The pH of the blood is monitored by chemoreceptors that are located within the carotid and aortic arteries. The medulla oblongata contains most of the chemoreceptors that monitor $CO_2$ levels within the blood.

**13. B.**

The nephron is the functional unit of a kidney. Each kidney contains over one million nephrons. Each nephron is composed of a tubule within a bed of capillaries. The tubule allows for the excretion of wastes while the capillaries reabsorb non-waste components back into the circulatory system. Capillaries also allow for the secretion of certain substances (such as penicillin) out of the circulatory system and into the tubule. The renal artery is the blood vessel that brings blood into each kidney. The renal vein allows for the flow of filtered blood out of each kidney. The urethra is a tube that provides a passageway for urine to be excreted from the urinary bladder to outside of the body.

**15. C.**

Glucose and amino acids are actively reabsorbed at the proximal tubule. This process requires large numbers of mitochondria, which provide energy in the form of ATP. Both glucose and amino acids are molecules small enough to pass through the filtration process (that occurs across the glomerulus) into the Bowman's capsule.

This requires immediate reabsorption because the remainder of the tubule moves closer and closer to the 'point of no return', which is the pelvis of the kidney (a region within the kidney into which all the nephron's collecting ducts empty).

## *Lesson 4—The Circulatory System*

### PRACTICE EXERCISE
### ANSWERS AND SOLUTIONS

**1.  a)** Capillaries are tiny connecting bridges between arterioles and venules that are the site for fluid and gas exchange between the blood and the tissues of the body.
   **b)** Coronary arteries deliver oxygen-rich and nutrient-rich blood to the tissue cells of the heart.
   **c)** Hypertension is the medical term for high blood pressure.
   **d)** Myocardium is the layer of strong cardiac heart muscle that lies between the inner endocardium and outer epicardium.
   **e)** Stroke volume refers to the amount of blood sent out as a result of a single contraction from either one of the ventricles to their respective arteries.
   **f)** Cardiac output takes into account heart rate and stroke volume and refers to the amount of blood that is pumped out the heart in one minute.
   Cardiac output = Heart rate × Stroke volume
   **g)** Heart rate is the number of times that the heart beats in one minute.

3. Because it is the mother's first child, there is no risk of erythroblastosis fetalis in this infant. The placenta will have prevented the mother's blood from mixing with the infant's blood during pregnancy; therefore, the mother will have not yet produced any Rh antibodies. However, once the infant is born, the placenta will tear during childbirth, and the mother's blood will now be exposed to the blood of the infant, which causes the production of Rh antibodies in the mother. A risk then exists if the mother chooses to have a second child. If that child is Rh positive, the antibodies the mother created during the first childbirth will now attack the unborn infant's blood through the placenta and cause it to agglutinate. Doctors can prevent this by injecting a fetal antigen competitive inhibitor via within 72 hours of the first pregnancy.
This prevents the mother from developing the Rh antibodies in the first place.

5. If lymph fluid cannot be collected in your lymph vessels, the resulting condition would be edema. This condition is characterized by fluid accumulation and swelling that occurs in the tissues when the lymph vessels do not properly drain excess interstitial fluid .

7. The lymphatic system is responsible for mounting and carrying out immune responses in order to protect the body against invasion and infection. Lymphatic fluid also transports fatty acids and fats throughout the body and removes excess interstitial fluid from cells.

9. Lymph vessels run completely independent of the circulatory system, but in close proximity. They are designed like veins both in wall structure and in that they have valves to ensure unidirectional flow and to prevent backup of the lymph fluid. Additionally, they vary in size from the tiny lymph capillaries that collect the interstitial fluid at the capillary bed, to the larger great thoracic and lymphatic ducts responsible for collecting all of the lymph from within the body and returning it to the blood.

11. The spleen has multiple functions. It has a blood reservoir that stores red blood cells; a "garbage dump" that collects the remains of abnormal, aged, and dead red blood cells; and it also acts as an immune response agent. It functions as a lymph node and initiates T and B lymphocytes in response to circulating antigens.

13. It is the job of the circulatory system to carry the hormones and chemical messengers produced by the endocrine system to their respective target tissues within the body.

15. The fibrous sac that covers the heart is called the pericardium.

17. The lub/dub sound represents the sounds made when the valves within the heart close. LUB is the sound made as a result of the atrioventricular valves closing during ventricular systole (contraction). DUB is the sound made when the semilunar valves close during ventricular diastole (relaxation).

19. An average (non-active) heart rate is 60–75 beats/min. An athlete will have a slower resting heart rate than the average person (as low as 45–50 beats/min). This is because athletes tend to have stronger hearts that need to beat less often (at a slower rate) than a non-athlete (with a weaker heart) to deliver the same amount of blood to the body.

21. a) The left and right atria of the heart fill with blood and then contract at the same time. This moves the blood though the atrioventricular valves into the ventricles.
   b) The left and right ventricles continue to fill while the atria relax. They then contract at the same time, pushing blood through the semilunar valves into the aorta and pulmonary artery. This simultaneously snaps the atrioventricular valves shut to ensure no backflow into the atria.
   c) The ventricles relax, and the semilunar valves close to ensure no backflow from the aorta or pulmonary artery.

23. Epinephrine affects the rate at which the SA (sinoatrial) node stimulates the atrial syncytium. It increases the rate of SA node firing, which in turn increases heart rate and blood pressure.

25. Systolic pressure is the pressure that occurs when the ventricles contract and push the blood out of the heart. Diastolic pressure is the pressure that occurs when the ventricles relax and fill with blood.

27. a) The blood is responsible for the movement of oxygen and carbon dioxide between the lungs and body tissues.
   b) The blood transports nutrients, hormones, water, heat, and waste products throughout the body.

**c)** The blood defends the body against bacterial infection, viral infection, and other foreign particles.

**29.** RBC production is increased by the bone marrow if it determines that the speed at which it is receiving oxygen is too slow. In other words, if the bones are not getting enough oxygen, the bone marrow will increase the rate at which RBCs are produced.

**31.** Agglutination is the clumping or curdling of transfused blood. It is caused when a patient receives the wrong blood type during a blood transfusion.

Ultimately, it is an immune response that is due to the specific type of protein antigen on the foreign donor's red blood cells. Because this antigen is different than the protein antigen of the patient's red blood cells, the patient's body recognizes the donor blood as a foreign substance and attacks as such.

**33.** The patient can be given type A blood because it is the same type as his or her own blood and thus will not trigger an immune response. He or she can also be given type O blood because type O blood does not have any antigens that would trigger an immune response.

## Lesson 5—The Motor System

### PRACTICE EXERCISE
### ANSWERS AND SOLUTIONS

**1.** Striated muscle is 'lined' and evolved into cardiac muscle and skeletal muscle. Smooth muscle has no visible lines. It is controlled by the autonomic nervous system.

**3.** The mammalian ribcage allows the lungs to expand when skeletal muscle contracts. The diaphragm and intercostal muscles work together to expand and contract the ribcage, which allows gases to flow in and out of the lungs, where high numbers of spherical structures (alveoli) maximize the surface area required for efficient exchange of gases.

**5.** The hydroskeleton is a 'skeleton' that does not have bone or chitin. Certain invertebrates, such as jellyfish and starfish, use an interplay of muscle and fluid to produce locomotion. The exoskeleton is a strong outer shell in organisms such as insects and arthropods. The endoskeleton relies on bone, cartilage, tendon, and vertebrate muscle. Skeletal muscle evolved into two distinct types: fast-twitch and slow-twitch.

**7.** The current model is the "Sliding Filament Model". Each cell carries out maximum contraction once it has been triggered by an incoming signal. However, results depend on the number of myofibrils recruited for the task, which in turn depend on the amount of force necessary for a particular muscular contraction. According to the model, actin proteins slide in between myosin proteins and thus pull the two Z-lines of the sarcomere together.

**9.** Actin and myosin

## PRACTICE TEST

### ANSWERS AND SOLUTIONS

**1. A.**
Mechanical digestion increases the surface area of food by breaking large portions into smaller portions. The primary mechanism is mastication. This process involves saliva, the tongue, and the movement of jaw and teeth. The process produces a paste called a bolus. Chemical digestion breaks molecular bonds through the actions of enzymes. This type of digestion requires a larger surface area for maximum efficiency. Peristalsis is the wave-like muscular contractions of the alimentary canal. This helps food move through the entire length of the digestive tract. Ingestion is the act of taking in food by way of the mouth.

**3. C.**
Gastrin is a polypeptide released into the circulatory system. Release into the stomach would cause its digestion by protein digesting enzymes, such as pepsin. Somatostatin is an inhibitory hormone that reduces the effects of hormones such as gastrin.

**5. A.**
Villi are small projections that increase the surface area of the small intestine. They are necessary to maximize the absorptive surface available for the passive and active transport of macromolecules.
Epithelial layers are the different surface layers that form the interior of the small intestine. They form the lumen, but they do not passively absorb all nutrients. Lipids are the only macromolecules passively absorbed. Burnner's glands secrete mucus into the lumen. This is essential for the protection of the epithelial layers from the initial acidic secretions of stomach contents that empt into the duodenum. It also acts as a protective layer against the enzymatic actions of proteases (protein hydrolyzing enzymes). Lacteals are vessels that collect passively transported lipids.

**7. D.**
The large intestine's primary function is the reabsorption of water. The absorption of nutrient macromolecules occurs throughout the length of the small intestine. The initial breakdown of proteins occurs within the stomach via the enzymatic activity of pepsin combined with HCl. The increase of surface area occurs through the initial mastication (chewing) of food and the churning of food throughout the digestive process (peristalsis).

**9. D.**
Inhalation is the result of a contracted and flattened diaphragm. This flattened structure produces the increase in thoracic space necessary to lower air pressure, which results in air rushing into the lungs. The diaphragm is curved when it is relaxed.

**11. A.**
Emphysema is a respiratory disease that describes the hardening of bronchioles and the bursting of alveoli. Smoking can greatly increase the risk of acquiring this disease. Bronchitis describes an infection of the bronchioles and bronchus. Pneumonia describes an inflammation of lung tissue that is often accompanied by abnormal filling of alveoli with fluids. This fluid response can be caused by a number of infectious organisms. Often the accumulated of fluids are coughed up. Pleurisy is an infection of the pleural membranes.

**13. C.**
The correct order is proximal convoluted tubule, Loop of Henle, and collecting duct.
The complete pathway is the glomerulus, Bowman's Capsule, proximal convoluted tubule, loop of Henle, distal convoluted tubule, and the collecting duct.

**15. D.**
The kidney carries out all of the above functions. This is achieved through the basic functional unit, the nephron. Filtration, reabsorption and secretion are use to carry out these vital processes.

**17. B.**
Cardiac muscle is unique because they require no external nervous stimulation. Their rate of contraction is controlled through a series of nerve bundles called nodes. The pacemaker (SA node) sets a nerve impulse of approximately 70 beats per minute.

This impulse is transferred throughout the heart in a series of steps that results in a uniform and organized cardiac muscle contraction. Cardiac cells are multinucleated and require high levels of oxygen and glucose. This is because the heart is the only muscle that must contract non-stop for an entire lifetime. Each individual cell acts in unison with its neighboring cell.

**19. B.**
The correct pathway is right atrium, pulmonary artery, pulmonary vein, and aorta. It is important to note that the right side of the heart represents the opposite or reversed orientation of your own heart. Another caution is the pulmonary system of blood vessels. Blood flow away from the heart is always through arteries.
This includes the artery leading to the lungs.

**21. D.**
Capillaries are the only blood vessels that normally allow for nutrient and gas exchange. This is because of their thin cellular walls, which selectively filter blood components across their blood vessel endothelium (inner surface cells).

**23. D.**

Baroreceptors are sensitive to artery stretching. They are located in the carotid arteries and the aorta. Their sensitivity to stretching allows them to react quickly to increased blood pressure. Their responses include a lowering of heart rate and force, as well as the lowering of arterial resistance to blood flow. Osmoreceptors detect the osmolarity (amount of water) of blood and are located only in the hypothalamus.

**25. C.**

Red blood cells bind oxygen and contain no nuclei. Red blood cells contain approximately 270 million hemoglobin proteins. Each hemoglobin contains four protein subunits surrounding $Fe^{2+}$ at its core. This metal ion is able to bind oxygen and then release it at the required location. Mature red blood cells lack a nucleus, so they must constantly be replenished. The average life span of a red blood cell is 120 days. Afterwards, they lose their smooth appearance and are selectively recycled.

**27. D.**

Leukocytes combat foreign invaders and make up the smallest number of blood proteins. They carry out a variety of different functions; however, each plays a role within the immune system. Their life spans vary from days to years. A cascade begun by the busting of platelets accomplishes blood clotting. Oxygen is transported by red blood cells.

**29. D.**

One-way valves are located within lymph vessels that transport lipids. Lymph system vessels are in close proximity to blood vessels; however, the lymph system contains neither red blood cells nor platelets. They rely on valves and muscular contractions to move lymph fluid through lymph nodes and back into the circulatory system.

**31. B.**

The terms vasoconstriction and vasodilatation are associated with smooth muscle. This involuntary control is necessary for the maintenance of blood pressure. Blood vessels can contract or relax, depending on signals received from baroreceptors. Although smooth muscle lines the digestive tract, the term associated with the digestion of nutrients is peristalsis. These rhythmic contractions help churn and move food along the entire length of the alimentary canal.
Striated muscle of the heart, or cardiac muscle, is associated with a coordinated heart contraction,

or heart beat.
The pressure generated during the contraction phase is known as systole, whereas the relaxed ventricle pressure is known as diastole.

**33. B.**

Respiration requires the skeletal muscle found within the diaphragm and the intercostals. These muscles are under voluntary and involuntary control. They are essential in creating an increase in thoracic cavity volume. This enables air to be drawn into an area of low pressure. Smooth muscle is under autonomic control and is found along the digestive tract and around most blood vessels. Alveoli and capillaries are not composed of muscle. They are thin-membrane structures that allow for the exchange of gases within the lungs.

**35. D.**

The sarcomere is the contractile unit that requires the filament myosin and its associated heads to be cocked through the actions of ATP. The filament actin is what the myosin head attaches to and pulls during a contraction. This interaction shortens individual sarcomeres.

**37. D.**

ATP use and tonus account for muscle heat generation. ATP is constantly used, even if a muscle is at rest. Tonus, the cyclic contraction of individual myofibrils, uses ATP to maintain balance and posture. Random firing also occurs. Muscle contractions help increase heat production; however, this is not essential to produce heat. Friction would seem to be a logical choice. The cocked heads actually keep actin and myosin far enough apart to avoid friction. This is important because an efficient contracting system would wish to maximize the energy put toward a contraction instead of overcoming the forces of friction.

# CREDITS

Many of the images in this book were created and adapted from a number of sources. The illustrations and photos that were not done by employees of Castle Rock Research Corporation have all been taken from public domain and other copyright-free sources, but we would like to acknowledge the contributions of various entities and individuals.

Many photos and artwork have been taken and adapted from www.Clipart.com.

The photograph that appears on page 73 was taken by I.K. Inha, who sadly passed away on March 4th, 1930. The image was downloaded from www.ymparisto.fi.

Mariana Ruiz Villareal has been a source of much inspiration and material, including the tracing she made of Ivica Letunic's phylogenetic tree of life illustration, which has been adapted and now appears on page 105.

The photograph of the tarantula hawk that appears on page 109 was taken by Dave Hood of Grant Ranch, California.

# BOOK ORDERING INFORMATION

## SENIOR HIGH SCHOOL TITLES

Castle Rock Research offers the following resources to support Alberta students. You can order any of these materials online at:

# www.castlerockresearch.com/store

| SOLARO.com - Study Online | | The KEY | | SNAP | Prob Solved | Class Notes |
|---|---|---|---|---|---|---|
| $29.95 ea.* | | $29.95 ea.* | | $29.95 ea.* | $19.95 ea.* | $19.95 ea.* |
| Biology 30 | Mathematics 30-1 | Biology 30 | Mathematics 30-1 | Biology 20 | Biology 20 | Biology 20 |
| Biology 20 | Mathematics 30-2 | Biology 20 | Mathematics 30-2 | Chemistry 30 | Chemistry 30 | Chemistry 30 |
| Chemistry 30 | Mathematics 30-3 | Chemistry 30 | Mathematics 20-1 | Chemistry 20 | Chemistry 20 | Chemistry 20 |
| Chemistry 20 | Mathematics 20-1 | Chemistry 20 | Mathematics 10 C | Mathematics 30-1 | Mathematics 30-1 | Mathematics 30-1 |
| Physics 30 | Mathematics 20-2 | English 30-1 | Social Studies 30-1 | Mathematics 30-2 | Mathematics 30-2 | Mathematics 30-2 |
| Physics 20 | Mathematics 20-3 | English 30-2 | Social Studies 30-2 | Mathematics 31 | Mathematics 31 | Mathematics 31 |
| Science 30 | Mathematics 20-4 | English 20-1 | Social Studies 20-1 | Mathematics 20-1 | Mathematics 20-1 | Mathematics 20-1 |
| Science 20 | Mathematics 10 C | English 10-1 | Social Studies 10-1 | Mathematics 10 C | Mathematics 10 C | Mathematics 10 C |
| Science 10 | Mathematics 10-3 | Physics 30 | | Physics 30 | Physics 30 | Physics 30 |
| English 30-1 | Mathematics 10-4 | Physics 20 | | Physics 20 | Physics 20 | Physics 20 |
| English 30-2 | Social Studies 30-1 | Science 10 | | Science 10 | Science 10 | Science 10 |
| English 20-1 | Social Studies 30-2 | | | | | |
| English 20-2 | Social Studies 20-1 | | | | | |
| English 10-1 | Social Studies 10-1 | | | | | |
| English 10-2 | | | | | | |

*Prices do not include taxes or shipping.*

Study online using **SOLARO,** with access to multiple courses available by either a monthly or an annual subscription.

**The KEY Study Guide** is specifically designed to assist students in preparing for unit tests, final exams, and provincial examinations.

The **Student Notes and Problems (SNAP) Workbook** contains complete explanations of curriculum concepts, examples, and exercise questions.

The **Problem Solved** contains exercise questions and complete solutions.

The **Class Notes** contains complete explanations of curriculum concepts.

If you would like to order Castle Rock resources for your school, please visit our school ordering page:

# www.castlerockresearch.com/school-orders/